Meat Technolog

Meat Technology

A Practical Textbook for Student and Butcher

FRANK GERRARD

M.B.E., F.Inst.M., M.Inst.R., M.R.S.H.,
Gold Medallist of The Worshipful Company of Butchers
Diploma of The National Federation of Meat Traders
Past President, The Institute of Meat

NORTHWOOD PUBLICATIONS LTD
London, EC1V 7QA

First edition 1945
Second edition 1951
Third edition 1964
Fourth edition 1971
*Fifth edition 1977

*Published by Northwood Publications Ltd
(Trade and technical publishing division of the Thomson Organisation Ltd)

© Northwood Publications Ltd and Frank Gerrard, 1977

ISBN 7198 2607 1

A 'Meat Trades Journal' book

By the same author
SAUSAGE AND SMALL GOODS PRODUCTION

Printed in Great Britain by The Anchor Press Ltd
and bound by Wm Brendon & Son Ltd
both of Tiptree, Essex

Contents

CHAPTER

Evolution. Skeleton. Organs. Organs of reproduction. Lymphatic system. Main lymphatic nodes of edible offal. Nomenclature.

Barley beef. Young bulls. The live animal. Inspection. Quality points. Handling points. Suggested scale of points for judging a butcher's beast. Indications of age. Dentition.

British Friesian. Aberdeen-Angus. Devons. Dexter. Galloway. Hereford. West Highland or Kyloes. Shorthorn. Red Poll. Sussex. Welsh Black. Charolais. Typical yields. Blonde d'Aquitaine. Limousin. Simmental. Chianina. Comparisons of continental breeds. Identification of crosses. Carcase appraisal. Fatstock guarantees. Some cattle grading schemes.

Pre-slaughter care. Slaughter. Handling of offals. Specification for dressing the carcases of cattle presented for beef premium. Carcases ex-KKCF. Costing ex-KKCF. Hindquarters ex-KKCF. Care of hides. Offals of the Ox. Estimation of dry rendering yields. Sampling. Endocrine glands. Duties of butchers and slaughtermen. Line slaughtering. Export slaughter houses.

Live weight to carcase weight. Live weights. Calculation of dressing percentages. Slaughter record.

Meat constituents. Muscle colour. Tenderness. Tenderstretch

process. Quality. Influence on yield. Suggested scale of points for judging beef carcase. Bone content. Beef grading. United Kingdom grades and grading. MLC beef carcase classification scheme. Some continental methods. Future developments.

From "The Experienced Butcher", 1816

*Be open in everything—Have no secrets of trade—
Truth is not ashamed of the light—Your customers
know that you are at great expenses—That you must
live by your trade.*

*When a tradesman is known for upright dealing,
he will have all the custom worth having, and his
gains, if not so great as some, yet it will be the more
pleasant in the getting, more satisfactory in the using,
and alone delightful in the thinking on.*

*Next to honesty, cleanliness and civility are the
greatest recommendations of tradesmen, and of none
more than butchers; the real nature of their business,
and the prejudices of the world make these qualities
the more particularly requisite in them.*

*We have one common interest, and must all live
by one another.*

Preface to first edition

The object of this book is to provide in a concise form some of the information I should have found of value on entering the meat industry. Book learning can never replace practical experience, but the period of apprenticeship can be considerably reduced and given a vital interest when it is supplemented by intelligent study. It is to be hoped that instructors in meat technology will find that the use of any scheme, whereby the grading of the live animal can be definitely associated with the carcase, is to be encouraged, as it will do much to enhance the knowledge of the student. It has been impossible in a book of this scope to cover all the various methods of cutting; the graphs and the pricing tests are intended as a guide for the preparation of similar figures applying to individual conditions. The figures given are based on the theoretical maximum, no allowance being made for the normal trade loss.

The sections on anatomy are intended to deal briefly with those portions with which the butcher is concerned in his daily craft. Questions have been included in the Appendix to enable the reader to check his general knowledge, and the Bibliography will provide a means of extending this knowledge or perhaps provide an incentive to specialize in in a particular section of the vast ramifications of this industry.

Familiarity with Mother Nature does not breed contempt. When we witness her handiwork of a million years, bearing the recent marks of the scientist, we should approach our privilege of craft with a new veneration.

I wish to acknowledge with sincere gratitude the inspiration and invaluable help of Dr John Hammond and the very kind assistance of Dr Callow.

The plates illustrating breeds were provided by kind permission of the *Farmer and Stockbreeder*; those of carcases by permission of the Ministry of Agriculture and Fisheries (HMSO), whilst photographs of slaughter practice were generously loaned by the Smithfield and Argentine Meat Co. Ltd, the Hide and Skin Improvement Society, Messrs Industrial Waste Eliminators Ltd and Devis & Sons Ltd.

My thanks are also due to the Publishers for their willing help, making publication possible under difficult war-time conditions.

Smithfield LCC Institute, London, 1944.

ix

Preface to fifth edition

Since the last edition was published in 1971, changes in the pattern of meat trading have taken place at an accelerating rate. The greatest single factor affecting the meat industry has been the influence of the European Economic Community, probably on account of the continued demand for lean meat and the export trade to the continent. In addition the EEC regulations have, in terms of volume, adversely affected our imports from oversea sources outside the EEC.

At the time of going to press, sales of livestock are based upon metric weights, wholesale carcase markets still retaining their weights in pounds, but the date for metrication at retail level has yet to be determined.

In addition to the acknowledgements made in previous prefaces, mention must be made of the valued assistance afforded by the Economics Branch of the Meat and Livestock Commission.

London 1977   Frank Gerrard

List of Figures

1 Cattle and beef

Evolution

The ox is a member of the Bovidae family of hollow-horned ruminants and this family is of great interest to the butcher as it includes not only Oxen (Bovinae) but also Sheep and Goats (Caprinae).

They are characterized by the following features: cloven hoofs, four compartments in the stomach, the absence of incisors in the upper jaw, and the duplex forms of the cannon bones.

Our present stock of domestic cattle is derived from the Wild or Forest Ox (Aurochs). Records prove that it existed over the whole of Europe up to about the eleventh century, and it is probable that they retreated from West Europe before the thirteenth century. A number of references appear to suggest that some of these cattle survived in Poland as late as 1627. Skeletons remaining to this day indicate that it was a massive animal, and our White Park Cattle (Plate 1) and probably the Welsh breed (Plate 15) are the nearest relatives at the present time.

In Britain a number of herds of White Cattle were enclosed, and it is generally agreed that these cattle were drawn from a common stock and practically all these cattle were white with black markings. Over twenty herds were known to have been originally enclosed, but unfortunately the majority of these herds have been dispersed. There are, however, representatives at the Whipsnade Zoo, Bedfordshire, which to the student is well worth a visit.

It is possible that the Normans introduced Red Cattle into Southern England and these may have played a part in the development of our present breeds. Robert Bakewell (1725–95) developed the principle of inbreeding to aid selection and fix type, and the method did much to establish such breeds as the Beef Shorthorn. The brothers Charles and Robert Colling, working upon the methods of Bakewell, continued his work and placed the Shorthorn breed on a very high level. This work of improvement was continued by Booth, who developed a type from which our Beef Shorthorn originated, while Bates concentrated on the Dairy Shorthorn.

Other species of Oxen include Zebu, which is the domesticated Ox of India, and it has been successfully crossed with Hereford and Shorthorns to produce types suitable for tropical climatic conditions and resistance to certain animal parasites.

The African and India Buffalo, the Yak of Tibet, the Bantin of Malaya, the Gaur of India and frequently the Bison are included in a subgenus.

Our modern British breeds can be conveniently considered under three main headings.

BEEF BREEDS

Aberdeen-Angus
Some strains of Shorthorn
Hereford
Devon

Galloway
Belted Galloway
West Highland
Sussex
Charolais

DUAL-PURPOSE BREEDS

British Friesian
Some strains of Shorthorn
Red Poll
Lincolnshire Red Shorthorn

Welsh Black
South Devon
Dexter
Longhorn

DAIRY BREEDS

Dairy Shorthorn
Jersey
Guernsey

Ayrshire
Kerry

The butcher is obviously most interested in the two former groups, though one must not lose sight of the fact that the sausage manufacturer obtains some of his material from old cow and bull beef irrespective of the above classification, and that much of the 'bobby' veal must be considered as a by-product of the dairy industry.

To the above list the recent imports of Blonde d'Aquitaine, Limousin, Simmental and Chianina, may be added. Whilst some of these may be used as pure breeds for beef production, in general, the bulls are crossed with dairy type dams.

Plate 1   The Hevingham herd of British White Park cattle

Plate 2   Longhorn heifer (*Farmer & Stockbreeder*)

CROSS BREEDS

Many feeders prefer a cross-bed animal, working on the assumption that many of these animals will fatten more readily than either of their parent types. Thus the 'Blue-grey', a product of a White Shorthorn bull and a Galloway cow, is very popular along the Border, and by using an Aberdeen bull on a Lincoln Red cow a very good butchers' beast can be obtained. In fact it is probable that a large percentage of the steers obtained from Ireland are by beef bulls out of a dual-purpose or even a dairy type of cow. It is therefore obvious that the possible combinations are extremely numerous, not that these animals would of necessity be 'scrubs', as much would depend on the method of feeding, and a very large proportion of our home-killed meat supplies are obtained from such cattle.

Skeleton (Fig. 1)

HEAD

Without entering into detail, the head can be considered as follows.

(1) Lower jaw, with 8 incisors and 12 cheek teeth (in the adult).

(2) Cranium, or brain case, and frontal bone and 12 cheek teeth (in the adult) (see 'Dentition' for greater detail).

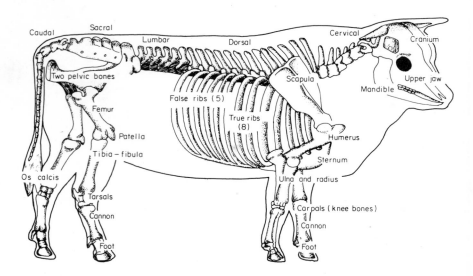

Fig. 1   Skeleton of bovine animal

VERTEBRAE

(1) Cervical vertebrae	7 bones
(2) Dorsal vertebrae	13 bones
(3) Lumbar vertebrae	6 bones
(4) Sacral vertebrae	1 bone (5 segments fused)
(5) Coccygeal vertebrae	very variable, up to 21 bones

RIBS

13 pairs
(12 or 14 pairs occasionally) } 8 pairs of true ribs,
5 pairs of false ribs

STERNUM

Breast-bone   1 bone (7 segments)

PELVIS

Pelvic bones

HIND LIMB	FORE LIMB
Femur and patella	Scapula
Tibia-Fibula	Humerus
Tarsals	Radius and Ulna
Cannon and foot bones	Carpals
	Cannon and foot bones

Organs

DIGESTIVE SYSTEM

The lips are wide and thick with no central fissure as in the sheep, and the muzzle is bare. The lower lip also possesses a narrow bare strip. The inner lining of the cheek has a large number of papillae, some of these up to $\frac{1}{2}$ inch (13 mm) in length. The front of the hard palate is covered with transverse ridges, varying from 15 to 20 in number, and behind this is situated the soft palate.

The tongue is frequently pigmented. These black marks are common and have no pathological significance. The organ is pointed at the tip and is covered with a thick mucous membrane, its upper surface being very rough. Near the root on either side of the tongue are small rounded marks (circumvallate papillae), whilst towards the tip of the blade there are a number of conical papillae.

The pharynx is short and wide, and the entrance to the oesophagus (weasand and food-pipe) is relatively large.

The oesophagus is about 2 to 2½ inches (5 to 7 cm) in diameter and about 2½ to 3 ft (0·75 to 0·9 m) in length. Its mucous lining is covered by a muscular coat.

The abdominal cavity is very large, to some extent at the expense of the chest cavity, as the last three ribs form part of the abdominal wall. The stomach of the ox is very large; in fact, in medium-sized animals it has a capacity of 40 gal (180 litres). It occupies the entire left half of the cavity, except for the small space occupied by the spleen, and it extends well over the middle line into the right half. It is a compound stomach consisting of four sections.

(1) *Rumen,* paunch or the plain tripe.
(2) *Reticulum,* fore-stomach or honeycomb.
(3) *Omasum,* Bible-bag, prayer-book, manifold, or manyplies.
(4) *Abomasum,* rennet-bag or true stomach.

Nature's adaptation is well exemplified by the modifications in growth of these compartments as the calf matures and changes from a milk diet to a bulky herbivorous feed. When the calf is born the first two divisions are together about half as large as the abomasum, whilst at the end of three months these proportions are reversed, and at maturity the capacity of the rumen represents about 80% of the total capacity, the reticulum about 5%, with the omasum and abomasum approximately the same size. The effect of this growth on the position of the kidneys is obvious to the practical butcher, giving us the 'open' or 'raison' side, owing to the paunch displacing the kidney knob to the right and slightly backwards, frequently causing a slight rotation of the kidney.

The rumen is oval in shape and is in contact with the left abdominal wall; its capacity in the adult is over 30 gal (136 litres). It is lined with a mucous membrane and dotted with papillae. It must be considered as a reservoir for food, as it does not contain any digestive glands. If there is insufficient fluid present, the rumen loses its power of contraction and the ability to mix the food thoroughly, so that the quantity of water consumed by the ox is large and the salivary secretion is extremely heavy. Thus it will be seen that, should these two be deficient, the normal digestive processes are seriously impaired.

The reticulum is the smallest of the four parts and it lies opposite to the 6th, 7th and 8th rib (approximately the gristle end of the fore-rib). It is above the end of the sternum (brisket) and is in contact with the diaphragm and the liver. Its mucous lining is intersected by prominent cells, four-, five-, or six-sided, about ½ inch (13 mm) in height, giving a 'honeycomb' appearance.

The omasum is really an organ of mastication, and, as the fluid is continually draining away, the contents are relatively dry. The cavity contains about 100 leaves or folds arising from the wall, their lower ends being free. This formation gives rise to the descriptive names applied to it in various parts of the country. As the two openings from the reticulum and the abomasum are situated at the lower surface, food must be forced upwards between the leaves against gravity.

Abomasum. This portion contains digestive glands and is the true stomach. The mucous lining is of a reddish colour and it is soft and smooth to the touch. In the rear portion of this organ there are spirally directed folds. By the time the food has reached this part, it is in a very finely divided fluid state.

INTESTINES

The intestine of the ox is best expressed in relation to the body length of the animal. This is about twenty times the length, so that with a mature beast the length of the small intestine is approximately 130 ft (40 m), the caecum about 30 in (76 cm), and the colon roughly 35 ft (10·5 m).

SMALL INTESTINE

The first length, the duodenum, is about 3 to 4 ft (1 m) in length; it receives the bile duct and also the pancreatic duct about a foot farther back.

The rest of the small intestine is arranged in coils situated between the rumen and the abdominal wall. The end portion runs forwards between the caecum and the colon, to which it is attached. The average diameter of the small intestine is about 2 in (5 cm).

LARGE INTESTINE

Caecum (bung or blind gut). This is continuous with the colon, the average diameter being about 5 in (13 cm).
Colon. The colon is at first the same diameter as that of the caecum, diminishing slowly to about 2 in (5 cm).
Rectum. The rectum is relatively short and is usually covered with peritoneum as far back as the first joint of the tail.

BEEF CASINGS (Fig. 2)

Casings

Trade term	Anatomical term
Weasand	Oesophagus
Narrow middle and middle	Colon
Bung gut	Caecum
Bung	Caecum (blind end below ileocaecal valve)
Wide middle	Colonic end, rectum
Fat end	Rectum, anal end
Round	Small intestine (Duodenum, jejunum, and ileum)

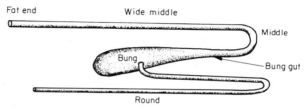

Fig. 2   Beef casings

LIVER

This organ is situated almost entirely on the right of the middle line. It consists of one large lobe partly divided and a thumb piece (caudate lobe). Its curved surface is in contact with the right part of the diaphragm, the last two ribs, and with the flank. The under surfaces are in contact with the omasum and the reticulum. The groove formed by the oesophagus is much shallower than in the horse. The average weight of the liver is about 10 to 12 lb (4·5 to 5·4 kg) or a little over 1 % of the live weight of the animal.

(The liver of a new-born calf is relatively larger than in the adult.)

GALL BLADDER

Consists of a pear-shaped sac and it can be considered as a diversion of the bile duct, enlarged so as to form a reservoir for the bile. It is approximately 5 inches (13 cm) in length, and situated above it is the portal lymph gland, near to the portal vein.

PANCREAS

This organ is sometimes substituted for sweetbread and is referred to by the butcher as the gut-bread. It is attached to the liver and is quadrilateral in shape. The duct leaves the pancreas to enter the duodenum about 12 in (30 cm) farther back than the bile duct.

SPLEEN

The spleen is about 20 inches (51 cm) in length, 6 inches (15 cm) in width, and at its centre approximately 1 in (2·5 cm) thick. It has an elongated elliptical form, the extremities being rounded and thin. In an adult animal its weight is about 2 lb (0·9 kg). It is situated across the stomach between that organ and the belly-wall.

THYMUS (SWEETBREAD)

This organ consists of two distinct portions and it is situated in the throat of the animal, extending down into the chest. It reaches its maximum development in the calf at about 6 weeks, and then gradually shrinks, until in aged animals there is only a vestige of the original organ. It is thought to be associated with the sex glands. At its maximum development it may weigh up to 1½ lb (0·7 kg).

RESPIRATORY SYSTEM OF THE OX

The nostrils of the ox are relatively small and are not capable of the great dilation of those of the horse. The nasal cavity is not completely divided by the septum and it is short and wide. The larynx is comparatively short and thick. The trachea (windpipe) is about 26 inches (66 cm) in length with a diameter of roughly 1½ in (4 cm). It consists of approximately 50 rings of cartilage. At the beginning of the tube the ends of the ring are slightly apart, but towards the lungs the ends meet, forming a dorsal ridge. There are three chief bronchi entering the lungs. The left lung is smaller than the right, it is divided into three lobes, whilst the right possesses four or five lobes. The average weight of the lungs is about 7 to 8 lb (3·2 to 3·6 kg).

EXCRETORY SYSTEM

The kidneys consist of two lobulated structures situated one each side of the lumbar vertebrae. The left kidney is displaced, giving the 'open' side. Each kidney has about twenty lobes, and the renal artery enters and the renal vein and ureter leave the kidney at a well-marked depression, the hilus. The kidney is enclosed by a thin capsule, which can be easily removed from a healthy organ.

The bladder acts as a reservoir for the urine. It is situated on the floor of the pelvis, but when distended may extend forward into the abdominal cavity.

The urethra is a tube carrying the urine from the bladder to the exterior. In the male it is long and leaves the pelvis via the sciatic arch to enter the penis. In the female it opens into the lower portion of the vulva, about 6 in (15 cm) from the exterior.

The skin of the ox will, by insensible perspiration, lose about $1\frac{1}{2}$ gal (7 litres) of fluid per 24 hours. Oxen sweat visibly from the muzzle, which in healthy animals should be cool.

HEART

The heart is a hollow muscular organ situated between the lungs. It is enclosed within a membrane, the pericardium. This bag consists of two layers, and between them is a small quantity of oily fluid, which acts as a lubricant. The ox heart contains two bony structures, which are to be found between the two upper compartments (auricles).

THICK SKIRT

The thick skirt or body skirt is a muscular portion usually considered as the pillar of the diaphragm. In some styles of dressing it is left attached to the carcase.

FATS

In addition to the kidney suet, three types of visceral fat are usually recognized by the slaughterman. The 'caul' (omentum), which extends from the stomach to the colon and surrounds the viscera (normally this is removed immediately after opening up the animal), the 'gut' fat (mesenteric), which is attached to the intestines, and the 'reed' fat obtained from the vicinity of the third and fourth stomachs.

PLEURA

Is a semi-transparent membrane lining the chest cavity and covering the lungs. This membrane may only be removed from the carcase in the presence of an inspector, as in many cases of tuberculosis evidence of the disease is frequently found upon it. A similar membrane, the peritoneum, lines the abdominal cavity.

Organs of reproduction

In the female these consist of the ovaries, uterus, vagina, vulva, and udder. The ovaries are small ovoid bodies, a little over 1 in (2·5 cm) in length. They are to be found, one on each side of the pelvic inlet, approximately 18 in (46 cm) from the exterior.

The uterus, or breeding-bag, is a hollow, muscular organ and during pregnancy becomes greatly distended and then projects from the pelvic cavity into the abdominal cavity, lying against the right abdominal wall. It is attached to the walls of the pelvis by folds of peritoneum.

The vagina is a muscular passage, continuous with the neck of the uterus, extending to the vulva. The vulva opens to the exterior by a small opening beneath the anus.

The udder is composed of four compartments, each with a milk sinus situated above the teat. The milk ducts of each quarter are entirely independent of those of any other. Above the outer side of each hind-quarter is situated the supramammary lymphatic gland.

The reproductive system of the male includes the testes, penis, and vas deferens. In the fœtus the testicles are situated at the roof of the abdominal cavity near the kidneys. Later they descend, one through each inguinal canal, to the scrotum. In castrated animals these canals become infiltrated with fat, whereas in the entire male they remain open (see p. 117).

Lymphatic system (Fig. 3)

Although meat inspection and diagnosis is not within the province of the butcher, he has a moral responsibility to his clientele, and Memo. 62, Foods,* allocates certain duties to him. It is therefore essential that he should be able to recognise diseased or abnormal conditions if he is to carry out his responsibilities faithfully. It is, of course, frequently found that a carcase may show evidence of disease in a deep-seated gland which could not be recognised by the normal routine inspection. Thus it is necessary that the slaughterman and meat cutter should have a few general ideas regarding the lymphatic system, to enable him to take appropriate action should his suspicions be aroused.

This system ramifies throughout the body and its organs, and it contains lymph, which carries nourishment to and bathes the cells, carrying away the waste products. At intervals throughout this system there are enlargements, nodes, more popularly known to the butcher as 'kernels'. If germs manage to enter the tissues, they frequently spread through the lymphatic system and are filtered out by the lymphatic

---

* A system of meat inspection recommended by the Ministry of Health for adoption by local authorities.

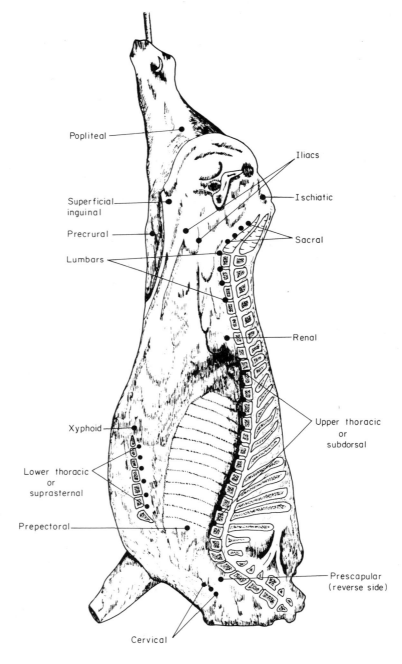

Fig. 3   Lymphatic nodes

nodes where the white cells destroy them. Thus any inflammation or changes in the glands provide ready evidence of disease, which might be difficult to identify in the tissues first affected. In some cases the system is not capable of dealing with the invasion and the infection enters the blood circulation, in which case the disease will become *generalized*. This frequently happens in tuberculosis, and with septic germs would cause blood poisoning. The sizes of the nodes vary considerably; for example, the large one found in the clod and silverside, to the small ones situated in the brisket skirt, and they are usually embedded in fat. The normal colour of the carcase nodes can be described as a bluish-grey, though those of the viscera are usually darker. If affected by disease they may become enlarged and congested with blood, soft and watery, show small greyish marks, contain a pus or matter or a gritty substance. Any of the foregoing conditions merit *expert* opinion.

A careful examination of imported beef will show that it is the custom to inspect the prescapular node in the forequarters, and the superficial inguinal or supramammary, and the precrural in the hindquarters. In Australian hinds the stifle joint also is examined for the possible presence of worm nodules (*Onchocerciasis*). Figure 3 indicates the positions of the more important nodes, and the experienced butcher should have little difficulty in locating them.

Main lymphatic nodes of edible offal

HEAD

Submaxillary.	On the inside of the angle of the jaw bone.
Parotid.	Below the root of the ear.
Pharyngeal.	Above the pharynx (inside tongue bones).

LUNGS

Bronchial.	Near branches of bronchi, on trachea.
Mediastinal.	Chain, between the lungs.

LIVER

Portal.	On under side of liver.

GUT FAT

Mesenteric.	Large number forming chain in gut fat.

STOMACH AND SPLEEN

Gastric.   Chain of small glands along the blood-vessels of the stomachs and spleen.

Nomenclature

The names applied to male and female bovines of different ages vary considerably throughout Great Britain and the Commonwealth. Those given below are fairly commonly used, and the definitions can be considered as representative of their general application.

ENTIRE MALES

Bull. An adult entire male of the bovine species.
    Bull calf. An entire male of the bovine species up to one year.
    Yearling bull. An entire male of the bovine species in its first year.

CASTRATED ANIMALS (MALES)

Steer calf. Bovine animal, castrated* whilst young.
    Steer, ox, bullock, stot. These terms are applied to castrated males. over two years, whilst in some countries ox is applied only to working oxen. There is, of course, a certain elasticity in these expressions, due to the demand for early maturity.

FEMALES

Heifer calf. Cow calf, quey calf, young female bovines.
    Heifer. Strictly speaking, is a female bovine which has not produced young, but the expression 'one-calf heifer' is frequently met with. In some parts the distinction is made by using the term 'maiden heifer' and in some areas of Scotland 'heifer' implies a speyed† animal. Also 'cow heifers' are widely recognized.
    Free-martin. A cow calf born as a twin to a bull calf is, on maturing, usually barren, and this term is applied to such an animal.
    Cow. A bovine female which has produced young.
    Cow heifer. Females which have calved or reached an advanced stage of pregnancy and which have not more than six permanent incisor teeth.

---

*Castration, emasculation, which is extensively practised if animals are primarily for food.
†Speying, or spaying, an operation on the female to prevent pregnancy.

GENERAL

Slink veal. The carcase of an unborn or still-born calf.

Calf. Young bovines from birth to six months.

Stirk. The application of this term varies considerably; it usually implies weaned calves in some parts both male and female.

Bud. A young bovine animal.

Stores. Lean cattle prior to fattening.

Baby beef. Cattle finished at an early age, say between 11 and 15 months.

In calver, or in calf. A female which has been successfully mated. The term 'springer' is also met with in some localities.

Barren, farrow, or eild, are applied in various parts to females which have been mated unsuccessfully.

Stag or seg. A male castrated after masculine features have developed or one not effectively castrated or an animal in which one or both testicles have failed to descend into the scrotum.

2   Growth

During pre-natal growth the various tissues compete for nutrients from the maternal blood stream. The brain, central nervous system, and essential organs have the initial priority, followed by bone, muscle, and finally fat.

Thus on a low plane of nutrition fat growth would be the first tissue to be affected, but with a further restriction the rate of muscle development would be retarded.

In young animals the head is relatively large, the legs are long, the body is short and lacks depth. Breeds of calves differ somewhat at birth in average weight, Charolais probably producing the heaviest. The actual size is, of course, controlled by the mother. Growth takes place in waves from the extremities, and the practical butcher knows that the point of lowest development of bone and muscle lies between the rump and the loin. As growth progresses, modifications take place, so that the relative body length increases, followed by a deepening of the trunk. The best example of this type of growth change is probably that which takes place in the ruminant stomachs. In a young calf the fourth stomach (abomasum, rennet-bag, or reed) is the largest of the four compartments, but as the animal develops and consumes bulky foods the first stomach (rumen, or paunch) rapidly increases in size until in a mature beast it may be capable of holding 30 gal (136 litres) of water. If in the live animal this balancing-up process of growth is rapid, we have an early maturing beef breed or possibly a dual purpose animal, whereas in dairy breeds the final conformation is different and the development of body form is less rapid and complete.

The graph following (Fig. 4) based upon the figures for Hereford × Friesian cattle (Pomeroy) indicate that the percentage of shin, leg and neck declines with maturity, whilst the sirloin, coast and flank all show an increasing trend, throughout the two-year period of this work. The first of these joints to reach a staple percentage is the sirloin. The round which formed the largest proportion by weight, showed an increasing trend up to 6 months, followed by a consistent decline.

It is of interest that from 12 months onwards the percentage of sirloin tended to be greater in the Herefords than in the Friesians, but the percentage of round tended to be less.

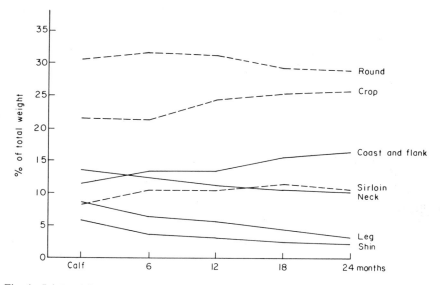

Fig. 4 Joint weight as percentage of total joints for Hereford × Friesian (less kidney knob), channel, and cod fats). More valuable joints indicated as dashed lines

In baby beef production, a well-bred beef type is usually kept going from birth with the specific object of producing baby beef. In this case stockiness will start developing at about 12 months, or in show specimens earlier. From the butchers' standard, however, it is inadvisable to permit the deepening process to continue too far as this will reduce the relative proportions of prime roasting joints by increasing the flank and brisket.

In the more general method of beef production the breeder, or feeder, usually permits a 'store period' in which the animals grow rangy, and this is followed by intensive finishing. This method is probably influenced by the fact that poor grass and hay are cheap and the quantity of labour involved is small.

Fat cattle coming on to the market can be considered broadly under three headings.

(A) Light weights, of about 12 to 15 months, weighing around 8 cwt (400 kg).

(B) Medium weights, from animals of 20 to 30 months, weighing about 9 to 11 cwt (460 to 560 kg).

(C) Heavy weights, obtained chiefly from cattle which have been allowed to reach their full growth prior to fattening.

TABLE 1

Analysis of Aberdeen-Angus, Shorthorn Cross, and Devon carcases

	A Aberdeen-Angus, heifer		B Shorthorn-Cross steer		C Devon steer	
Live weight	8 cwt 2 qr		11 cwt 3 qr		15 cwt	
Carcase weight	548 lb		576 lb		998 lb	
Dressing %	57·56		57·44		59·4	
Joints	% of carcase		% of carcase		% of carcase	
Hindquarter flank	3·3		3·2		3·8	
Dug fat	1·6		(cod) 1·7		(cod) 1·8	
Goose skirt	0·5		0·6		0·7	
Rump	7·0		6·9		6·7	
Loin	10·2		9·9		9·6	
Thick	5·1		5·3		4·9	
Leg	4·0		4·0		4·9	
Pubic bone	0·42		0·75		0·67	
Topside	5·5		6·7		5·8	
Silverside	8·6		8·9		8·4	
Kidney	0.46		0·4		0·31	
Suet	6·0		4·5		3·7	
Total hindquarter	——	52·68	——	52·85	——	51·28
Shin	2·5		2·8		2·75	
Forequarter flank ⎫	{ 4·9	12·5	{ 4·7	9·8	{ 4·5	11·2
Brisket ⎭	{ 7·6		{ 5·1		{ 6·7	
Clod ⎫	{ 3·6	8·7	{ 4·7	9·2	{ 5·4	9·1
Stocking ⎭	{ 5·1		{ 4·5		{ 3·7	
Fore-rib	5·5		6·1		6·0	
Top-rib ⎫	{ 3·9	9·4	{ 4·4	10·1	{ 4·8	9·8
Back-rib ⎭	{ 5·5		{ 5·7		{ 5·0	
Leg mutton cut ⎫	{ 3·0		{ 3·0		{ 3·1	
Chuck ⎬	{ 2·9	8·2	{ 3·7	8·6	{ 4·3	9·6
Blade ⎭	{ 2·3		{ 1·9		{ 2·2	
Total forequarter	——	46·8	——	46·6	——	48·45
Loss	0·52		0·55		0·27	
Total	100·00		100·00		100·00	
Carcase bone	13·5		14·8		14·2	
Remarks	Choice, small bone, suet excessive		Good, well-fleshed, rather heavy boned		Good, well-finished rather massive forequarter	
	Live Grade A+		Live Grade A+		Live Grade A+	

The above were quartered between the 10th and 11th rib and cut straight across.

Barley beef

There is a good deal of interest in the use of barley beef for the pre-packing trade and a recent test carried out on a really good Friesian of 8½ cwt (430 kg) at just over 11 months resulted in a yield as given below.

The beast was carefully selected and represented a good example of the feeder's art. The conformation was generally good with a very high percentage of hindquarter although, as is common with the Friesian, somewhat lacking in second thigh.

At this stage of growth there was little if any 'deepening' of the carcase, thus providing a low proportion of the less valuable flanks and briskets. Immediately following slaughter the two sides of the carcase were placed in a cooler at approximately 34°F (1°C) and the weight loss some 76 hours later was only about 1½% of the initial weight.

The inedible offal yield (Table 2), particularly the stomach and hide, was relatively small.

TABLE 2

Offal yield of Friesian 'barley beef' carcase

	lb	oz			Approx. % of live weight
Head, ex tongue	23	8			
Tongue	4	4			
Breads	1	8			
Liver	11	12			
Spleen, melt	1	8			
Heart	4	4			
Tail	2	8			
Thick skirt	2	0			
Lungs and trachea	7	4			
			58	8	6·14
Caul fat	14	0			
Gut fat	8	4			
			22	4	2·35
Paunch and honeycomb, empty	15	0	15	0	1·58
Hide	36	0	36	0	3·78
					13·85

The body was then prepared by cutting a 10-rib forequarter and using a modified London and Home Counties method of cutting to give the following results (Table 3).

TABLE 3

Analysis of Friesian 'barley beef' carcase
Cold weight of carcase, 538 lb

	% of carcase	
H$\frac{1}{4}$ flanks, cut full	4	
Thick flanks	5·7	
Silvers, long cut	9·35	
Topside, ex fat	5·75	
Legs	6·45	
Rumps	6·7	
Loin, ex short cut	9·35	
Goose skirt	0·55	
Clods and stickings	10·4	
Shin	2·85	
Coasts, flank and brisket, cut full	8·5	
Fore-ribs	5·7	
Middle-ribs	9·4	
Steakmeats	7·45	
	———	92·15
Kidneys		0·35
Suet and cod fat		7·50
		———
		100·00

That ratio of H$\frac{1}{4}$ to F$\frac{1}{4}$ joints worked out at 55·7% to 44·3% respectively.

The relatively high figure for the rump was obtained by de-boning the aitch bones and rump bones in one piece to permit a greater latitude in cutting off the rump and fillet.

On subsequent de-boning and removal of the gristles the total amount

TABLE 4

Typical Friesian carcase
Cold weight of carcase, 608 lb (276 kg)

	% of carcase
Potentially saleable meat	71
Fat and suet	11
Bone, gristle and loss	18
	———
	100

of potentially saleable meat worked out at practically 74·3% carcase weight, of which approximately 18·2% was bone gristle and loss, etc., with a total fat figure of 7·5%. It should be emphasized that this was probably an ideal beast in terms of yield and the resultant boneless meat was subjected only to a moderate degree of trim. An example taken from a somewhat more representative carcase gave the yield as shown in Table 4.

In terms of potentially saleable meat the appropriate factors by which the cost price of the carcase should be multiplied to find the saleable meat cost would be 1·346 in the case of the 538 lb (244 kg) carcase and 1·408 for the heavier carcase.

It should be noted that this difference is almost entirely due to the quantity of suet and fat trim in the heavier carcase.

Young Bulls

In most European countries, beef from young bulls contributes materially to the supply of meat and such beef usually attracts a premium. There has been an increasing interest in the production of this class of meat in the United Kingdom. There is little doubt that this was stimulated by the importation of large quantities of young bull beef from Yugoslavia, mainly from Simenthal cattle, and small importations from Cuba.

Extensive trials carried out in this country prove that growth rates and food conversion are far superior in bulls, as compared with steers; the former do not of course suffer the characteristic setback associated with castration. In general it may be found that bull beef can be produced for about 1p per lb dead weight less than steers under similar conditions. Thus, this form of production can be attractive to the farmer and, if such animals are slaughtered at a relatively early age, they do not present any great management problems.

From the aspect of the retailer, such beef carries very little surplus fat and may yield from about 6% to 10% more lean than comparable steers.

A consumer acceptance survey in a number of retail shops in the Midlands indicated ready repeat sales with a market increase in the demand for briskets and flanks. It was considered that sides from young bulls were worth up to 1p per lb more than those from steers, by the multiple firm concerned.

The extreme leanness of such beef may be attractive to many buyers but, if tenderness is the main criterion of quality, the meat may often be found inferior to that from young steers.

Obviously, the treatment by tenderizing techniques could completely change this picture.

The following comparison carried out in this country and its general implications is given in Table 5.

· TABLE 5

Comparison of carcases from four steers and four bulls

Both groups had the same sire and were reared under identical conditions of management and feed. Age at slaughter 10¼ months. Pure Friesian.

	(Average)	
	Bulls	Steers
Carcase weight, cold	471 lb	453 lb
Weight of F¼'s	237 lb	226 lb
Weight of H¼'s	234 lb	227 lb
Radius-ulna, length	370 mm	365 mm
Leg metatarsal-pubis, length	778 mm	763 mm
Eye muscle, length	142 mm	142 mm
Eye muscle, depth	60 mm	58 mm
Fat over eye muscle	4·2 mm	5·2 mm
Colour 0–12 (12 = darkest)	10·5	9·75
Kidney suet 1–5 (1 = most)	3·5	2·5

General implications

(1) The carcase weight of the bulls is slightly higher (3·97 %) than that of the steers.

2) There is little difference between the H¼ and F¼ meat in spite of the lower suet content of the bulls.

(3) From the length of bone in relation to the weight of the quarter (fores 6·2 in steers, 6·4 in bulls; hinds 3·0 for both) it would appear that at this stage of growth castration had not yet affected bone length.

(4) Whilst the length of the eye muscle, an early developing part, has not been affected by castration, the depth, a late developing part, has been very slightly increased.

(5) The muscle is darker in bulls than in steers and might thus imply more flavour.

(6) The kidney fat is greatly increased by castration.

(7) The subcutaneous fat is slightly increased by castration.

(8) In the author's opinion the differences would be more marked if the animals had been slaughtered at 12 months.

The following data (Fig. 5 and Table 6) illustrate the effect of fattening and maturing on carcase composition. A proportionate decrease occurs in the bone content of the various joints as the fat is laid down, with the consequent increase in the calorific value of the joints.

The live animal

LOCAL PREFERENCES

As a rule there is a local preference for the breed or type of animal predominating in the particular area, and though, for example, the Friesian is widely distributed throughout the British Isles, and for that matter the world, many breeds are to some extent restricted to certain localities. In addition to this factor there are preferences shown in some parts as regards sex, finish, and weight. Some buyers consider that heifers mature more quickly and provide better flesh with a smoother finish, whilst others contend that steers have the advantage as they are reputed to carry a greater ratio of more valuable cuts. Again, in areas devoted to dairying, heifers would be more easily obtained than steers. It is probable that these preferences are based rather on custom than scientific fact and that quality and finish are more important in the long run than the factors outlined above.

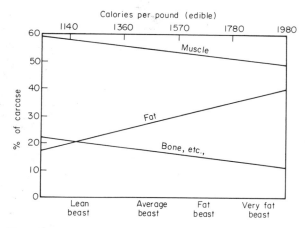

Fig. 5 Effect of fattening and maturing on carcase composition
(Chart based upon data kindly supplied by Dr. E. H. Callow)

Consumers show marked preferences in the quantity of fat they require with their meat, and this in turn is reflected in the degree of finish in the live animal. With the extension of the mechanical rather than the physical, the amount of fat required generally is obviously reduced. The town worker will want leaner meat than his agricultural brother, and the worker in the heavy trades, iron-working, stevedores, etc., must have more calories than, say, textile workers engaged in a warm, humid atmosphere. Usually a demand for lean animals indicates

TABLE 6

Analysis of three fattened Shorthorn steers

Joints	Fat baby beef		Fat 2-year-old		Fat 3-year-old	
	Bone and loss (%)	Calories (per lb)	Bone and loss (%)	Calories (per lb)	Bone and loss (%)	Carlories (per lb)
Clod and sticking	23	1050	25	1235	21	1385
3-rib and leg-of-mutton piece	22	960	18	1185	12	1440
3-rib piece	26	1035	23	1445	16	1765
6-rib piece	25	1300	22	1685	17	2010
Loin*	14	1380	15	1555	10	2120
Rump	17	1590	16	1700	15	1540
Round	18	985	13	1255	10	1410
Aitch-bone	30	1150	29	1250	27	1505
Hind shin	55	405	55	465	46	715
Thick flank	8	1480	7	1580	6	1665
Plate	24	1415	16	2010	11	2280
Brisket	22	1645	21	1730	14	2025
Fore shin	54	405	53·5	395	48	565
Suet	—	3840	—	3840	—	3840

*Loin, including thin flank.
(Figures compiled from *Beef Production in Great Britain,* Wood and Newman.)

a lower consumption of meat. In London and the Home Counties a side of beef of about 280 to 300 lb (127 to 136 kg), not excessively fat, seems to be about the ideal, and such a side might be obtainable from a good beast of about 9 to 9½ cwt (457 to 482 kg) live weight. There appears to be slight variations in the weight demands in different parts of the country. For example, Southern Scotland has a preference for a somewhat heavier carcase, whilst South Wales usually demands much lighter weights.

Inspection

Though inspection of an animal from the aspect of health or disease is obviously the province of the veterinary world, a few general observations may prove of value to the student and the butcher.

The type and general appearance of the animal is of importance. For example, the possibility of disease in an old, emaciated cow is much greater than is the case with a well-finished prime young steer. It is of course obvious that, generally speaking, the older the beast the greater the probability of its having contracted disease. The normal temperature of the ox, 101·4°F (38·5°C), is not greatly above that of the human, and in a healthy animal the ears, hoofs, and horns should be cool to the touch. The eye should be clear and bright, the animal alert, and it should attempt to move away when approached. The coat should be smooth and lie close to the hide, the skin mellow to the touch and freely moving on the underlying structure. There should of course be no bare patches or signs of parasitic conditions. The breathing should be steady and regular, and, if a cough can be induced by pinching the larynx, this may indicate possible trouble. There should be no offensive discharges and one should look for any abnormal swellings, particularly around the lower jaw. (A moist muzzle with a certain amount of clear fluid is normal.) The dung should be free from blood, and an abnormal smell may indicate physic. The urine should be straw-coloured, not cloudy, and discharged in a strong continuous stream. In the United States it has been found that about 25% of the animals marked as suspect in the ante-mortem inspection are condemned at the time of slaughter.

Quality points

The animal should be viewed from the side and, in beef types, should present a straight back and under-line with good depth, the body generally rectangular in form, with the head short and broad between the eyes. From the back the rump should appear long and broad, the ribs well barrelled, and the thighs thickly fleshed. The legs should be straight and short, meat extending well down to the hocks and the bone fine. A coarse tail frequently indicates a big-boned animal. The skin should be mellow and the hair fine.

Handling points (Fig. 6)

The flank will give a general idea of the quantity of fat laid down, as a double fold can be grasped. In very poor animals little more than a double layer of skin can be felt (3). The degree of fat on the barrel can be judged by placing the thumb and finger on either side of the last rib (4). If the finger-tips are placed on the backbone above the hip, the thumb can be brought down on to the end of the hip bone (the point at which the gristle of the rump is cut through to separate the rump and loin), and this will provide a very good guide as to the fatness (2). The cod fat, or in the case of a heifer the dug fat, can be examined by holding the tail and passing the right hand between the back legs. The two fat pockets on either side of the tail (1) should also be handled for

Suggested scale for judging a butcher's beast

	Max.	Award
GENERAL		
Form. Straight top line and under-line deep, low, and well-sprung ribs	10	
Condition. Development of muscle and degree of finish	10	
Weight. According to age and trade requirements	10	
Quality. Fine hair, mellow skin, uniform finish, sufficient firmness to indicate large ratio of muscle	10	
	— 40	—
HINDQUARTERS		
Back. Straight, smooth and even	10	
Loin. Thick and broad	8	
Thighs. Full and well fleshed	4	
Rump. Long, wide, and even, head and tail smooth	3	
Hip-bones. Smooth and well covered	2	
Pin-bones. Well apart, not too prominent	2	
Flank. Full and level with under-line	2	
Legs. Fine bone, straight and short	2	
	— 33	—
FOREQUARTERS		
Ribs. Well barrelled, thickly fleshed	8	
Chest. Large girth, full crop	4	
Shoulders. Well fleshed, neat, and smooth	3	
Shoulder vein. Full	2	
Neck. Short and thick	2	
Brisket. Well forward and wide	1	
Legs. Straight, fine shank	2	
	— 22	—
HEAD		
Muzzle. Broad, wide jaw, large nostrils	2	
Face. Short and broad	1	
Horns. Fine texture, or in polled, no sign of horns	1	
Ears. Medium size	1	
	— 5	—
Total	100	

additional indication of finish, and finally there should be no dropping away behind the shoulders (5). The type of animal required by the average butcher, to cater for modern consumer demand, is a beast of

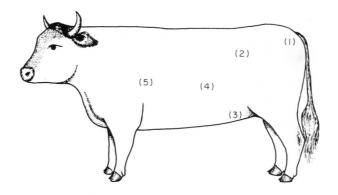

Fig. 6   Handling points

about 8 to 9½ cwt (406 to 482 kg) with a good dressing percentage (not obtained at the expense of excessive fat) which will yield him a carcase with a high proportion of the valuable cuts in conjunction with small bone. Long and continual experience is necessary to become an expert in judging the live beast, though in many cases there are individuals who appear to possess an instinctive flair for 'knowing' the type of carcase obtainable from a given animal. With this fortunate type of individual, first impressions of weight, quality, and probable dressing percentage appear to be the most valuable. With the introduction of the weighbridge the question of judging the live weight of a beast assumes less importance, but the average good judge should be capable of placing a beast within a 5% weight error, either way.

Indications of age

The period of gestation in the cow is about 40 weeks, though this may show considerable variation, and extremes of 35 weeks to over 45 weeks have been recorded. In an unborn or stillborn calf the lungs will be collapsed and will sink in water, proving that the animal has not breathed, the feet will be unscratched and the flesh is deficient in fat and easily torn. Normally the navel cord of the calf dries up during the first week of its life and falls off during the second week. The scab remaining will probably be cast about a month after the birth of the calf. In horned breeds the thickening of the skin on the skull can be noticed at about three weeks, indicating the formation of horns. At these points the hair becomes thin, and the horn-cap can usually be seen at about 8 to 10 weeks. At around 3 months a moveable horn-point is present which on flaying is removed with the skin. In bull calves the horn becomes fixed rather earlier than in the case of heifers, that is at about 4 to 5 months.

Dentition

For normal commercial purposes the age of cattle is usually judged by the incisor teeth, though for show purposes the molars may also be examined.

The dental formula for a 'full mouth' is the following.

	Molars	Premolars	Incisors	Premolars	Molars	
Upper jaw	3	3	0 | 0	3	3	} 32 teeth
Lower jaw	3	3	4 | 4	3	3 .	

The dental formula for the *temporary* teeth is as follows.

	Premolars	Incisors	Premolars	
Upper jaw	3	0 | 0	3	} 20 teeth
Lower jaw	3	4 | 4	3	

The temporary incisors can easily be recognized by their small size, whitish sheen, and rather rounded form. These milk teeth are erupted in pairs from the centre outwards, their place being taken by the permanent incisors. In addition to the number of 'broad teeth' present, in the case of a 'full mouth' the degree of wear on the crown and the formation of necks caused by the gums receding will provide an indication of probable age. Feed and probably breed may influence the teething events and the rate of wear, but the following will indicate average periods of eruption of the teeth in the ox.

Temporary	Eruption
1st pair of incisors ⎫	
2nd pair of incisors ⎪	
3rd pair of incisors ⎬	Birth to 3 weeks
4th pair of incisors ⎭	
1st cheek tooth	At about 3 weeks
2nd cheek tooth ⎫	
3rd cheek tooth ⎭	Birth to a few days

Permanent

1st pair of incisors	$1\frac{1}{2}$ to 2 years
2nd pair of incisors	2 to $2\frac{1}{2}$ years
3rd pair of incisors	3 years
4th pair of incisors	$3\frac{1}{2}$ to 4 years
1st cheek tooth	2 to $2\frac{1}{2}$ years
2nd cheek tooth	$1\frac{1}{2}$ to $2\frac{1}{2}$ years
3rd cheek tooth	$2\frac{1}{2}$ to 3 years
4th cheek tooth	5 to 6 months
5th cheek tooth	1 to $1\frac{1}{2}$ years
6th cheek tooth	2 to $2\frac{1}{2}$ years

Below are the regulations of the Smithfield Club regarding dentition in cattle.

'Cattle showing the back part of the second upper molar (fifth cheek tooth) half up, will be considered as exceeding one year and four months.

Cattle having their central permanent incisors cut will be considered as exceeding 1 years and 6 months.'

Cattle having their central permanent incisors fully up will be considered as exceeding 1 year and 9 months.

Cattle having their second pair of permanent incisors fully up will be considered as exceeding 2 years and 3 months.'

(Recent investigations indicate that considerable variation can occur in dentition, in some cases amounting to several months as compared to average.)

3   Some British breeds of cattle

Apart from the general external distinguishing features of the different breeds, other factors are involved in comparing their value as economic producers of beef.

Certain breeds and their crosses may thrive under upland and hill conditions, whilst others respond more favourably to a kinder environment.

Breed and even different sires within a breed, may cause varying degrees of difficulty in calving, chiefly due to the size of the calf.

Breeds can differ in their efficiency in converting feed into live weight gain, some authorities claiming that this can amount to as much as 5 to 6%. Differences in growth rate of different breeds and sires within breeds, may be up to almost 10%. A rapid growth to slaughter weight, increases the throughput and consequently the return obtained on the capital invested. However, the major consideration to the meat trade is the carcase, and it is the *carcase* weight gain which is significant, provided that the carcase composition will provide a high proportion of meat as prepared for retail sale. This will be influenced by the amount of fat trim, proportion of bone and in terms of cash, a high yield of the more expensive portions, chiefly from the hindquarter. Below is a brief outline of the characteristics of some beef and dual-purpose breeds of interest from the aspect of beef production.

British Friesian

Over 73% of our beef is now obtained from the dairy herd, and in this respect the Friesian and its crosses are numerically the strongest. Therefore this breed is dealt with in rather more detail than the other breeds referred to.

British Friesians (Plate 3) are descended from the stock which has provided most parts of the world with the universal 'Black and White'. It was not, however, until 1909 that the breed acquired pedigree status in this country. This was probably due to the prohibition on the importation of live cattle into Britain in 1892. A special importation of selected breeding animals from Holland was permitted in 1914 and there is little doubt that this stock played a most important part in improving the breed. Further importation took place, chiefly with the object of obtaining an increase in butterfat. Today the British Friesian Cattle Society is the largest association of this type in the country.

Looked upon originally purely as a dairy breed, the Friesian's value as a producer of beef has been emphasized by the current demand for lean meat. It is generally agreed that to produce good beef from a young Friesian means keeping the animal 'going' from birth. With this procedure a good carcase can be obtained at about two years. Many producers favour a Hereford × Friesian, which tends to produce a somewhat stockier carcase with a little more quality.

As a pure breed some remarkable weight/age results have been obtained and records from official sources give the following figures for steers (Table 7).

TABLE 7

Weight/age figures for British Friesian steers

Age (years months days)			Live weight (kg)	(kg/day)
–	11	24	456	1·29
1	1	21	502	1·21
1	1	26	528	1·26
1	2	2	554	1·30
1	2	23	501	1·12
1	4	25	649	1·27

BREED DESCRIPTION—THE BULL

Head. Fairly large and distinctly masculine, broad near the horns, and tapering without undue length to nose, without Roman nose, the whole head being clean cut and without dewlap. The head should be carried high to denote stylishness. The ears should be fairly large, thick, well set on and carried evenly. The muzzle should be broad, with prominent nostrils.

Eyes. Large, bold, alert, and set wide apart.

Horns. The horns should grow straight from the head, not too long, and turn inwards and forwards evenly, but not upwards. They should not be coarse but should be thick and white at the base and gradually taper to the darker point.

Neck. Moderately long, thick, straight, and deep, well let into the shoulders.

Shoulders. The shoulders should be strong, well laid in, and broad at the points.

Body. Deep, with strong loin and well-sprung ribs, showing a good barrel with straight and parallel top and bottom outlines, freedom from hollows (particularly behind the shoulders) and with loose skin.

Quarters. Long and straight on top, hips level but not unduly wider than the pin bones, thighs wide and well let down, well fleshed outside down to the hocks. The buttocks should be wide and flat, without patches at the side of the tail-head.

Tail. The tail, the switch of which must be entirely white, should be set on level, in a line with the back, should not be too coarse and should be carried in a perpendicular line to a point just behind and below the hocks.

Legs. The legs should be strong, straight and short, have nice but not too heavy bone, with good joints and feet, and should be placed well outside each corner of the body. The hocks should be clean, flat and broad.

Colour. Black and white are the only colours permissible. All four legs and the tail switch should be white. The black and white markings should not be mottled or intermingled and, except under special circumstances, a bull with a black hair spot on the foot or such spots on the feet is not eligible to have its entry registered.

Aberdeen-Angus

This is the premier beef breed (Plate 4) and, as its name implies, it originated in the north-east of Scotland. Its ancestry is uncertain, but black polled Scottish cattle were recorded four hundred years ago. Later, crossing was carried out with the Guernsey, Ayrshire, Shorthorn, Galloway, and Fife cattle (the latter now extinct), but it is impossible to estimate to what extent these influenced the modern beast. It is probable that William McCombie must be given the credit of popularizing this breed to the outside world.

CHARACTERISTICS

Polled, the poll being more pronounced than in the Galloway and there should be no indication of horn growth. Uniform black in colour, though white patches under the belly are tolerated. The coat of calves and the winter coat of older cattle may have a brownish tinge. The head should be moderate in length, wide between the eyes, ears placed well

Plate 3   British Friesian bull (*British Friesian Cattle Society of Great Britain & Ireland*)

Plate 4   Aberdeen-Angus steer

Plate 5   South Devon steer

Plate 6   Devon heifer

apart, not loose or hanging. The back straight and broad, the ribs well sprung, the tail hanging close to the hindquarters and light of bone. A coarse tail usually goes with big bone. The hindquarters should be well fleshed, the flank full, and the upper and lower line straight. It is an early maturing breed, admirably suited for the production of 'baby beef'. This breed has been extensively used in various parts of the world for grading up stock and when crossed with horned cows will produce 100% black polled calves. The flesh is of excellent quality and appears to be particularly prone to marbling, and this is considered as a sign of quality by the butcher.

Devons

There are two types, the South Devon or Hams (Plate 5), a large some-what coarse breed, and the Devons (Plate 6), which are more compact and produce beef of the highest quality. The latter are sometimes referred to as the North Devons and locally are termed 'Red Rubies'.

CHARACTERISTICS

Compact, well-balanced form; neat, well-formed shoulders. The hair is red in colour, thus explaining the local term applied to them. The skin is an orange-yellow, particularly round the muzzle and eyes, and inside the ears more of an orange-red. The horns are creamy white in colour, carrying a black tip. It is claimed that these cattle are economical feeders and produce a high ration of valuable joints with a small proportion of bone.

Dexter

This breed is closely associated with the Kerry and it is the smallest of our British breeds (Plate 7). It is thought that the breed probably originated from a freak dwarf (as did the Ancon breed of sheep), and this theory is substantiated by the large proportion of monstrosities (bull-dog calves) which are produced when a cow of this breed is mated to a Dexter bull. They do, however, produce a good butcher's beast when crossed with an Aberdeen-Angus or Shorthorn bull, whilst a Red Poll cross gives a good dual-purpose beast.

CHARACTERISTICS

The colour should be entirely black or red. The body well rounded and plump with a relatively heavy head. The legs are very short and toes turned in, particularly those of the hind feet. In the female the horns are fairly fine and point upwards, whilst in the bull they are thicker and less elevated.

Galloway

This is a polled breed (Plate 8), commonly found in the south of Scotland, particularly Dumfries, Kirkcudbright, and Wigtown. There is also a belted variety (Plate 9) which was at one time very popular in the Tyneside area.

CHARACTERISTICS

Black in colour with a brownish tinge, the hair being fairly long and inclined to be wavy. The poll is flatter and more rounded than in the Aberdeen-Angus. The head is short and very broad and the nostrils wide. Ears are set rather far back and should point upwards. The back is straight, the legs short and strong with muscle extending well down to the hocks. It carries a heavy hide, but gives a mellow touch. This breed produces excellent beef, usually marbled, and it generally shows up well in the carcase competition of the Smithfield Club Show. (A Galloway was junior champion at under two years in 1923, scaling over 13 cwt (660 kg)). The belted variety is similar in general conformation but it possesses a white belt; unlike the normal Galloway it has good dual purpose qualities.

Hereford

The Hereford breed (Plate 10) is fairly widely distributed. Not only is it largely found in Herefordshire and Shropshire, but it also predominates in Montgomery, Radnor and Brecon. It is a hardy breed and is therefore popular for range conditions, and a polled variety of Hereford has been produced which renders de-horning unnecessary. The Hereford is possibly closely connected with the Devon, Sussex, and Welsh Black, and orange-yellow skins are common to them.

CHARACTERISTICS

Dark red, with a white face, brisket, belly, feet, and switch, and a white marking extending along the spine over the shoulders. Horns of medium length with a wax-like colour, black tips are considered objectionable. The eyes are full and the eyelids red in colour, the nostrils broad and the muzzle flesh-coloured. The body is rectangular in form, thick and

Plate 7   Dexter heifer (*Farmer & Stockbreeder*)
Plate 8   Galloway bull

Plate 9 Belted Galloway bull (*Farmer & Stockbreeder*)

Plate 10 Hereford heifer

deep with the legs well placed. The brisket stands well out between and in front of the legs. The Hereford will cross well with other breeds; the bull crossed with a Galloway gives a white-face polled beast which feeds well and gives a good butchers' beast.

West Highland or Kyloes

This breed (Plate 11) is found chiefly in Argyll (the north-western parts) and the Western Isles of Scotland. It is a very hardy breed, slow maturing, the cows yielding a small quantity of rich quality milk. The flesh is of very high quality but it usually takes over three years to produce a good beef steer.

CHARACTERISTICS

Black appears to be the original colour, though now dun, brindled, with various shades of red and yellow predominate. The hide is thick and the coat is shaggy, thick and glossy. The horns are long in both male and female, light in colour, coming out level with the head and rising towards the point. The body is well developed, particularly the back and hindquarters, whilst the legs are powerful and short. The tail carries a good switch and is long, almost reaching the ground. Cows of this breed will cross successfully with earlier maturing beef breeds but, as would be expected, these crosses do not possess the hardiness of the dam.

Shorthorn

The Shorthorn (Plate 12) was at one time numerically the strongest of all British breeds; it embraces beef-producing strains as well as dual-purpose and dairy types. It is also very popular in the Argentine, the Dominions, and the United States. In some parts of the world it is referred to by its older name, the Durham. The breed as a whole has the valuable characteristic of adaptation to a wide range of climatic conditions. It has a marked ability to pass on its characteristics to its progeny and is therefore of great value in grading up native stock. The majority of Shorthorns in this country consist of dual-purpose types, the few pure beef strains being relatively poor milkers.

CHARACTERISTICS

The horns are short and blunt, somewhat oval in section and set fairly widely apart. The colour may be red, white, and roan, the latter colour being most common. The white type is used in this country to cross with

Galloway cows to produce the 'Blue-grey'. The muzzle, palate, lips, and eyelids should be flesh-coloured. The back is straight, wide across the hook bones, and the hindquarters square in outline as compared with most other beef breeds.

Red Poll

The Red Poll (Plate 13) enjoys a very high reputation as a dual-purpose beast. They are found chiefly in Norfolk and Suffolk. The breed has developed from the Polled Suffolk Duns, a breed with a good milk record, and the Old Red Norfolk Horned breed, which was a small, early maturing beef type. The modern Red Poll has retained much of these virtues.

CHARACTERISTICS

The colour is red (dun may sometimes occur) and the presence of horn growth or scurs is an objection. The form is compact, with a good upper line and a fine bone. The tail tassel is white, and in the case of the cow the udder may also be white. The breed is usually well represented at the Smithfield Club Show and it supplies a high-quality carcase.

Sussex

This is one of the largest and heaviest of British breeds (Plate 14). It is found chiefly in Sussex, Surrey, and Kent, and on account of its size and strength was at one time extensively used for draught purposes. The breed has proved popular in South Africa on account of its hardiness.

CHARACTERISTICS

They bear some resemblance to the Devon but are less compact and pleasing in form, the colour is dark red with a white tip to the tail. The horns are strongly developed and somewhat irregular in form. Of recent years greater attention has been paid to form, early maturity, and depth of flesh with the object of producing a good beef animal with a hardy constitution.

Welsh Black

There are two main varieties of this breed (Plate 15), the North Wales or Anglesey and the South Wales, the latter being referred to as Pembroke or Castle Martin cattle. The South Wales varieties tend towards dairy standards, whilst those cattle from the North can be considered as

Plate 11   Highland cattle

Plate 12   Beef Shorthorn heifer

Plate 13   Red Poll steer

Plate 14   Sussex steer (*Photo by Joan Pitt, Sussex Cattle Society*)

Plate 15   Welsh Black steer

Plate 16   Mature and young Charolais bulls (*Farmer & Stockbreeder*)

good dual-purpose beasts. There was at one time a steady trade with stores of this breed for grazing in the Midlands.

CHARACTERISTICS

Black in colour, the winter coat possessing a brown tinge, the horns are strong and well developed, showing considerable variation in form. The neck and forequarters are inclined to be massive and in some cases the hindquarters appear light. They do, however, yield a better dressing percentage than their general appearance suggests.

Charolais

This breed originated in Central France and the first importation of Charolais semen into this country took place in 1955. In late 1961, a number of young bulls were imported and were distributed to A.I. centres in England and Wales (Plate 16). A British Charolais Society has now been formed and interest in this breed, particularly for crossing purposes has rapidly increased. The original French Charolais Herd book is dated 1887 and is published at Nevers. The following breed characteristics are specified.

TABLE 8

Summary of some British breeds of cattle

Breed	Beef	Dual purpose	Relative weight	Colour	Horned	Polled
British Friesian		×	10	Black and White	×	
Aberdeen-Angus	×		9	Black		×
Dexter		×	5	Black or Red	×	
Devon	×		8	Red	×	
South Devon		×	11	Lighter Red	×	
Hereford	×		10	Red, White Face and Belly	×	×
Highland	×		7	Dun or Brindle	×	
Galloway	×		8	Black, Black and White Belt	×	×
Shorthorn	×		10	Red, White, Roan		
Shorthorn		×	10	Red, White, Roan	×	
Red Poll		×	8	Red		×
Sussex	×		10	Deep Red	×	
Welsh Black		×	8	Black	×	
Charolais	×		12	White or Straw	×	

The relative weights are intended to provide some comparison of size based on mature animals of comparable finish.

CHARACTERISTICS

Hair colour white or light wheat. The head relatively small, short with wide forehead, flat, or slightly concave. The top of the head is straight, head short from eye level to muzzle. Horns round, white and tapered. Ears of medium size, thin and almost hairless. Eyes large and prominent, cheeks heavy and the muzzle broad.

The neck short with a short dewlap. The chest deep, ribs round and neatly laid into the body. Top-line horizontal with the under-line, very muscular loins wide and thick, hips not too prominent, but very wide as is the rump. The buttock deep and well fleshed down to the hock, the tail well set in with body, tapered and ending in a fine switch. Legs short and well set, not too fine in the bone. Skin not too thick, but soft to the touch.

For full-grown cattle the weight of average cows varies between 1540 lb (700 kg) and 1760 lb (800 kg), for bulls, between 2200 lb (1000 kg) and 2640 lb (1200 kg).

Typical yields

Following is a summary of work carried out by Spillers Ltd in conjunction with J. Sainsbury, comparing intensively fed Devons, Friesians, Lincolns, and Sussex, from the aspect of beef production. Forty-one carcases were involved in this test.

	Devon	Friesian	Lincoln	Sussex
Average age at slaughter (days)	348	329	347	339
Live weight (farm) (lb)	850	872	855	849
Empty live weight (lb)	816	833	818	811
Cold carcase weight (lb)	483	485	477	483
Killing out %, empty weight	59·2	58·2	58·3	59·5
% carcase composition				
Bone and gristle	16·32	19·49	17·44	16·34
Suet, rendering fat, and excess trussing fat	17·36	10·11	14·89	13·94
Total trim, bone and fat	33·68	29·60	32·33	30·28
Trimmed retail cuts	64·35	68·43	65·82	67·89
Trimmings and cutting loss	1·97	1·97	1·85	1·83
	100	100	100	100

During the course of the dissection, the following comments were recorded on colour of fat, colour of lean, and degree of marbling.

Fat colour. The fat of all the carcases was the characteristic 'creamy' colour associated with the method of intensive feeding (high concentrate/low roughage, both concentrates and hay on offer, *ad lib*).

Flesh colour. The muscle colour of almost all the carcases was relatively light, with the following variations.

	Devon	Friesian	Lincoln	Sussex
Pale	1	2	3	1
Bright (good)	8	4	6	9
Dark	3	4	–	–

Marbling. The degree of marbling was assessed visually at the 12th rib.

	Devon	Friesian	Lincoln	Sussex
Well marbled	2	–	2	3
Moderate	1	1	1	3
Slight	9	3	6	4
None	–	6	–	1

Almost all samples were tender, in the case of 7 samples (5 Sussex, 2 Devon) there was a slight degree of 'chewiness' not typical of beef of this age. In no case did this amount to undesirable toughness.

All the samples were tasted by a panel, alongside prime Scotch beef and, by comparison, the flavour was delicate, the degree of variation being the following.

	Devon	Friesian	Lincoln	Sussex
Above average (good)	5	2	5	–
Satisfactory	4	6	4	9
Below average	3	2	–	1

Retail yield. As against a datum line of 100, representing all carcases in the trial, the mean retail yield of each group was the following.

	Devon	Friesian*	Lincoln	Sussex
	97·1	102·2	98·9	102·1

*This excludes two Friesian carcases which were so deficient in 'finish' that they were sold at reduced prices.

Blonde d'Aquitaine

The breed originated in the south-west of France where it had a high reputation as a draught beast and for beef. Following agricultural mechanization, emphasis was concentrated on its selection for beef production.

The first importation of Blondes into the UK took place in 1972 and a Blonde d'Aquitaine Breeders Society of Great Britain was formed.

CHARACTERISTICS (Plate 17)

The coat should be a light wheat colour, ranging from light to darker shades, often with lighter rings around the eyes and muzzle. Lighter colour on the inner sides of the leg and under the belly. Horns, light colour, darkening at the tips, hooves also light in colour. Head not too massive, with a straight or slightly convex profile. Forehead and muzzle broad, face triangular. Mucous membranes, pinkish in colour.

Body long (a feature very marked in calves) forequarters well fleshed. Back broad and flat with thick muscular loins. Deep rounded chest and ribs, a broad rump, well developed second thighs and a smooth tail setting. Legs, fine boned and well placed. In terms of muscle: fat: bone ratio, and the area of the 'eye' muscle, they compare most favourably with other continental breeds, (see Table 9) for crossing with dairy type cows.

Limousin

Apart from its wide recognition in France as a beef breed, it has been very successful in many other countries in Europe and in North America, both under ranch and feedlot conditions. In 1971 the Limousin Cattle Breeders (UK) Ltd imported two Limousin bulls which were used on Friesian cows. Subsequently, detailed cutting tests were carried out on seven steer carcases, to assess their value in terms of vacuum packed primal cuts. The average yield of saleable meat was 73·6%, based upon the initial cold carcase weight, two of them achieving the exceptional level of 75·2%. The average cold carcase weight of the seven bodies, being 518 lb (235 kg) at an average age of 344 days.

CHARACTERISTICS (Plate 18)

Coat, wheat coloured, but not too dark, lighter under the belly and around the perineum, horns and hooves, blond. Head, short with a broad forehead and muzzle; thin horns, slightly rounded at the tops. Muscular shoulder; deep rounded chest and ribs: broad back with

Plate 17   Blonde d'Aquitaine bull (*Anglo-French Beef Sires Ltd*)
Plate 18   Limousin bull (*Limousin Cattle Breeders (UK) Ltd*)

prominent muscling. Large rump, broad at the pin bones; deep well rounded thighs. Legs well placed and finely boned. Objections include, spots on coat, mucous membrane or horns and faulty stance.

Simmental

This breed, with its many types, is numerically the most important breed of cattle in Europe. The breed originated in Switzerland, their colour being a dun-red or 'leather-yellow' and white. They were recognized as a breed in 1862, the herd book dates back to 1890. They are known under various names, such as the Tachete Rouge in France, Red Pied Fruilli in Italy, Kula in Bulgaria and the Yugoslav Pied. There are also Russian, Polish, Rumanian and Czechoslovakian strains. Of recent years there has been an increasing interest in the German variety, the Fleckvieh, this type being recognized as being excellent producers of beef, combined with good milking characteristics. The British Simmental Cattle Society was formed in 1970 when a number of bulls and females were imported from Germany and Switzerland.

CHARACTERISTICS (Plate 19)

The coat colour is red and white, but varying from a dark dun to almost yellow dominant on a white background. Typically, the white is on the face, legs, tail and under the body, but there can be white patches over the shoulders and on the flanks, but not usually at the tail head. Large areas of both colours is the breeding objective, rather than smaller intermixed patches. The back is long and level, chest broad and deep, hindquarters well developed, with flesh extending well down the hocks, and relatively short legs. The head is somewhat long with a straight profile, but with a wide 'grazing' muzzle, when viewed from the front.

Chianina

The name is derived from Val di Chiana, a valley situated between Lake Trasimeno and the river Arno. Considerable discussion still exists regarding the probable origin of the breed. Whilst the herd book dates back only to 1956, a number of breeders were concentrating on improvement, well before this date. This involved consideration of conformation, weight for age coupled with periodical measurements in order to assess the relative changes taking place during growth. The most impressive characteristic is their size and the following are the average figures obtained from 8 high standard adult bulls:

Live weight	1532 kg	(30 cwt)
Height at withers	180 cm	(71 in)
Circumference (thorax)	268 cm	(105 in)
Body Length	202 cm	(80 in)

At the Royal Smithfield Show (1974) a cross from a Chianina bull and Friesian dam, achieved a liveweight gain of 3·7 lb (1·7 kg) per day, on cereal feed.

CHARACTERISTICS

At birth the hair tends to be a reddish colour, changing to white at about 6 months. In the case of males, grey hair appears on the neck and shoulders during the winter. The muzzle, hooves and switch of the tail are black and the horns are a medium length, elliptical in cross section. Initially the horns are black in colour, becoming yellow with maturity. The head is relatively small, the length of leg (an important feature in draught cattle) has, with the emphasis on beef production, been reduced. As would be expected there is a heavy muscular development with good body depth and well barrelled ribs.

Comparison of continental breeds

The Danish Research Organization (EGVET) have been conducting a large scale investigation involving eight continental breeds (semen from five bulls within each breed) and some 1350 dairy type cows.

The preliminary results relating to the carcase composition of males, intensively fed to reach 300 kg (660 lb) at 12 to 15 months, emphasize the superiority of the Blonde sire, in this test, as shown in table. 9.

Identification of crosses*

It is generally agreed that crossbreds are usually more fertile, have a lower mortality rate and an 'hybrid vigour' which results in better growth. In addition to the crosses previously mentioned, Charolais, Simmental, Limousin and more recently Blonde d'Aquitaine bulls have been increasingly used in the UK for crossing purposes, chiefly on account of the yield of lean meat obtained from such carcases.

With first crosses uniformity is increased, but if such first crosses are mated, there is an increased variability, so that the progeny may appear with the undesirable characteristic of both parents. There is so much

*I am indebted to Dr Pomeroy for the use of his notes on this subject.

Plate 19   Simmental-Fleckvieh heifer (*Norwood & Sons*)

Plate 20   Chianina bull (*Chianina Cattle Breed Society of Great Britain Ltd*)

TABLE 9

Sire breed	K. Out %	% Lean	% Fat	% Bone	Lean to fat ratio	Area of eye muscle cm²
Blonde d'Aquitaine	57·1	74·5	10·0	15·5	7·3	69·9
Charolais	54·2	71·1	12·6	16·4	6·1	65·4
Limousin	56·2	70·9	13·8	15·2	5·4	68·5
Simmental	54·3	70·7	12·5	16·8	6·1	66·1
Chianina	55·2	70·0	12·4	17·7	6·1	60·7
Romagnola	54·8	69·9	13·3	16·8	5·7	67·8
Danish Red and White	53·6	69·1	14·1	16·8	5·4	60·1
Hereford	54·1	65·7	17·8	16·5	4·0	58·7
Average	54·9	70·2	13·3	16·5	5·8	64·7

Summary:
  (1) Differences between breeds for muscle to bone and muscle to fat ratios are large. Blonde d'Aquitaine, Limousin and Charolais being superior.
  (2) Under this system of feeding little difference in growth and feed conversion was observed.
  (3) Easiest calvings followed the use of Hereford and Limousin bulls, whilst most difficult births can be expected from Romagnoli, Chianina and Charolais sired calves.

indiscriminate cross-breeding of cattle that crosses are frequently difficult to identify with certainty and the problem is aggravated by the dominance of some of the breed characteristics. Thus the dominance of the black coat and polled condition of the Aberdeen-Angus is such that, while it is relatively easy to decide that a polled black animal is not a pure Aberdeen-Angus, it is almost impossible to decide what other breed went into the cross. The 'Blue-grey' or black and white roan produced by crossing an Aberdeen-Angus with a White Shorthorn is an exception to this general rule.

In general, pure breeds can be identified with a fair degree of certainty and it is considered unlikely that any pure bred animals have been wrongly identified as crosses. On the other hand, some cross-bred animals may approach a characteristic breed type so closely that they may be recorded as pure bred. This could happen, for example, where a Hereford × Shorthorn cow has been backcrossed to a Hereford bull.

First cross Hereford × Shorthorns are unlikely to be confused with pure Herefords for the following reasons.

(a) The white face of the Hereford is incompletely dominant and red patches appear on the face of the crossbred, particularly around the eyes.

(b) The red coat in the Hereford is a deep ruby colour whereas in the cross it has a pronounced yellowish tinge.

(c) The white 'flash' along the top of the back and the tuft of hair between the horns of the pure Hereford tend to be markedly reduced or even to be absent altogether in the cross.

(d) The horns tend towards the Shorthorn type.

(e) The shape of the head tends towards the Shorthorn type, longer than the Hereford and with a broad, flat muzzle.

Similar considerations apply to the Hereford × Ayrshire cross but in this case the coat has an even more pronounced yellowish tinge, the upcurving Ayrshire horn is dominant, and sometimes but not always the broken coat pattern of the Ayrshire tends to appear. Hereford × Friesian crosses can be confused with Hereford × Welsh but they usually have white patches, particularly in the under-line and feet. Furthermore, the Friesian coat is sleek and shiny compared with the rough, hairy coat of the Welsh and this characteristic appears in the cross. However, this characteristic can be affected by the condition of the animal since animals in poor condition tend to have rough, hairy coats.

Throughout Dr Pomeroy's survey the temptation to take account of conformation in identifying breeds and crosses has been resisted. For example, on this basis an animal with a beefy conformation might be classified as a Hereford; one with an intermediate conformation as a Hereford × Shorthorn and one with a dairy conformation as a Hereford × Ayrshire. However, Brookes has shown that the so-called beef or dairy conformation can be markedly affected by the way in which an animal has been reared. Consequently, identifying breeds and crosses on the basis of confirmation might have the effect of crediting the Hereford breed with an undue proportion of animals with a good beef conformation and debiting the Ayrshire crosses with an undue proportion of animals with a bad beef conformation.

HEREFORD × FRIESIAN

The cutting test overleaf was carried out on 8 left sides obtained from a uniform group of 8 Hereford × Friesian steers. Cold side weights ranged from 258 lb (117 kg) to 281 lb (128 kg), the average being approximately 272 lb (123 kg).

CHAROLAIS CROSSES

The principal use of beef bulls in this country is for crossing on dairy breeds, to produce cross-bred beef. The Charolais crosses on account of their growth rate and high proportion of lean meat yielded an

TABLE 10

Primal cuts as a percentage of gross weight (Cut 10-rib fores)

H¼ flanks	2·89*	
Rumps and loins, ex	18·05	
Kidneys and suets	3·03†	
Thick flanks	5·35	
Legs (jointed)	4·51	
Buttocks and A bones (with cod and skirt)	18·12	
	———	51·95
Shins	3·02	
Clods and stickings	9·27	
Coasts	9·13*	
Crops	25·10	
	———	46·52
Loss—evaporation, etc.		1·53
		———
		100·00

*At this stage of growth the deepening of the animals had not developed, consequently the proportions of these cuts would be less than those from a fully mature beast of similar type.

†It is generally accepted that the 'open' side (left) will tend to carry less kidney suet than the right side. The kidneys and suets range from 2·75% to 3·6% of the side weight.

attractive carcase, very suitable for present day demands. Initially the emphasis was on Friesian cows, but it was considered by some producers that the Charolais, would add little to the really good Friesian, as they were both fairly large, lean and carried somewhat large bone. However, it was found that the size of the Charolais bone was not directly related to its weight. Attention was then focused on the Ayrshire and Channel Island cows, the resultant carcases proving very acceptable to the butcher. In general, the muscular development of the Charolais, corrected the lack of fleshing in the dairy type and conversely, the bone formation of the Charolais was modified, whilst the fat deposition was somewhat increased, as compared with the pure Charolais. The following tests will provide some comparison of typical crosses, using a Charolais on a Friesian (Plate 21) and on an Ayrshire (Plate 22).

Carcase appraisal

Carcase dissections carried out by Messrs T. Wall and Sons, and the Ministry on Charolais and Hereford cross carcases out of Friesian dams, can be summarized as follows.

Plate 21   Charolais/Friesian steer (*British Charolais Cattle Society Ltd*)

There was little difference between the two types of cross in the proportion of prime cuts, although the Charolais crosses had a 1% advantage in prime cuts from the hindquarter.

There was a marked superiority of Charolais crosses in the percentage of lean meat.

Consumer acceptability on colour, tenderness, and flavour, was equal to that of the traditional crosses. The reduced fat cover was in line with the current market requirements.

Fatstock guarantees

Prior to decontrol in 1954, the Government had complete control of fatstock and guaranteed prices were fixed weekly, in advance. With decontrol the producers were suddenly face with the problem of disposing of their stock on an open market.

Under the Agriculture Act, 1947–57, provision was made for guaranteed prices on open markets to producers of certain agricultural products, including fat cattle, fat sheep, and fat pigs.

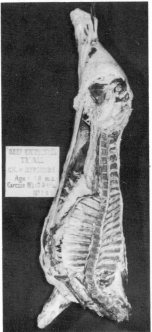

Plate 22   Charolais/Ayrshire steer

Left   Side of the carcase

Above   Close-up of the rib eye

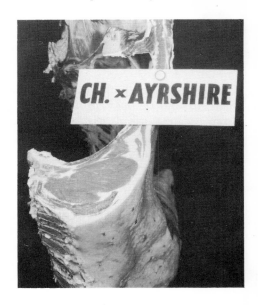

TABLE 11

*Charolais × Jersey: Primal cuts as a percentage
of carcase weight (491 lb) (Cut 10-rib fore)*

	%
Rump and loin	17·9
Kidney and suet	1·6
Top-piece, ex leg	25·5
Crop	24·4
Clod and neck	10·5
Flanks and brisket	11·6
Leg, jointed	5·1
Shin	3·2
Loss	0·2
	100·0

Hindquarter 54·1 % of side

TABLE 12

Carcase dissection

	Charolais × Friesian (%)	Hereford × Friesian (%)
Lean	59·3	52·3
Fat	21·6	29·5
Bone	14·6	13·8
Cutting loss, etc.	4·5	4·6
	100·0	100·0

The Fatstock (Guarantee Payments) Order, 1960, made provision for guarantee payments to producers of fatstock. These arrangements are known as the Fatstock Guarantee Scheme.

Certain functions under the Scheme have been delegated to the Meat and Livestock Commission which was established in 1967.

The guaranteed price was fixed annually for the following year (Annual Price Review) by the Government in consultation with the National Farmers' Union, and among the many factors which are considered, the following are probably the most important.

(1) Production costs (feed, labour, etc.).
(2) Profit trends in production.
(3) Probable consumer demands.

(4) Livestock population trends.

(5) Potential overseas supplies.

In the overall assessment the Government could influence production by varying support as between, say, milk production, beef production, pork, or mutton and lamb.

The scheme applied to fat steers and clean fat heifers, fat lambs and other clean fat sheep, home-bred clean fat pigs and the carcases obtained from such animals, and the carcases of young bulls and other male cattle, complying with the required standards, minimum weight, and other qualifications.

Other qualifications included certain quality standards and the weights. If the cattle or sheep are imported, they must, for attested cattle, have been in this country for at least 13 weeks and for sheep for periods specified.

Pigs are rather more complicated, as adjustments are made depending upon the number of pigs certified.

In addition the guaranteed price per score dead weight is also related to the basic rations of feeding stuffs, and adjustments are made in the guaranteed price to take account of changes in the cost of feed.

In order to obtain guaranteed payments, producers must present their fatstock at approved certification centres, which are places approved by the Minister for the purposes of the scheme.

There are two types of centre.

(a) Live weight certification centres, i.e. livestock markets or other places at which fatstock is sold live.

(b) Dead weight certification centres at which carcases are certified, i.e. slaughterhouses or other places including bacon factories at which fatstock is slaughtered.

Full details of the Scheme and price schedules are given in *Fatstock Guarantee Scheme* which is published annually by the Ministry of Agriculture, Fisheries, and Food.

Some cattle grading schemes

(*Courtesy Meat Commission Economic Information Service*)

The following tables will tend to highlight some similarities and differences in grading systems for cattle.

In all these schemes the major divisions are those of steers, heifers, bulls and cows and with one exception (Irish Republic) they are linked to some weight standards. In some cases minimum killing out percentages form part of the schemes and in Italy dentition is incorporated for their Viteloni (young bulls) and age standards also apply to West Germany and the Netherlands.

Plate 23 *Above* Charolais/Jersey young bull
          Right Side of the carcase

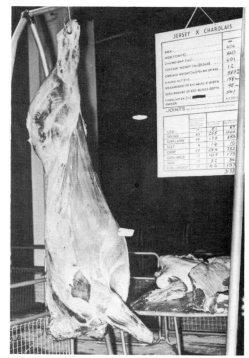

Some of the standards for conformation are given in great detail, but there is less emphasis on the state of fatness. In France, for example, the various features for assessing conformation within the five top grades (six in all) are based upon 13 physical characteristics plus the degree of fatness.

Great Britain		Northern Ireland	
Class	Grade	Class	Grade
Steers	Light (7½–9¼ cwt) Medium (9½–11 cwt) Heavy (11¼ cwt and over)	Steers	U LM (450–600 lb d.w.) LH (over 600 lb d.w.) T
Heifers	Light (6½–8 cwt) Medium/heavy (8¼ cwt and over)	Heifers	U/L T
Cows	1st quality 2nd quality 3rd quality	Steers and Heifers Cows	E

Irish Republic

Class	Grade	Conformation	Fleshing	Fat Covering
Steers	1 (b) 2 3 4 5	Very good Very good to good Good Very good to good Moderate	Very good Very good to good Good Very good to good Moderate	Light Medium, even distribution Light Heavy Variable
Heifers	● (b) 2 3	Very good to good Very good to good Moderate *or* Good	Very good to good Very good to good — —	Light–Medium, even distribution Medium–slightly heavy, even distribution Variable Heavy
Cows	1 (a) 2 (b) 3	Very good Good Moderate to poor	Very good Good Moderate to poor	— — —

(a) Cow heifers and best young cows.
(b) Grades quoted in *European Weekly*.

Netherlands

Grade	1st Quality (a)	2nd Quality (a)	3rd Quality	Manufacturing Cows
Conformation	Good to very good	Average	Below average	Bad
Neck	Very well muscled	Well muscled	Less well muscled	Thin
Withers	Very well filled	Well filled	Below average	Badly muscled
Shoulders	Very well fleshed	Well fleshed	Below average	Badly fleshed
Back	Broad and well fleshed	Slightly narrower	Narrower, lacking in flesh	Very narrow prominent bone structure
Loin	Wide and well filled	Average	Below average	Thinly fleshed
Croup	Well filled	Average	Slightly hollow	Very hollow
Brisket and Plate	Short and thick	Rather thick	Not well filled	Long and flat
Hindquarters flank	Short	Average	Long	Very long
Fatness	Very lean	Lean	Below average	Light fat covering
Age	(as a rule) not older than 4 years	(as a rule) not older than 7 years	(as a rule) older than 7 years	Every age

Remarks:

1st Quality also include especially meaty animals that are (i) insufficiently finished, (ii) excessively fat, (iii) obviously older than 4 years.

2nd Quality also include meaty animals that are (i) insufficiently finished, (ii) excessively fat, (iii) slightly older than 7 years.

3rd Quality also include less meaty animals that are insufficiently finished and young as well as animals of average meatiness that are (i) without fat covering, (ii) excessively fat, (iii) old.

(a) Grades quoted in *European Weekly*.

Western Germany

Class and Grade		Description	Live-weight (lb)	Minimum Killing Out %
Steers	A(a)	Young steers, well fleshed of good conformation lightly finished for slaughter.	1173+	57
	B	Other finished steers.	1173+	56
Bulls	A(a)	Very well fleshed and very good conformation. Fattened bulls, young in perfect condition (solid, sturdy hindquarters, wide firm back, deep chest, solid thighs). Fattening period completed, young animals of 1¼–3 years. Breeding animals, not too old, fully fattened.	882–1323	58
		OR Bulls for production of sausages and cold cooked sausage; as a general rule the presence of a milk tooth is required.	1985	60
	B	Poorer conformation at slaughter than A. Young bulls for fattening and bulls which are not too old for breeding.	1045+	55
	C	Mature bulls.	1045+	48–55
Heifers	A(a)	Well fleshed and good conformation, equivalent to Steers Grade A.	913+	60
	B	Animals of high quality but not good enough for Grade A. Estimation of quality of heifers B and C same as for steers.	913+	55
	C	Poorer conformation.	913+	52
Cows	A	Cow heifers of good conformation. Finished for slaughter.	1323–1764	60
	B(a)	Cows of average conformation. Must not have calved too often.	1140+	53
	C	God manufacturing quality cow.	1140+	49
	D	Old inferior quality animals.	1140+	40

(a) Grades quoted in *European Weekly*.

France

Conformation	F	R(a)	A	N(a)	C	E
	Excellent	Very Good	Good	Average	Mediocre	Poor
Profiles	Well rounded	Fairly well rounded	Blocky	Less Blocky	Generally thinly fleshed	
Blemishes	None	Few in relation to F	Maximum of 2 in relation to F	More numerous and marked in relation to A		F
Sticking	Very thick	Thick	Quite thick	Generally thin	Thin	O
Withers	Wide and full	Wide and full	Still muscular	Narrow, not hollow	Hollow	R
Blade bone	Very plump	Plump	Well developed	Less well developed	Badly developed	
Shoulders	Very well muscled	Well muscled	Average	Lacking in muscle	Thinly muscled	M
Back	Wide and well fleshed	Wide but slightly well fleshed	Tapering slightly at the shoulders	More pronounced tapering up to shoulder	Narrow and poorly fleshed	A
Rib	Very rounded	Rounded	Slightly rounded	Flat	Very flat	N
Hip bone	Not apparent	Not apparent	Could project very slightly	Could project	Projecting	U
Rump	Very well rounded	Well rounded	Blocky	Slightly thinly fleshed	Thinly fleshed	F
Round (of beef)	Rounded, short, thick	Less rounded but still thick	Blocky but still thick	Blocky but lacking thickness	Long and flat	A
Topside	Well rounded	Rounded	Blocky but still thick	Blocky but lacking thickness	Thinly fleshed	C
'Cleft'	Very short	Short	Average	Long	Very long	T
State of fattening	Well finished	Well finished	Well finished	Well finished	Adequate	U
Minimum Weight						R
Steer	660lb	R1: 660lb R2: 530lb	617lb	All weights	All weights	E
Heifer	660lb	R1: 660lb R2: 530lb	529lb	All weights	All weights	
Cow	660lb	660lb	573lb	All weights	All weights	
Bull	660lb	660lb	All weights	All weights	All weights	

(a) Grades quoted in *European Weekly*

Italy

Class	Grade	Description	Liveweight (lb)	Minimum Killing out %
Vitelloni Young bulls	1(a)	Young bulls: weighing more than 397lb. All milk-teeth present. Animals of first quality	818	55·0
	2(a)	All other not classified in Grade 1	818	55·0
Cows	1	Cows which have already calved. Animals of chosen quality	997	47·8
	2(a)	Animals of lower quality than Grade 1	997	47·8
	3	For manufacture	997	47·8

(a) Grades quoted in *European Weekly*.

Belgium

The Belgian system of cattle classification depends basically on the killing out percentage and the judgement of the buyers. What grading there is, is summarized in the table below.

Classification	Grade	Average Liveweight (b)	Percentage of market	Minimum Killing Out %
Steers and Heifers				
60%	1	1003	17	60
55%	2(a)	1003	19	55
Bulls				
60%	1	1105	13	60
55%	2(a)	1105	14	55
Cows				
55%	2	1127	14	55
50%	3(a)	1127	17	50
For manufacture	4	—	6	—

(a) Grades quoted in *European Weekly*.

Denmark

There in no official grading system in Denmark, but the following is a description of the kind of animal found in each class.

Class	Grade	Description
Steers	(Prime quality) (a)	Steers, 500 kg (9¾ cwt) and over, of best quality. (Also referred to as 'Swiss steers'.)
Heifers	(Prime quality) (a)	Small heifers of best quality. (Also referred to as 'Good shop heifers'. Chiefly a home market race.)
Cows	(1st quality)	Young cows of best quality.
Cows	(2nd quality) (a)	Older export cows of best quality.
Cows	(3rd quality)	Cows of inferior quality. Lowest quotation refers to 'Cows only fit for sausage meat'.
Calves	(Prime quality) (a)	Milch calves of best quality.

(a) Grades quoted in *European Weekly*.

4 Slaughter

Pre-slaughter care

As the condition and keeping qualities of the carcase will depend to a great extent on the care expended prior to slaughter, these precautions should be considered as an essential part of the slaughter technique. Ante-mortem inspection enables suspected animals to be segregated, thus protecting animals and workers in the case of contagious diseases. Also, many diseases are notifiable by law.

It is generally agreed that a period of fasting is essential and the consensus of opinion indicates 24 hours as a minimum, many people preferring 36 hours. The hunger or fasting pens should be clean, efficiently drained, and neither too cold nor too hot. Plenty of water should be available, as this in conjunction with fasting will ensure that the minimum quantity of intestinal content, and consequently bacteria, will be introduced into the slaughter-house. This fasting will also prevent the blood system being gorged with partly assimilated food substances, which are thought to affect the condition of the beef.

Nervous excitement and physical exertion should be avoided as these result in a rise in temperature, which will cause imperfect bleeding. Excessive muscular fatigue will mean that the reserve of glycogen in some of the muscles will have been used up. This substance changes to lactic acid after slaughter and the rate of setting is greatly influenced by the formation of this acid. It is also probable that bacteria would be adversely affected by this acid medium; in fact, bone sour in hams is most commonly found in hams obtained from fatigued pigs. The rate of cooling will, of course, play a part, and rapid reduction of temperature at the centre of the flesh will not permit the germs to develop. It is considered that, to obviate the possibility of 'bone-taint' in beef, the temperature at the centre of the round should be reduced to below 48°F (9°C) within 48 hours of slaughter. It is therefore obvious that fasting, resting, copious draughts of water, and the minimum of strain prior to actual stunning are the fundamental points.

Harsh droving methods should be avoided, and the use of an electric goad will prevent bruising and render tail twisting unnecessary. The animal will move away from the slight shock and this permits penning with a minimum of trouble. The packing-house practice of passing animals through a shower, or even a bath, removes any dirt adhering to the hide or feet and again reduces the probability of contamination of the finished article.

Slaughter

ROPING

Where a stunning-pen is not available the animal is secured by tying with a rope, tied with a bow-line knot round the neck, placing the knot away from the windpipe to avoid choking. The rope is passed through a ring either in the floor or low down in the wall, so that the animal's head can be secured in a suitable position. In some cases a chain is employed.

In the United Kingdom, the practice of 'roping' became illegal as from January 1963, the provision of a stunning pen being compulsory for the slaughter of cattle, i.e. bulls, cows, steers, and heifers. Prior to the enactment of the 1958 legislation, it is probable that less than 10% of the slaughter-houses in England and Wales, were provided with stunning pens.

STUNNING

With the exception of 'Kosher' slaughtering, cattle are rendered insensible previous to 'sticking'. Quoting Edelman, Mohlar, and Eichhorn (*Meat Hygiene*): 'Bleeding is most thorough when the heart and respiratory functions remain in action as long as possible. These functions depend principally on the intactness of the medulla oblongata, with the respiratory, cardiac, and vasometer centres, and consequently the most satisfactory methods are those in which the medulla oblongata is not injured.' Various methods of producing insensibility are employed, and the more common are as follows.

(a) Knocking with a 4-lb sledge-hammer on a 4-foot shaft. This system is usually preferred in packing-houses, and as the brain of the animal is not damaged it results in very efficient bleeding.

(b) Mechanical devices can be broadly divided into two types: those in which a captive bolt is operated by a blank cartridge or a strong spring, and with this pattern the end of the bolt is similar to that of a pole-axe. The other type are instruments firing a free bullet. The chief objections to these are that the bullet may be deflected and cause injury to workmen in the slaughterhouse and that the medulla oblongata is generally damaged.

(c) A leather mask has been used, this mask covering the animal's eyes, the portion over the brain carrying an iron bolt which is struck by a hammer to penetrate the brain-case. The time involved and the difficulty of fitting such a mask on to a restless animal would preclude its use from centres where many animals are dealt with.

(d) Neck stabbing, sometimes termed pithing, consists of inserting a knife between the base of the skull and the first bone of the vertebrae, to cut through the spinal cord. Though this system produces paralysis of the body, the animal does not become unconscious until anaemia of the brain follows sticking. No muscular contraction can occur during the bleeding, so probably more blood is retained than with other methods.

ELECTRICAL STUNNING

Here a high-frequency current of comparatively low voltage (60–80 V) is applied to the animal through electrodes in contact with the head. This method is used almost exclusively for pigs and sheep, though in some parts it has been applied to cattle. The chief difficulty in the latter case is fitting the apparatus to the head of the beast, whilst with pigs and sheep a form of tongs can be easily handled and rapidly applied.

The current is applied for a few seconds, producing instantaneous unconsciousness, and if the animal is not stuck it will slowly recover and appear normal in the space of a few minutes.

Very efficient bleeding is obtained and the consumption of current is extremely low.

Pithing, as applied to normal slaughter technique, consists of inserting a cane or metal spike through the hole in the skull into the brain to the spinal cord; this breaks up the brain and renders the animal insensitive to pain. This practice is not universally followed; in fact where a knocking hammer is used, the brain-case is not penetrated. Destruction of the medulla oblongata previous to sticking would appear seriously to affect the action of the heart, respiration, and reflex muscular contractions, and this would prevent thorough bleeding. Against this is the question of the possibility of a workman receiving injury from a beast, owing to muscular contraction, should he commence operations too quickly after bleeding without pithing. The practice of pithing animals does not appear to be in use to any great extent outside Great Britain.

With the Kosher method the animal's throat is cut across and unconsciousness is produced by the cessation of the blood-supply to the brain and nerve centres.

ANAESTHETISING—PIGS (see p. 212)

Various types of apparatus for anaesthetising pigs by the use of carbon dioxide have been in use in many countries for a considerable period, but their use was not permitted in the United Kingdom until 1958, and it is necessary to obtain from the local authority, a certificate of approval prior to use.

STICKING

The object of bleeding is to remove the blood as completely and rapidly as possible from the carcase, as blood produces an ideal media for the multiplication of bacteria and their distribution throughout the carcase. An incision is made just in front of the sternum, cutting into the main blood-vessels. Usually this cut is made whilst the animal is hoisted, better bleeding being claimed, but it must be remembered that in this position pressure will be built up on certain organs more so than in the case of a carcase lying on the floor. In sticking, care must be exercised to avoid 'over-sticking', i.e. puncturing the pleura, or blood will flow back into the chest cavity, staining the chest wall. In such a case 'stripping the pleura' may only be carried out in the presence of an inspector, as its removal may mask evidence of diseased conditions.

DRESSING

The order in which the various operations are carried out will, of course, vary, and be influenced by the equipment available. The present practice, particularly in the larger abattoirs, is towards line dressing, whereby once the animal has been hoisted to the bleeding-rail the carcase is never again lowered to the floor, throughout the complete process (see p. 92). However, in many cases, much of the dressing is still carried out on the floor and the following outline will give some indications of the general procedure.

Directly the animal is dropped and 'pithed', the slaughterman stands with his back to the animal, with one foot below the head, the other in front of the forelegs, so that the skin of the throat is drawn taut. The end of the brisket is located and an incision is made from just in front of the brisket, on the centre line of the neck towards the head, exposing the windpipe. The throat bread is removed, and its position will provide a good indication of the position of the main blood-vessels. The knife is then directed towards the point of the brisket, and by moving it in the direction of the backbone the blood-vessels are cut just outside the chest cavity. The chest cavity must not be cut into. The blood drains from the body assisted by pumping the front leg. The animal is scalped, by chopping off the horns, and the head is skinned out, usually by a junior. A cut is made across the larynx, the weasand tied off, and the head is detached by cutting through the muscle and the occipital joint.

The front legs are jointed, leaving the knuckle bones (carpals) on the carcase. The hide is sometimes removed from them previous to jointing, though this is not the common practice in England. The hind legs are jointed by cutting through the tendons so that the toes will fall forwards with hide attached. The slaughterman usually grips the foot between his knees and makes an incision down the hide, over the round to a point just behind the cod fat or, in the female, the udder. Flaying continues down and over the round, and the joint of the rear hocks are found and the feet removed above the knuckle joints (tarsals). In some parts the hind feet are left attached to the hide, and they are used to provide a grip when removing the hide. The gam cords are opened up in readiness for hoisting. A rip is then made from the incisions caused by sticking, in a straight line over the brisket, along the middle line of the belly to the tail. The hide is removed from the neck and brisket, some slaughtermen leaving the hide on the fore shanks, as it will protect them from blood and dirt when the animal is hoisted and the offal is being removed. 'Siding' is carried out in long, firm strokes until the hide is within about 6 in (15 cm) of the floor. Care must be exercised to ensure that the 'fell' or 'vellum' is not cut. At this stage it is desirable to spray over the exposed surface with clean water. The abdominal cavity is then opened up by making a small cut behind the brisket, inserting the hand, and cutting up the middle line towards the cod fat, the hand being used to protect the viscera from damage. The caul fat is then removed, the bladder emptied, and the viscera pushed to one side, so that the buttock can be split, in the case of young animals, with a knife. The brisket is cut down to the bone and sawn through, and the food-pipe and windpipe loosened. A beef tree is placed through the hocks and the carcase half hoisted, to facilitate removal of the tail and flaying; the back gut is released and the bladder is usually removed at the same time. The hide on the tail is then ripped, on the inside of the tail, and if a tail extractor is used, the tail can be easily skinned out by pulling away from the hide with a dry cloth. The hide is then removed from the round and rump. Following this, the carcase is hoisted up, and the weight of the intestines and stomach, with spleen attached, is sufficient to remove them from the abdominal cavity.

The liver can be taken out by cutting its attachment to the diaphragm, making certain that the gall-bladder is not punctured. The diaphragm which separates the abdominal and chest cavities, is cut through at the white connective tissue, leaving the thin skirt on the carcase. The contents of the chest cavity, i.e. the pluck, can then be removed, and the aorta which is near the vertebrae is trimmed out. The flaying is then completed and the hide removed. The body can be completely sawn down which makes a very clean job of the chine, or, in some cases, split with a sharp cleaver, though in older animals the rump and loin may be sawn, the division being completed with the cleaver.

Washing and Hot Shrouding

It is obviously better to avoid contamination of the carcase, than to attempt subsequently to remove it.

There is ample proof that the use of wiping cloths can add materially to the bacterial count, rather than reducing the contamination, and the use of such cloths is now illegal. It would appear that the American method of high-pressure spraying, followed by hot shrouding, has much to recommend it. The details of the process are given below.

The normal mains pressure is boosted to as much as 275 lb/sq. in (19 kg/cm²) and the temperature of the water maintained at 110°F (43°C.) The spray nozzle delivers about 4 gal (18 litres) per min. It is claimed that the blood from superficial bruises can be dispersed, reducing the necessity of trimming. It is important that the water spray be directed at the carcase at the correct angle and care is taken to ensure that the water does not come into contact with the bone. This is frequently followed by 'hot shrouding', the carcase being covered with a hot damp sheet of heavy muslin. Some packers place the cloth in a weak brine solution, which is kept at about 120°F (49°C), the cloth being wrung out prior to wrapping the carcase. The cloth is stretched tightly over the surface, excluding the bone, care being taken to obviate wrinkles. Pins are inserted (4 in (10 cm) galvanized) to retain the cloth and in situations such as the round rump and loin, where the cloth may not adhere closely to the side. The cloths give the beef a smooth appearance and tend to modify any 'patchy' fat and tend to give a whiter colour. The cloths remain on the carcase during the initial chilling and are removed the following day. Following use, the cloths are steeped in cold salt water to remove the blood, followed by sterilizing in a solution of sodium hypochlorite.

Handling of offals

Head

The tongue is loosened by cutting along the inside of the jawbone towards the base, and after inspection of the glands it is completely detached and thoroughly washed and scraped, working from the tip to root, against the papillae. Tongues are cut either long or trimmed to give a short-cut tongue. Care must be exercised or the lingual artery may be damaged and this will prevent efficient pumping. Normally it will require 24 hours' cooling before it is pumped with pickle and placed in brine. During the cooling period it should be hung from the root end, to preserve the shape and prevent damage to the blade. Lean tongue trimmings can be used for made-up goods, and the fat should be rendered. The cheek meat should be carefully removed from the head, and the lower jaw separated from the skull. The head is split and the brain released from its attachments and removed. The lips, when thoroughly cleaned, can be broken down on a mincing machine and boiled down for jelly stock for beef brawn.

PLUCK

In the ox this consists of the trachea, lungs, and the heart. The glands, bronchial and mediastinal, are examined, and the lung tissue itself may be incised. The bag surrounding the heart (pericardium) is cut through and the heart detached by cutting through the blood-vessels. Any free blood should be squeezed out and the heart hung up to cool. If the heart is intended for manufacturing purposes, it should be remembered that there are two small bony structures situated below the aorta. If the lungs are to be used for edible products they should be thoroughly examined, as at times, following the process of slaughter, food material from the stomach may be found in the bronchial tubes.

LIVER

It is essential that the gall-bag should not be punctured whilst it is attached to the liver. It should be removed by cutting through the duct, whilst pinching the neck of the bag and pulling it away to avoid spilling the gall. After examination the glands should be trimmed away and the liver hung to cool. In some cases a transverse cut is made across the thin end of the liver to permit it to drain.

SPLEEN

Is removed from the paunch and hung up to cool. It can be used for retail sale as melt and skirt or retained for manufacturing purposes.

STOMACHS

There are four divisions in the ruminant stomach, and before these are cut all the adhering fat should be carefully removed, or it will become contaminated with the content and its value seriously depreciated. To protect the carcases hanging in the slaughterhouse the stomachs should not be opened on the killing floor. The third and fourth stomachs (omasum and abomasum) are detached and these two are then separated. Normally the third stomach (bible-bag) is disposed of intact, though it can be emptied and cleaned prior to cooking for animal feed. The fourth stomach (reed or rennet) can be considered as an edible product and is opened up and well washed. The first and second stomachs (paunch and honeycomb) are opened up and emptied of their contents. Tripe dressing is rather a specialised trade, and firms doing this work use washing machines that are fed with hot water at about 140°F (60°C), the revolving vanes removing the mucus lining. Various chemical agents are employed in the water to assist in the removal of the lining and to bleach the tripe. This process is followed by cooking, cooling in cold water, and trimming. Normally about 40–45% of the green weight is available as the finished product.

Cow Heels

Are prepared by the firms handling tripe. They are cleaned and, after scalding, the hair can be easily removed, and usually the hooves are loosened by immersion in boiling water, so that they can be pulled off prior to boiling until they are tender.

Sweetbreads

These are removed during the dressing process and are washed off in clean cold water.

Intestines

As in the case of tripe, the preparation of casings is carried out by specialist firms, but every effort should be made to collect the adhering fat, as far as is possible without damaging the casings.

Weasand (Oesophagus)

After it has been cut from the paunch it should be washed through, hung up, and the outer muscular coat stripped away with the help of a sharp knife. Great care is necessary or the inner lining will be punctured. It is turned inside out and one end tied, followed by inflation and tying off the other end. They should be thoroughly dried before use.

BLADDERS

These may be inflated in a similar fashion if there is any demand for them.

FATS

The total fats available will depend upon the live weight and the degree of finish in the animal. For example, the caul, reed, gut fat, and trimmings from a show beast of 13 to 14 cwt (660 to 710 kg) might be in the region of 75 lb (34 kg), and a very good ox might produce 55 lb (25 kg). On the other hand, poor animals may only yield about 20 lb (9 kg) of raw fat. In a good commercial beast of 10 cwt (508 kg) about 30 to 35 lb (14 to 16 kg) of fat might reasonably be anticipated. The fats should be dealt with as quickly as possible and cooled rapidly to obtain the best product.

Specification for dressing the carcases of cattle presented for Beef Premium

(EEC marketing for year 1976/77)
The following offals shall be removed:
1. Hide.
2. Head and tongue; but in Northern Ireland, unless the Department of Agriculture agrees to the contrary, the ears must be examined by the certifying officer before slaughter, after which they may be removed. In Great Britain, in every case, and in Northern Ireland where the Department has agreed not to inspect before slaughter, the ears must be left naturally attached to the carcase until it has been examined as a carcase to determine eligibility for premium, after which they may be removed.
3. Feet.
4. Guts and tripes with accompanying glands:
     a. Liver;
     b. Spleen;
     c. Pancreas.
5. Caul and gut fat.
6. Heart and heart fat.
7. Heart bread and neck bread (thymus glands)
8. Lights (lungs, trachea and larynx).
9. Thick skirt (pillar of diaphragm)*
10. Tail.*
11. Genito-Urinary organs, excluding kidneys. (When the kidneys are

---

* Where it is the trade practice to leave the thick skirt or tail or both these offals on the carcase, a weight deduction of 2 lb (1 kg) will be made in respect of the thick skirt and 3 lb (1½ kg) in respect of the tail.

removed before the carcase is weighed, an addition of 3 lb (1½ kg) shall be made to the carcase weight.

Where the kidneys, kidney knobs and channel fats have been removed the minimum qualifying weights will be reduced by 16 lb (8 kg).

12. Large blood vessels of abdomen and thorax.

CONDITIONS OF WEIGHING CARCASES OF CATTLE

Carcases must be dressed according to the specifications above, when they are weighed, except the ears may be removed before weighing after the carcase has been accepted as being eligible for certification; if they are not so removed a deduction of 2 lb (1 kg) i.e. 1 lb (½ kg) for each ear will be made.

Carcases shall be weighed:
a. If weighed hot, within 1 hour of slaughter;
b. If weighed cold, within 24 hours of slaughter except where prior approval for an extension of this period has been given.

When carcases are weighed 'hot', the 'cold' weight will be ascertained by making rebates as follows:

	Hot weight (kg)	Rebate (kg)
	125 and under	2
Sides of beef	126 – 175	2½
	over 175	3

Carcases ex-KKCF

It is well recognized that the most important single factor affecting the retail yield of trimmed boneless meat, is the amount of kidney knob and channel fat in the carcase. Arising from this, the national organizations concerned have agreed that the carcases of beef cattle sold by deadweight may be weighed either including or excluding the kidney knob and channel fats.

Removal of these fats will reduce the carcase weight, on average, by some $3\frac{3}{4}\%$. Thus an average body of 575 lb (261 kg) with KKCF, would weigh 553 lb (251 kg) without KKCF, and the killing out percentage would be reduced by some 2% on average.

This means that to convert a price per lb for the average carcase with KKCF, to an equivalent price per lb for the same carcase ex-KKCF, it is necessary to multiply it by 1·0389, irrespective of carcase weight. Conversely to convert from an ex-KKCF basis to a with-KKCF basis, the figure to multiply by, is 0·9625. (Four places of decimals are needed for accuracy to one-tenth of a penny.)

Variations

The figures relate to average cattle. The yield of KKCF (and the price comparison) varies considerably and the producer or buyer must decide if a yield of say $2\frac{1}{2}\%$ or 5% is more appropriate to a particular batch of cattle, rather than the national average of $3\cdot75\%$.

The producer of cattle with smaller than average KKCF is likely to be better off than the producer of cattle with above average KKCF, as he will be paid for a heavier carcase. The producer of cattle with above average KKCF, to obtain the same total return, would need a greater price increase, and this is most unlikely to be achieved.

Cattle killed at lower levels of external fatness, tend to be the dairy types, which have proportionally more KKCF.

Conversely beef types that tend to get slaughtered at higher levels of fatness may not be as fully developed in KKCF as their external fatness might suggest. Type and general level of fatness influence KKCF yield, much more than carcase weight. Indications from MLC and other carcase data, suggest the following:

Types which can be expected to yield *less* than average KKCF:

(a) Young bulls of Friesian or Charolais × Friesian breeding,

(b) Any carcase classified 1 for external fat (the leanest class) in the MLC beef classification system (see p. 000),

(c) Most Friesian or Charolais × Friesian steers produced on an intensive cereal system (barley beef), generally provided the external fat class does not exceed 2,

(d) Most Hereford × Friesian and other beef × Friesian steers produced in intensive or semi-intensive systems to 18 months of age, generally provided the fat class does not exceed 3,

(e) Most beef type steers, provided the external fat class does not exceed 4.

Types likely to *exceed* the average yield of KKCF:

(a) Most Friesians produced in 18 months or more extensive systems with a fat class of 2 or more,

(b) Most Hereford × Friesians or other beef × Friesians with a fat class of 4 or more.

Costing ex-KKCF

In the case of sides of beef with KKCF, quartered at the 10th rib straight across, it was usually assumed that in the average run of good commercial beef, the hind : fore ratio, would be about 51 : 49.

With the introduction of ex-KKCF dressing this ratio has altered, with a consequent change in the price differential of the two portions.

Thus based on the above, a straight side of beef of 300 lb (136 kg) would give:

Hindquarter 153 lb (69 kg) – 51%
Forequarter 147 lb (67 kg) – 49%

The removal of the KKCF calculated as $3\frac{3}{4}$% i.e. 11·25 lb (5·1 kg) from the side results in a weight of 288·75 lb (131·4 kg). Thus the hind ex-KKCF will then weigh 141·75 lb (64·4 kg) with the fore remaining at 147 lb (67 kg). This means that the original $H\frac{1}{4}$: $F\frac{1}{4}$ ratio of 51 : 49 is almost exactly reversed, becoming approximately 49·09 : 50·91. In this case, each 1p increase in the cost per lb of the $H\frac{1}{4}$ ex-KKCF represents a decrease of approximately 0·96p per lb in the $F\frac{1}{4}$ value. Conversely, each 1p increase in the cost per lb of the $F\frac{1}{4}$, means a decrease in the $H\frac{1}{4}$ value of approximately 1·037p per lb.

Hindquarters ex-KKCF

Whilst purchasing $H\frac{1}{4}$ ex-KKCF eliminates one of the major variables, the actual boneless, trimmed retail yield obtained, can vary with the different $H\frac{1}{4}$s. It may be found that, in terms of potential gross margin, the cost price in p per lb for comparable results from a well fleshed $H\frac{1}{4}$ with a minimum of fat trim and that of an excessively wasteful $H\frac{1}{4}$, poorly muscled, might represent as much as 4p per lb.

The following table relates the cost price and the percentage yield, to the cost price as prepared for retail sale. In these figures the negligible value of bone and trim has been ignored.

TABLE 13

Hindquarters ex-KKCF

Cost p. per lb	46	48	50	52	54	56	58	60
% Prepared	Cost Prepared							
74	62·16	64·86	67·57	70·27	72·97	75·67	78·38	81·08
73	63·01	65·75	68·49	71·23	73·97	76·71	79·45	82·19
72	63·89	66·67	69·44	77·22	75·00	77·78	80·56	83·33
71	64·79	67·60	70·42	73·24	76·05	78·87	81·69	84·51
70	65·71	68·57	71·43	74·28	77·14	80·00	82·85	85·71
69	66·66	69·56	72·46	75·36	78·26	81·16	84·05	86·95
68	67·64	70·58	73·53	76·47	79·41	82·35	85·29	88·23
67	68·65	71·64	74·62	77·61	80·59	83·58	86·56	89·55
66	69·69	72·72	75·76	78·79	81·82	84·85	87·88	90·91
65	70·77	73·84	76·92	80·00	83·07	86·15	89·23	92·31
64	71·87	75·00	78·12	81·25	84·37	87·50	90·62	93·75

Thus it will be seen that the cost of prepared meat from a very good quarter yielding 74% at 60p per lb would be similar to that of a quarter costing 52p per lb, but yielding 64%.

It must be emphasized that the figures above represent the *average* price of the meat as prepared and many of the portions will not fetch this average cost price.

Care of hides

The portions of an animal which require most protection are provided by nature with a thicker hide, whereas in the less exposed parts, such as the inner surface of the thighs, the hide is much thinner. In the winter the light summer coat is replaced by a much heavier growth of hair, though in the case of the tail the hair is permanent. The characteristic colour in the skin and hair is due to a pigment, which is formed from certain amino acids. Should the skin be badly damaged, colourless areas may develop. As with most other animal tissues, the quantity of water present in the hide decreases as the animal ages, and the hides from mature animals contain about two-thirds water and almost one-third of protein. Hides and skins can be considered as the most important by-product from cattle and sheep, yet in very many cases they are not granted the consideration they merit. This applies not only to the butcher, but frequently to the farmer as well. Parasites, barbed wire, and thorns all take their toll, and, in addition to their effect on the hide, such damage opens up the way to infection in the live animal. The highest value is obtained for leather that is free from damage and is obtainable in large pieces. Such leather can be utilised in belting and harness-making, as these require lengthy portions with no weaknesses.

Previous to slaughter, adhering dung should be washed away from the hide, and well-rested animals are easier to flay than those that are heated. Scores on the hide, though they are not deep enough to extend through it, may cause a weak place or a break in the leather when it is tanned. Scoring is usually caused by insufficient training and not holding the knife accurately. By maintaining a steady upward lift on the hide, by keeping it taut, and by using the flaying knife from heel to toe in long pressing strokes, with reasonable care much of this damage can be avoided. When ripping the hide, the object should be to leave it as square as possible, and in sticking, the incision should be made in a perfectly straight line between the brisket and the throat (Plate 24). The practice of dragging the carcase across the floor of the slaughterhouse is greatly to be deprecated, as it will result in damage to the grain of the hide. In some of the larger abattoirs the hides are subjected to a thorough washing by jets of water under pressure, followed by scrubbing to

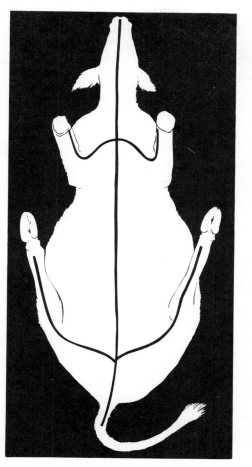

Plate 24   Correct lines for ripping.   *Left*: Floor dressing   *Right*: Vertical Line dressing
(*The Hide and Allied Trades Improvement Society*)

remove dirt and blood. In most slaughterhouses there are no such facilities, and immediately the hide is removed from the carcase it should be spread out in a cool situation to permit dissipation of the animal heat. If such hides are not collected immediately, they should be treated by sprinkling the flesh surface with *clean*, medium grain salt, not neglecting the edges and the shanks. It has been estimated that the loss to butchers in this country, caused by bad flaying and careless preservation of hides is well over £1 million per annum.

Offals of the Ox

Edible

Ox cheek and head trimmings	Stewing, brawn and sausage,
Tongue	Salting and boiling
Brains	Boiling, sauce, and sausage
Sweetbreads { (a) Thymus (b) Pancreas }	Frying or boiling
Heart	Baking, boiling, or sausage
Liver	Frying
Skirt { (a) Thick (b) Thin }	Stewing
Spleen (melt or milt)	Pies and flavouring soups
Tail	Soup and stewing
Kidneys	Stewing, soup and frying
Blood	Black puddings, blood and barley loaf, blood flour
Blood plasma	As a binder in sausage
Stomach { (a) Rumen	Cleaned and boiled for tripe
(b) Reticulum (honeycomb)	Cleaned and boiled for tripe
(c) Abomasum }	Cleaned and boiled for red or black tripe
Feet {	Cleaned and boiled for cow heel
	Calve's-foot jelly
Fats { (a) Suet	Pudding, paste, mincemeat, etc.
(b) Fat	Dripping
(c) Oleo stock	Oleo-margarine and confectionery
(d) Oleo stearine }	Lard compounds
Bones	Soup and gelatine
Lungs	Animal feed
Udder	Boiled or salted, smoked and fried

Pharmaceutical

Name	*Situation in animal*
Pituitary	Base of Brain
Pineal	Brain surface
Thymus	In neck
Spleen	Across paunch

Pharmaceutical (*cont.*)

Thyroid	In throat
Suprarenal	Near kidney
Ovaries	Near horns of uterus
Corpus luteum	Part of ovaries
Pancreatin (pancreas)	Near liver
Thromboplastin, lecithin, kephalin	Obtained from brain
Red-bone-marrow	Bones
Liver extract	Abdominal cavity
Ox gall	Gall-bag, attached to liver
Parathyroid	Near root of tongue
Testes	Scrotum

Inedible

HIDE, CURED	Leather
Collagen	Tissues rich in collagen are now reconstituted to form sausage casings
Body hair	Felting and plaster retardant
Tail hair	Upholstery, brushes, plaster retardant, felting
Ear hair	Artists' brushes
Trimmings	Glue, fat for tallow, fertiliser
FAT	
Soap tallow	Soaps and glycerol
Tallow oil	Lubricants, leather dressing, textile finishing
Tallow stearine	Soaps, leather dressing, glycerol
Cracklings	Meat scrap
Tankage	Animal and poultry feed and fertiliser
BONES	
Inedible tallow	Soap, lubricating oil, candles, glycerol
Glue	Furniture making, etc.
Bone meal	Sugar refining, case-hardening metals, animal feed and fertilizer
Long bones	Tallow, glue, knife handles, buttons, etc.
HORNS	
Pith	Glue
Shell	Buttons, combs, etc., and fertilizer
FEET	Neats-foot oil, tallow and bone meal
Sinews and dew claws	Glue, tallow, and fertilizer
Hoofs	Combs, buttons, etc., and fertilizer
BLOOD	Animal feed and fertilizer
Blood albumen	Textile sizing and weatherproof glue

Inedible (*cont.*)

INTESTINES

    Small (runners)   Sausage containers, gold-beaters' skin, sealing
    Large (middles and bung)   parchments, etc.

WEASAND (OESOPHAGUS)   Sausage containers

BLADDER   Putty containers

OX GALL   Used in paints and setting dyes

    Gall stones   Ornaments

MEAT SCRAP   Animal feed

The total value of the carcase and the by-products will vary with different types of beast, but it is estimated that in the United States the value of the carcase represents a little over 80% of the total, the hide about 12%, leaving approximately 7% as the relative value of the other by-products. It must, however, be borne in mind that the fullest possible use is made of all the by-products. The following summary (Table 14) taken from the *Packer's Encyclopedia* will provide a good indication of the yield normally anticipated from a good 1000-lb steer.

TABLE 14

By-products in lb, derived from a 1000-lb steer in good market condition

Trimmed tongue	5·00 lb	Round casing	105 feet
Cheek and head meat	5·00 lb	Weasand	1 piece
Brain	0·90 lb	Bladder	1 piece
Gullet	0·25 lb	Bung	1 piece
Lips	1·25 lb	No. 1 Oleo oil	22·00 lb
Heart	3·50 lb	No. 2 Oleo oil	1·80 lb
Liver	10·00 lb	No. 3 Oleo oil	0·75 lb
Kidneys	0·75 lb	Stearine	13·00 lb
Tail	1·25 lb	Prime tallow	4·10 lb
Sweetbreads	0·30 lb	No. 1 tallow	1·75 lb
Suprarenal glands	0·06 lb	Brown grease	0·16 lb
Plain tripe	6·50 lb	Hide	65·00 lb
Honeycomb tripe	1·50 lb	Thighs	1·45 lb
Switch	1 piece	Buttock bones	1·15 lb
Sinews and pizzle	2·62 lb	Cannon bone	1·00 lb
Dew claws	0·40 lb	Neat-foot oil	0·85 lb
Blood, green	35·00 lb	Grinding bones	13·00 lb
Blood, dried	7·00 lb	Horns	0·70 lb
Tankage	10·00 lb	Horn piths	0·90 lb
Hooves	1·85 lb	Shin bones	1·60 lb
Middle casing	32 feet		

(*Packers' Encyclopedia*, pp. 8, 146.)

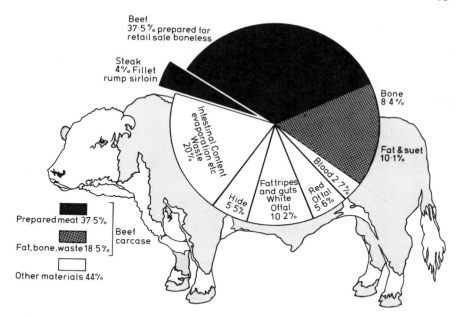

Beef
37·5% prepared for
retail sale boneless

Steak
4% Fillet
rump sirloin

Intestinal Content
evaporation etc
Waste
20%

Bone
8·4%

Fat & suet
10·1%

Blood 2·7%

Red
Offal
5·6%

Fat tripes
and guts
White
Offal
10·2%

Hide
5·5%

Prepared meat 37·5%

Fat, bone, waste 18·5%

Beef
carcase

Other materials 44%

Fig 7 Composition of beast. This sectional diagram illustrates the amounts of meat for the table, bone and fat, waste, and other products derived from a beef animal. The figures shown here are representative of a fair quality commercial animal of about 1000 lb (454 kg) liveweight giving a carcase yield of 560 lb (254 kg)

Estimation of dry rendering yields

The Commonwealth Scientific and Industrial Research Organization (C.S.I.R.O.) have developed the following method for calculating the theoretical yields obtainable from dry rendering operations.

Given the raw material analysis in terms of fat, water and if possible ash, the meat meal and tallow yields may be calculated, together with the protein content of the meal.

The calculated values agree fairly well with those obtained under practical commercial conditions. Where mixed batches of raw materials are used (a normal practice), calculations can be made to give a fair indication of the yields anticipated, provided that the proportion of the various products in the mix are known.

It is essential that the products be accurately specified in terms of trimming and the amount of residual water, arising from any washing processes. The following figures indicate the effect of differences in preparation, on the meat yield and tallow yield, in a meat deboning operation.

	Abattoir	Tallow Yield	Meat Meal Yield
Boning room,	A	15·9%	54·2%
beef bones	B	19·4%	58·3%
Boning room,	A	58·1%	13·4%
beef fats	B	64·4%	22·2%
	C	67·9%	9·4%

A significant feature which can be associated with preparation is that the protein content of the meat meal from bones, is markedly affected by the amount of residual meat present.

CALCULATION

An example of the method of calculating yields is given, based upon a sample of beef tongue roots:

Protein	16%
Fat	15%
Water	68%
Ash	0·9%
	99·9%

The raw analysis does not add up to 100%, due to experimental errors in analysis. In practice the total will usually fall between 98 and 102%.

METHOD

Assuming that the final meal contains 6% water and 9% fat, then weight of final meal from 999 lb raw material,

$$= 160 \text{ lb of protein}$$
$$9 \text{ lb of ash}$$
$$+ \text{ fat}$$
$$+ \text{water}$$

Let $x =$ final weight of meal, then amount of fat in meal is:

$$\frac{9}{100} x \text{ lb and the amount of water is } \frac{6}{100} x \text{ lb}$$

$$\therefore \text{ Meal weight } x = 160 + 9 + \frac{9}{100} x + \frac{6}{100} x$$

$$x = 169 + \frac{15}{100} x$$

$$x = 198$$

$$\therefore \text{ Final meal yield} = 198 \text{ lb} = 19\cdot8\%$$

$$\text{Fat in final meal} = \frac{9}{100} \cdot x = \frac{9 \times 198}{100} = 17\cdot8 \text{ lb.}$$

Fat originally present 150 lb

Tallow yield $= 150 - 17\cdot8 = 132\cdot2$ lb or $13\cdot2\%$

Protein content of meal $\dfrac{160}{198} = 80\cdot8\%$

TABLE 15

Meal and tallow yields from various Beef Offals

Offal	Raw Material Analysis				Yields			Comments
	% Water	% Protein	% Fat	% Ash	% Meal	% Tallow	% Protein in meal	
Abomasum	68–75	7–8	22–26	—	8–10	22–24	84–86	calculated values 6% water, 9% fat in meal
Rumen	78–84	14–18	2–4	0·7–1·0	19–21	8–10	71–73	
Entire digestive tract (likely average value)	72	15	11	2·5	18–20	0·5–1·5	79–81	
Liver	70	20	4	6·8	30–32	Nil	62–64	experimental values calculated to 6% water and 9% fat in meal
Lung	79	18	2	1·0	21–23	Nil	79–81	
Spleen	76	19	4	1·5	22–24	Nil	77–79	
Tongue roots	68	16˙	15	0·9	19–21	12–14	79–81	
Bone—3-month steer	46	20	14	20·5	46–48	8–10	40–42	calculated values 6% water, 9% fat in meal
Bone—48-month steer	32	21	21	26·5	54–56	15–17	36–38	
Skeleton-head— 48 months	55	18	7	20·2	44–46	1–3	39–41	
Average—all bones	38	19	21	22·1	47–49	15–17	38–40	

Sampling

The more representative the sample of raw materials used for analysis, the more accurate will be the results obtained. The analysis for fat and moisture should present little difficulty, but protein analysis is more complex.

However, if the water and fat content is known, a rough estimation of protein can be obtained if the protein is assumed to represent the difference. For example, in the case of tongue roots:

$$\text{Total} - (\text{water} + \text{fat}) = \text{Assumed protein}$$
$$100\% - (68\% + 15\%) = 17\%$$

With this method the calculated protein content of the final meal is always too high, by from 5 to 8%, due to the varying amounts of ash in the different soft offals. The protein figure can be adjusted by using the figures given for ash, in Table 15.

There is little species difference between various types of soft offal and there is likely to be as much variation between different batches of the same offals of one species, as there is between batches of the same offal from different species.

The foregoing applies only to soft offals and are not applicable to bones, on account of their high and variable ash content.

The protein content of green bones can vary from 18 to 24%, depending upon the part of the skeleton from which they are obtained.

Although the actual percentage of protein does not appear to change with the age of the animal, the ash content increases with age (with water decreasing); and the meal obtained from the bones of old animals would contain a lower percentage of protein, as shown in Table 15.

Endocrine glands

It is now appreciated that these ductless glands play a most important part in the development, relative growth of the various parts, general activity, mental development, and the whole life of the individual or animal. Such conditions as cretinism, excessive or retarded growth, abnormal fatness, extreme nervous conditions, and idiocy can frequently be attributed to derangements of these glands. A brief summary of these glands and their position is given below.

THYROID

Situated on either side of the trachea, consisting of two lobes connected by an isthmus of gland tissue. Its active substance is thyroxin, which regulates the energy rate and the production of heat in the body. A deficiency during the prenatal period will result in cretinism. According to Dr R. G. Hoskins, one hundredths of a grain of thyroxin makes the difference between normality and imbecility in the human being (this is the amount used daily in the body).

Endemic goitre and myxoedema are also conditions caused by a deficiency of thyroid secretion. An excess will result in an increased metabolism, nervousness, and muscular tremors. This gland is associated with the activity of the pancreas, the parathyroids, sex glands, and probably some others.

PARATHYROIDS

These are very small glands. Situated on either side of the trachea near to the thyroids, they can in fact be easily removed, in error, with the thyroid glands. Their removal from the live animal results in nervous spasms, or convulsions, resulting in death. The extract is used in the treatment of tetanus, and injections into the blood-stream result in an increase in the calcium and phosphorus content of the blood.

THYMUS

This gland, the sweetbread, consists of two portions, one situated in the throat, the other in the chest cavity. It reaches its maximum development very early and in calves may weigh up to $1\frac{1}{2}$ lb (0·7 kg). In three-year-old cattle it is extremely small, and in five-year-olds it has entirely disappeared. It is interesting to note that castration is said to delay the rate of atrophy. Thymus substance is used in the treatment of rickets. Persistence of the gland is thought to be the cause of some cases of sudden death in infants.

PINEAL

This is a small cone-shaped gland about the size of a pea. It can be found in a small brain cavity, above the pituitary body. Young males with pineal tumours have shown precocious sex characteristics and abnormal skeletal growth.

PITUITARY

Situated in a bony sac at the base of the brain, this really consists of two lobes, each with different functions. Together they are about the size of a large pea. The anterior lobe is associated with growth and can be responsible for both the giant and dwarf. This part of the pituitary gland is also involved in the regulation of heat production and it is intimately associated with the sex glands.

The posterior lobe has amongst other properties the ability to stimulate the involuntary muscles; it is therefore of value in obstetric cases.

SUPRARENALS

These two glands are situated close to the pelvis of the respective kidneys. The left gland is flattened and somewhat heart-shaped in outline, the right is like a boxing glove in shape (the left does not migrate with the kidney but retains its early position). The inner part of these glands contains a substance which has the ability of constricting the capillaries and thus raising the blood-pressure. From this portion of the gland is obtained adrenalin and similar products which are extensively used in surgery. The outer portion is associated with a disease known as Addison's disease, which causes general debility and emaciation.

SEX GLANDS

As well as their primary function these glands also secrete substances which influence secondary sex characteristics, e.g. the steer, in addition to losing its ability for procreation, never develops the head, crest muscle, and heavy forequarters of the bull, and if the ovaries of a hen are removed it will gradually take on the characteristics of the rooster. Various extracts from these glands have been used in cases of ovarian disturbances and in some forms of sexual neurasthenia. The breeder is making increasing use of these substances and it is possible to induce lactation without pregnancy.

In addition to the foregoing, there are other glands or tissues which supply pharmaceutical substances. The spleen when desiccated is valuable in supplying iron to the system; red bone-marrow is intimately connected with the formation of new blood-cells. The brain tissue supplies kephalin and lecithin, the former proving valuable in the clotting of blood and the latter for treating cases of snake-bite. Aid to digestion can be obtained from the pancreas, the stomach lining provides pepsin, and the abomasum of the calf rennin, whilst surgical ligatures are obtained from the intestine of the sheep.

The economic utilization of these substances can only be carried out where large quantities of animals are handled. Their removal, particularly the smaller glands such as the parathyroids, is a highly skilled operation. As a general rule the glands should be cooled as rapidly as possible after their removal from the animal, followed by freezing. The subsequent treatment of selection, de-fatting, grinding, and testing for activity is the province of the pharmacist, but the following table (Table 16) (C. Robert Moulton) will indicate the yields obtainable.

A number of pharmaceutical products originally obtained from natural sources have been replaced by synthetics.

TABLE 16

Weights of important glands or tissues of meat-producing animals

Weights in grams, ounces, or pounds

Portion	Bovine	Ovine	Porcine
Pineal body	0·32 g	0·04–0·12 g	0·10 g
Pituitary gland	3·0 g	0·37–0·55 g	0·33–0·78 g
Ovary	5·7 g	0·76 g	3·15 g
Testes	½ lb	2 oz	3–4 oz
Suprarenal	11–15 g	1·5–2 g	3–5 g
Thyroid	1–1½ oz	2–9 g	4–10 g
Thymus	⅓–½ lb	15–25 g	9–35 g
Pancreas	½–1 lb	1 oz	1½–2 oz
Stomach	16–20 lb	1–2 lb	2–4 lb
Spleen	1–2 lb	⅛–½ lb	⅓–¾ lb
Brain and cord	20–26 oz	6–9 oz	10–16 oz.

In the case of the parathyroid, one needs 600 glands to get 1 lb of fresh or 3600 to obtain 1 lb of the finished dry material.

Duties of butchers and slaughtermen

The following is extracted from Memo. 62, Foods,* and is of particular interest to the slaughterman.

(i) Evidence of disease in a carcase should not be modified or obliterated by washing, rubbing, stripping, or in any other manner, except under the direct supervision of the Meat Inspector, and in accordance with his instructions.

(ii) In *no* case either of 'back-bleeding', 'over-sticking', or 'sticking-in' should stripping of the serous membrane be permitted, except by, or under the direction of, the Meat Inspector, and in any such case in which immediate stripping is necessary to preserve the marketability of the carcase, the membrane should not be entirely detached from the carcase until it has been examined by the Meat Inspector, and he has authorized the detachment.

(iii) Notification of intention to slaughter animals *for emergency reasons* should be forwarded to the Veterinary Officer, Public Health Inspector, or Medical Officer of Health, and so far as practicable all such animals should be examined at the time of slaughter. If not so examined, the carcase and the whole of the viscera should be detained until it has been examined by the Public Health Inspector and a decision given.

*A system of meat inspection recommended by the Ministry of Health for adoption by local authorities.

In cases where such an animal is examined at the time of slaughter, the Inspector may require the carcase and the whole of the viscera, unless obviously unfit for food, to be detained for 24 hours thereafter to enable a later inspection to be made.

All carcases of such animals as may subsequently be passed for human consumption should be ribbed or quartered before being released.

(iv) When any dead or moribund animal is admitted into a slaughter-house, immediate notification of the fact to the Veterinary Officer, Public Health Inspector, or the Medical Officer of Health should be made by the owner or person in charge of the animal, and as soon as practicable after receipt of the notification an Inspector should examine such carcase or animal.

(v) Where the carcase has not been examined by the Public Health Inspector at the time of slaughter, the whole of the viscera and offal should be kept, pending inspection, in such a way as to enable them to be identified, by labelling or otherwise, with the carcase from which they have been removed.

Line slaughtering

In its basic form, line slaughtering implies the movement of the carcase' in contrast with what is termed booth slaughtering, where the carcase remains practically stationary, and the various by-products are man handled by the operatives, across the slaughter floor.

Obviously it is desirable that provision should be made for the various products, immediately adjacent to the point at which they are removed in the process of dressing. There must be no criss-crossing of the paths of edible and inedible products and as far as possible potential sources of gross contamination should be diverted from the carcase area, as rapidly as possible. Consequently, the general pattern of the line, will tend to take the following diagrammatic form (Fig. 8).

Basically, the length of the line will be determined by the number of slaughtermen employed and the output planned. In a completely mechanized conveyor system, adjusting the speed of conveyor will provide some degree of latitude. With the object of reducing the floor area required, it is seldom possible to install a practical unit in one straight line, as indicated in the diagram.

As the carcase is kept off the floor, much higher standards of hygiene can be maintained and there is a considerable saving in floor space and consequently building costs. With the traditional booth system of operation, a reasonable throughput might be in the region of about 1·25 beasts per man-hour, whilst with a fully conveyorized plant

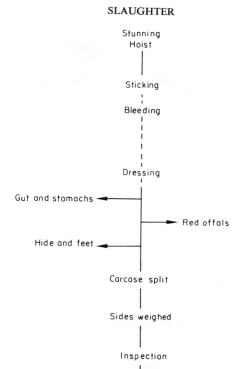

Fig. 8 Diagram of slaughter operations

operating with a good team, this figure can frequently be doubled.

The detailed plan on p. 92 (Fig. 9) indicates a modern lay-out for a single-floor abattoir, which will have a final capacity of 80 beasts an hour and that for sheep of 300 per hour, the dressing in both cases being conveyorized. Greater efficiency is obtained with a two-storey structure, with the by-products below the killing floor, so that the materials pass down shutes and no labour is involved with the trucks. Such a design is, however, more expensive in terms of initial cost. This abattoir has been designed to comply with the high standards demanded by the US Dept. of Agriculture and the EEC countries.

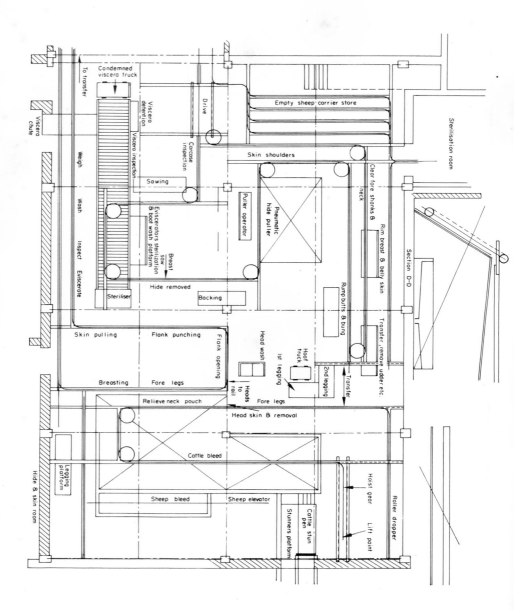

Fig. 9   Plan of modern abattoir layout. (By courtesy of Brook and Crowther Ltd.)

GENERAL DESCRIPTION OF OPERATION

Cattle enter the stunning pen from the lairage and, after stunning and automatic hoisting onto the bleed-line, they are conveyed over the bleeding trough, the minimum bleeding time being $7\frac{1}{2}$ minutes. At the end of the blood trough the neck pouches are opened to get rid of the blood which has collected and then the head is skinned and removed for washing (US Regulations require that in dressing the heads must come off first). The weasand is rodded and tied off, to obviate any risk of contamination from this source, and the foreshanks are removed.

The bleeding conveyor carries the carcase onto the first legging platform, where the free leg is skinned and removed, after which the transfer hoist is inserted and the carcase is lifted until the shackle chain can be detached.

The second leg is skinned and removed whilst on the hoist, after which the carcase is hooked onto two standard dressing rollers and the hoist hook is removed.

The dressing rollers are fed into the dressing conveyor which puts a slight spread on the hind legs, as it travels past the various skinning platforms.

A pneumatically operated hide puller grips the open edges of the belly skin and pulls the hide backwards across the sides, leaving the fell on the carcase. The operator controls the amount of pull and stops at the far line so as not to damage the fat covering the back. From the puller, which works on the moving carcase the body passes the packing platform and the hide is removed and taken directly to the hide room.

The breast-bone is sawn through and the body then passes over the moving top viscera table, where it is cleared of both red and green offal, which fall onto the table. The table is a slat conveyor in stainless steel, with its own built-in sterilizer.

All the viscera is inspected on the table, whilst the carcase is being split by a heavy power saw capable of handling 80 cattle per hour and operated from a platform which moves sideways and downwards, as the carcase passes.

The carcase is inspected immediately after sawing, in a position alongside the viscera inspection, and then goes away for trimming, weighing, and washing, or onto a suspect loop for further inspection.

Clean viscera is pulled off the moving table top onto the chute to the gut room and red offal is lifted onto trucks for the red offal room. Condemned material automatically discharges into the container for removal.

The sheep line is designed to pass the hide room and the viscera table at the correct time in the various operations and also to carry heads, in sequence and not touching each other, to the inspection area.

Export slaughterhouses

EEC Directives lay down detailed regulations regarding the design, construction, operation, cold storage facilities and inspection for slaughterhouses concerned in the intra-Community trade in fresh meat.

In England and Wales, inclusion on the list of approved Export Slaughterhouses is granted by the Animal Health Division of the Ministry of Agriculture; and in Scotland by the Scottish Department of Agriculture and Fisheries.

Before a slaughterhouse can be included on the list, it must be inspected by a veterinary officer of the appropriate department who will assess the construction and hygiene standards. In addition there are periodical checks to ensure that standards are maintained, in order to retain inclusion on the list.

For exports to the United States or to American forces in other regions, the United States Department of Agriculture (USDA) have somewhat similar regulations and they are responsible for the approval and continued inspection of such 'Export Slaughterhouses'.

5 Dressing percentages

Live weight to carcase weight

The dressing percentage is a comparison of the carcase yield in relation to the live weight of the animal or, expressed in another fashion, the pounds of dressed carcase obtained from every 100 lb (45 kg) of live animal. This figure will depend upon a number of factors, the more important being the stage of maturity, the degree of finish, the breed, and the intestinal content. As in the case of many other old customs, the butchers' stone of 8 lb (3·6 kg) has a good practical basis, as it assumes that the loss of 6 lb (2·7 kg), as compared with the farmers' stone, represents the loss to be anticipated as between live animal and carcase weight. This ratio would give a figure of over 57%, which is a reasonably high estimate for the average run of modern cattle. It is probable that the old preference for more heavily fatted beasts than those required today have influenced this standard. When a beast is slaughtered there is an initial loss by evaporation, therefore dressing percentages should always be calculated on cold carcase weight. This shrinkage will vary with different classes of cattle and the loss will be influenced by the storage condition. In most packing houses where carcases are weighed hot a deduction of 2% is usually made. Under adverse storage conditions this figure can easily be exceeded.

Yields may range from about 45% up to 70%, though these figures are extreme and will seldom be met with. The world record dressing percentage is held by an Aberdeen-Angus at 76·78%. This does not mean that such a beast would prove ideal from the butchers' standard, as such a figure could only be obtained at the expense of excessive fat. In fact, figures above 60% are usually provided by animals which carry too much fat for the present consumer demand for lean meat.

The dressing-out percentage is not an entirely satisfactory method of defining the carcase yield. For example it has been found that the dressing-out percentage of a beast which has not been fasted, as compared

95

with its *empty gut* live weight, can vary by up to as much as 12%. In addition, the head and the hide weight will vary with different breeds and with their degree of development. It is usually found that the Hereford will give the heaviest hide, followed by the Angus and Shorthorn and in general dairy breeds will tend to have the lightest weight hides.

Usually the 'killing fats' (omentum and mesenteric) will probably run at about 3% of the live weight, but may range from as low as 1% in poor cows to 6% or even more in ripe cattle.

Under normal commercial conditions of resting and slaughter a beast dressing out at about 55% should give a reasonably lean carcase, suitable for many types of retail trade. It is usual to consider offals under two main classifications, edible and inedible, but in considering gross figures for these, it is necessary to define which should be included under the appropriate heading.

A distinction may be made between 'red' and 'white' offals, although sweetbreads are included in the former and blood, if used for black puddings, should be classified as edible.

Similarly, fats, depending upon their quality and the heat processing to which they are subjected, may become an edible product or technical tallow. Thus calculations of the total yield obtained must be related to the specific conditions.

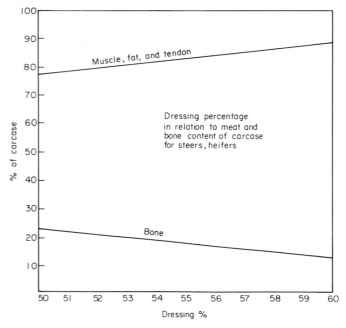

Fig. 10   Dressing percentages for steers and heifers

Live weights

Under the Markets and Fairs (Weighing of Cattle) Acts, all markets and fairs where tolls are charged, and all auction marts, are required to provide a weigh-bridge, and sellers are bound to have all cattle weighed if requested. The Act of 1926 enforces weighing of all cattle fit for immediate slaughter, and the announcement of the weight to intending purchasers previous to the sale (except where exemption from the provisions of the Act has been obtained). The Act does not apply to sales by private treaty. Thus, under normal circumstances the buyer is familiar with the weight, and though the conformation and degree of finish are important points, as the weight is known, one important factor of possible error is eliminated.

A number of methods of calculating the weight from measurements have been evolved and many of these methods have been developed on the assumption that each stone (14 lb (6·4 kg)) of the live animal occupies 576 cubic inches (0·944 m³)

There is also a cattle gauge, based on the slide-rule principle, which is used for calculating weight from measurements, with corrections for different types of animals. The measurements are taken in feet, length from the square of the shoulder to the square of the buttock, and girth immediately behind the shoulders.

Calculation of dressing percentage

As already stated, the carcase yield of a beast is expressed as a percentage of the live weight of the animal. The dressing percentage is calculated as follows:

$$\frac{\text{cold carcase weight (lb)}}{\text{live weight (lb)}} \times \frac{100}{1}$$

The calculation is simplified when dealing with metric units as the carcase weight and live weight are both expressed in kilograms. For example, a beast weighing 480 kg and yielding a carcase of 269 kg, would have a dressing out percentage of:

$$\frac{269}{480} \times \frac{100}{1} = 56\% \text{ (approx)}$$

Assuming that a beast costs 50p/kg live weight and that the dressing out percentage is 56% 'sinking the offal', the carcase cost per kg would be:

$$\frac{50}{56} \times \frac{100}{1} = 89·28\text{p. (approx } 40·49\text{p/lb)}$$

For wholesale butchers wishing to include a profit in this form of calculation, the following adjustments should be made:

$$\left(\frac{p/kg}{\text{Dressing }\%} \right) \times \left(\frac{100}{100 - X} \right) \%$$

X is the percentage desired profit on sales. As an example if we require 5% profit on sales and using the figures above, then:

$$\left(\frac{50}{56} \right) \times \left(\frac{100}{95} \right) \% = 93 \cdot 99 \text{ p/kg (app. } 42 \cdot 63 \text{p/lb)}$$

If it is desired to allow a credit for offals, against the value of the carcase, the total value of the offals should be divided by the cold carcase weight in order to find the appropriate amount to be deducted from the side value. For example, if the offal is worth £15 and the cold carcase weight is 269 kg, then:

$$\frac{1500}{269} = 5 \cdot 576 \text{p/kg credit (2·53p/lb)}$$

To relate the cost of the boneless beef, as prepared for sale, to the cost of the live animal, the following method can be applied:

$$\left(\left(\frac{P}{D} \times \frac{100}{1} \right) - \text{Offal credit} \right) \times \left(\frac{100}{\% PM} \right) = \text{cost boneless meat}$$

Where P is the p/lb or p/kg of live beast,
D the dressing percentage and
$\%PM$ the prepared boneless meat as a % of the cold carcase weight. Thus for a beast costing 26p/lb (57·31p/kg.), dressing out at 56%, allowing a credit of 2·68p/lb for offal and assuming that 70% of the carcase is boneless meat, then

$$\left(\left(\frac{26}{56} \times 100 \right) - 2 \cdot 68 \right) \times \left(\frac{100}{70} \right)$$

$$\left(46 \cdot 42 - 2 \cdot 68 \right) \times \left(\frac{100}{70} \right)$$

$$43 \cdot 74 \times \left(\frac{100}{70} \right) = 62 \cdot 48 \text{p/lb (137·74p/kg)}$$

The slaughter record (p. 103) will be found useful for students and for the butcher who wishes to run a test to check the cost of beef in relation

TABLE 17

Test on Aberdeen-Angus heifer (about 24 months)

Condition: very good butchers' beast.
Live weight, 952 lb; carcase (hot), 560 lb carcase (cold), 548 lb.

Edible offal	lb	oz	Inedible offal	lb	oz
Blood	38	0	Hide	69	0
Breads	1	8	Feet	16	0
Head, ex	22	8	Omasum, empty	6	0
Tongue, long	6	4	Casings, empty	12	0
Weasand and meat	1	0	Lungs and trachea	7	6
Rumen and reticulum,			Mesenteric and fat		
empty	15	0	trimmings	17	2
Abomasum, empty	3	12	Gall-bag, bladder,		
Spleen	1	2	etc.	2	12
Liver	14	2		130	4
Thick skirt	2	0			
Tail	2	1			
Omentum	16	13	Stomach and intestinal		
Heart	4	7	contents	128	0
	128	9			

Summary

	lb	oz	Approx. % of live weight
Carcase, cold	548	0	57·6
Edible offal	128	9	13·5
Inedible offal	130	4	13·7
Carcase loss, hot to cold	12	0	1·2
Intestinal contents	128	0	13·4
Loss	5	3	0·6
	952	0	100·0

Bone in carcase, 74 lb 2 oz; percentage of bone in carcase, 13·5%.

to that of the live animal. A periodical analysis of a sample beast will probably well repay the time spent in weighing the offals, etc., and working out the sheet, and will provide valuable data against future purchases.

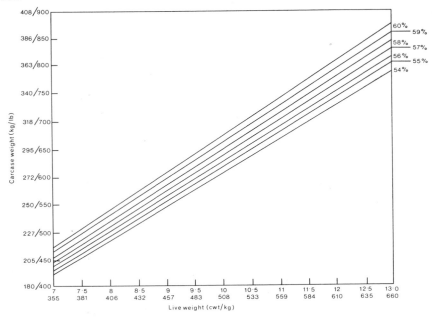

Fig. 11   Conversion of live weight to carcase weight (54% to 60%)

Conversion of lb and cwt quantities into nearest Metric equivalents

cwt	lb	kg	cwt	lb	kg	cwt	lb	kg	cwt	lb	kg
—	1	0·454	1	112	51	—	661	300	—	1213	550
—	2	0·907	1½	168	76	6	672	305	11	1232	559
—	3	1·36	—	200	91	—	700	318	11½	1288	584
—	4	1·81	—	220	100	6½	728	330	—	1323	600
—	5	2·27	2	224	102	—	772	350	12	1344	610
—	6	2·72	2½	280	127	7	784	356	12½	1400	635
—	7	3·18	—	300	136	—	800	363	—	1433	650
—	8	3·69	—	331	150	7½	840	381	13	1456	660
—	9	4·08	3	336	152	—	882	400	13½	1512	686
—	10	4·54	3½	392	179	8	896	406	—	1543	700
—	20	9·07	—	400	181	—	900	408	14½	1568	711
—	30	13·61	—	441	200	8½	952	432	14	1624	737
—	40	18·14	4	448	203	—	992	450	—	1653	750
—	50	22.68	—	500	227	—	1000	454	15	1680	762
—	60	27·21	4½	504	229	9	1008	457	—	1764	800
—	70	31·75	—	551	250	9½	1064	483	—	1984	900
—	80	36·29	5	560	254	—	1102	500	—	2000	907
—	90	40·82	—	600	272	10	1120	508	—	2205	1000
—	100	45·36	5½	616	279	10½	1176	533	—	3000	1380
									—	4000	1814
									—	5000	2268

TABLE 18

Test on Hereford Steer (about 30 months)

Condition: up to show standard.
Live weight, 1140 lb; carcase (hot), 708 lb; carcase (cold), 694 lb.

Edible offal	lb	oz		Inedible offal	lb	oz	
Blood	24	8		Hide	68	0	
Breads	2	0		Feet	24	0	
Head, ex	32	12		Horns	3	8	
Tongue, cut long	9	2		Omasum, empty	7	8	
Weasand and meat	1	12		Casings, empty	14	0	
Rumen and reticulum,				Lungs and trachea	9	0	
empty	16	0		Mesenteric and fat			
Abomasum, empty	3	0		trimmings	27	0	
Stomach fat	2	0		Gall-bag, bladder			
Spleen	2	2		etc.	3	8	
Liver	11	8				156	8
Thick skirt	2	1					
Tail	1	14					
Omentum	11	8		Stomach and intestinal			
Heart	4	8		contents		148	8
		124	11				

Summary

	lb	oz	Approx. % of live weight
Carcase, cold	694	0	60·9
Edible offal	124	11	10·9
Inedible offal	156	8	13·7
Carcase loss, hot to cold	14	0	1·2
Intestinal contents	148	8	13·1
Loss	2	5	0·2
	1140	0	100·0

Bone in carcase, 84 lb; percentage of bone in carcase, 12·1%.

TABLE 19

Test on Shorthorn steer (about 27 months)

Condition: very good butchers' beast, somewhat fat.
Live weight, 1092 lb; carcase (hot), 650 lb; carcase (cold), 639 lb.

Edible offal	lb	oz		Inedible offal	lb	oz		
Blood	23	0		Hide	70	0		
Breads	1	8		Feet	21	0		
Head, ex	27	0		Horns	30	0		
Tongue, cut long	6	1		Omasum, empty	7	0		
Weasand and meat	0	15		Casings, empty	17	0		
Rumen and reticulum,				Lungs and trachea	8	0		
empty	28	0		Mesenteric and fat				
Abomasum	4	10		trimmings	23	0		
Stomach fat	2	0		Bladder, etc.	3	0		
Spleen	1	8					152	0
Liver and gall bag	14	14						
Thick skirt	3	0						
Tail	2	4						
Omentum	15	4		Stomach and intestinal				
Heart	4	8		contents			153	0
			134	8				

Summary

	lb	oz	Approx. % of live weight
Carcase, cold	639	0	58·5
Edible offal	134	8	12·3
Inedible offal	152	0	13·9
Carcase loss, hot to cold	11	0	1·1
Intestinal contents	153	0	14·0
Loss	2	8	0·2
	1092	0	100·0

Bone in carcase, 89 lb; percentage of bone in carcase, 14%.

SLAUGHTER RECORD

Beef

Date...............

Breed....... Sex....... Age....... Remarks.......................

Grade....... Weight....kg........   at...... per kg   =   £ p

Transport, etc.   =

Cost at slaughterhouse   =

Live weight at slaughter ....kg........   Shrinkage ......%

Carcase weight, hot ......lb   Carcase weight, cold ......lb

Cold carcase weight percentage of live weight as purchased ......%

Offal	Weight		% of live weight	Offal	Weight		% of live weight
	lb	oz			lb	oz	
Head				b. fwd			
Tongue				Sweetbreads			
Feet				Lights			
Paunch				Melt			
contents				Liver			
Paunch empty				Heart			
Intestinal				Skirt			
content				Fats			
Intestines empty				Weasand			
Hide				Tail			
Blood				Trimmings			
				Miscellaneous			
				Loss			
c. fwd				Totals			

£ p

Cost of beast at slaughterhouse
Add charge for slaughter and storage

Less value of offals

Net cost of carcase   Carcase cost per lb

6   Carcase quality

Carcase quality as such still awaits a scientific definition and may have different values for various buyers. However, we are aware of some of the numerous factors which contribute to the general appraisal of the quality of a carcase and these extend through many facets from conception to its final consumption.

Our beef breeds have a world-wide reputation and, even today, where the vast majority of our beef is associated with the dairy herd, the beef sire still plays an important role. For example, the Hereford × Friesian is a very popular cross, introducing a little more quality, although it may take longer to reach slaughter weight. The average age of slaughter has decreased considerably over the years and there appears to be an increasing proportion of semi-intensively fed cattle of about 18–24 months. Heifers mature at an earlier age than comparable steers and may carry somewhat more fat, but are usually lighter in bone. The age at which castration is carried out can influence the carcase and recently there has been an increased interest in the use of young bulls for beef.

Environment will influence type, the slow maturing Highland cattle as compared with intensively fed barley beef, ready for slaughter at about one year, being good examples, although the plane of nutrition is obviously of importance.

Considerable progress has been made in the eradication of disease, probably the most spectacular being that of TB; even so much can be done to reduce the diseases which may prevent cattle from attaining their full growth potential.

Too little attention has been given to the study of individual variation in resistance to stress. Individual animals vary in their resistance to nervous stress and the balance between the degree of fasting and the stress of a hungry restless beast is important. One of the chief causes of poor keeping quality in the case of carcases from fatigued animals is the excessive retention of blood which will provide an ideal media for the multiplication and distribution of bacteria.

In the healthy live animal, it may be broadly assumed that the flesh is almost entirely free from bacteria. This is due to the delicate balance maintained by various defensive factors, including the white blood cells, serum reactions, and the pH of the flesh. The main defences against the heavy bacterial load in the gut appear to be the unfavourable pH, the protective mucous lining from the mouth to the anus, and the large number of mesenteric nodes in the mesentry. Fatigue and prolonged starvation reduces the resistance of the gut wall to bacterial invasion, whilst the combination of both fatigue and hunger permits the invasion of bacteria, more readily than any single factor.

Another important factor is that a fatigued animal will tend to use up its glycogen in its muscles, and following death the pH, which normally falls from about 7·2 to 5·7 will not fall to the same extent and the higher pH will favour the growth of putrefactive organisms. The main sources of potential contamination appear to be the hide, feet of animals, faeces voided on the floor, swabbing cloths, hands and clothes, and splashing with contaminated blood and faeces when hosing down.

Whilst the initial contamination will basically determine the commercial storage life, both temperature and humidity control will have a marked effect on the rate of multiplication of micro-organisms. Reference to the post-mortem changes in meat is given on p. 253.

The resistance of fat to chemical breakdown is not entirely controlled by the storage conditions. Rancidity can be caused by mould growth, bacteria, enzymes, and oxidation with atmospheric oxygen, resulting in objectionable odour and off flavours. The type of fat laid down on and within a carcase will depend upon the species of animal, the type of feed, and the plane of nutrition. Of our food animals, pork fat appears to be the most sensitive to such changes and, even at low freezer temperatures, the anticipated storage life is less than that of beef or mutton, under comparable storage conditions. The diagram indicates some of the main factors which have an influence on the ultimate quality in its widest sense, of carcase meat (Fig.12).

Meat constituents

Before we consider the question of what influences carcase quality it may be as well to examine the meat constituents. To the lay mind 'meat' implies edible substances obtained from muscles, fat, organs, and glands of the many food animals, but to the trade the term is usually applied to the dressed carcase. Therefore, we must obviously include not only the above-named portions but also the bones, ligaments, and tendons.

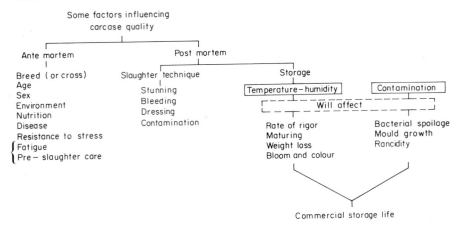

Fig. 12　Some factors influencing carcase quality

BONE

Bone is usually considered under four main headings.

(a) Long bones, with enlarged ends, e.g. clod and silverside, etc. These are mainly concerned with effecting movement of the animal.

(b) Flat bones, which protect vital organs and provide attachment for muscles.

(c) Short bones, such as the knuckles.

(d) Irregular bones. These would include the vertebrae and the bones of the base of the skull.

Bone is a connective tissue in which earthy salts have been deposited to increase the strength. This process of bone formation (ossification) provides valuable evidence as to the probable age of the carcase. Bone consists of about one-third animal or organic matter, and about two-thirds inorganic matter, the latter consisting chiefly of phosphate of lime, with much smaller quantities of carbonate of lime, phosphate of magnesia, and carbonate and chloride of sodium. In the calf up to about the fourth week cartilage and not bone (ossa cordis) is found in the heart, and up to approximately the sixth week from birth the shank bones are easily separated with a knife, or by boiling. The bones in earlier maturing animals become ossified at a younger age than late maturing types. It has also been found that animals maintained on a high plane of nutrition, irrespective of breed, will tend to show early ossification of the bones.

In bovine animals under two years the ischio-pubic symphysis can be split easily with a knife, but will later require to be sawn, owing to ossification. Up to about two years, the tips of the first four or five dorsal vertebrae are entirely cartilaginous. Following this, bone centres appear and these 'buttons' are almost entirely converted into bone at about the sixth year. A border of cartilage can be distinguished between the dorsal spine and the 'button' decreasing up to about the ninth year, by which time it has disappeared. At this stage the 'buttons' are of lighter colour than the bones of the spine, and after about twelve years the buttons become yellowish-grey in colour and very hard and compact. It has been suggested that the increase in the rate of ossification at these points, by increasing or improving the level of nutrition, are not so marked as changes in the rate of ossification elsewhere or the rate of change in the dentition.

(I am indebted to Mr J. K. Walley MRCVS, for the observations above on ossification.)

LIGAMENTS AND TENDONS

The ligamentum nuchae in the neck and shoulders (yellow in colour) is characteristic of the former, and the tendon of Achilles (white) is an example of the latter. These white and yellow connective tissues vary considerably in chemical composition, the tendon being rich in collagen, whilst the ligament is poor in collagen and contains a relatively high proportion of elastin. As collagen can be converted into gelatin by boiling, this difference is of importance when preparing a 'jelly stock'.

FAT

Fat is deposited in and on the animal as a reserve store against future needs. It appears to be laid down in the following order. Around the intestines, the kidneys, and then on the rump, extending along the back and round the barrel and under the belly. The neck and shanks are the last portions to become covered with fat. Thus with stocky beef types and Down breeds it is more easy to obtain a good finish on these parts than, say, in dairy breeds or leggy mountain sheep. To some extent the body fat will resemble the fat taken up in the feed. When an animal fattens, the size of the fat cells increases as they become distended with fat. According to Moulton, the diameter of the cells in a poor steer is only about one-third of that found in a very fat animal. It appears probable that the wide variations in colour may be influenced by the size of these cells and the relative amount of connective tissue. Breed plays an important part, and the characteristic yellow fat of the Jersey and Guernsey is familiar to the butcher, and possibly the public's objection to a bright yellow fat is based on its association with dairy cows. In aged cows the typical yellow fat is probably due to the concentration of pigment, as the fat is used up for the production of young and milk, and the relative increase in the proportion of connective tissue. Even in grazed beef cattle, loss of condition, when feed is scarce, will tend to produce a rather yellow fat. Every butcher is familiar with the difference between, say, suet fat and that laid down on the surface of the carcase, and this variation is Nature's method of maintaining the right consistency throughout the animal. The internal fat having a higher temperature than the external fat must have a higher melting point, whereas the external fat is almost in contact with the atmosphere and would not require such a high melting-point. For example, the melting point of brisket fat in an average beast might be as low as 90°F (32°C), and the kidney as high as 120°F (49°C). This point is important from the aspect of palatability, as fat with a melting-point or setting-point at a higher temperature than that of the human body will tend to cause that 'furry' effect on the palate usually associated with cold mutton fat. Generally the fat of sheep is white and should be firm and odourless, but frequently, particularly in mutton which has been stored for a period, a tallowy smell and flavour will develop.

The fat of the pig is fine, smooth, and firm, and will give a melting-point between 100 and 122°F (38 and 50°C).

Fat-soluble flavours are retained in the fat; therefore, the final flavour of the meat is greatly influenced by the fat. Also, during cooking or when consumed, the volatile substances influence our impression of palatability, as taste and odour are closely related. We are all familiar with 'fishy' pork, 'orange' beef, and the effect of some types of weed on both milk fat and body fat. Desirable flavours can of course be taken up in the same manner.

'Marbling', the infiltration of fat between the muscle fibres, is always taken as an indication of quality; it shows that the animal is well finished, and the fat introduces flavour into the meat and, on cooking, exerts a basting effect on the muscle bundles. Recent work, however, appears to indicate that whilst marbling fat has an effect on flavour and probably palatability it is not correlated with tenderness.

Meat obtained from the carcases of young animals is frequently deficient in marbling fat, but may be extremely tender. A good example of this is the Yugoslav beef, which was imported into this country in relatively large quantities.

There is always a certain amount of fat present even in the poorest carcase and 'bobby' veal may contain 10% of fat. A carcase containing about 28% of fat would be suitable for the average retail trade where a too well finished carcase is undesirable.

The meat processor is particularly interested in the proportion of fat present, in his formulation of meat products. Although the skilled craftsman may be able to assess the lean : fat ratio with a high degree of accuracy, such individuals are few and far between. Whilst the fat content of a sample can be estimated by means of chemical analysis, this process will probably take some hours. Under normal conditions it may be found that by the time the basic materials have been analysed, the manufactured product has already been prepared. Consequently, to be of any practical value it is desirable that an analytical procedure should form part of the production line, so that suitable adjustment can, where necessary, be made. An apparatus under the trade name Anyl-Ray is now available which will permit instantaneous readings of fat content to be taken. A direct reading of the percentage of fat in a sample can be obtained in 3 seconds. The principle involves the use of controlled X-rays to measure the penetration of gamma rays. As the lean meat absorbs more energy than the fat, the energy transmitted will vary accordingly. The rays which have penetrated are picked up by a radiation measuring device, which in turn energizes a calibrated direct reading, in terms of percentage fat. As compared with chemical analysis, the simple average of deviation is stated to be 0·863%. This may have been influenced by sampling, by laboratory technique, or from the Anyl-Ray readings taken.

MUSCLE

Muscle consists of a number of fibres held together by connective tissue. A muscle fibre can be considered as a small elongated sac with a fine exterior membrane enclosing the meat proteins, myosin, and myogin, and with them certain salts and acids. The connective tissue contains a large percentage of collagen, a tough substance, which, as already mentioned, can be converted, on boiling, to a tender material, gelatin. The proportions of connective tissue in a muscle is dependent on the activity of the muscle in the live animal. The leg muscle of the ox is subjected to great stress during the movement of the animal, and consequently the amount of connective tissue present is much greater than in the fillet (psoas muscle), which has comparatively little work to do. Therefore, the joints containing much collagen are more suitable for boiling or stewing and those with little collagen are preferred for roasting and grilling.

DOPPELENDER (DOUBLE MUSCLE)

Genetically, a mutation might be briefly described as the inception of a heritable variation. A number of these mutations occur in our food animals and in practically all cases, they result in undesirable characteristics. For example, dwarfism in cattle is known to be due to recessive genes and the gene concerned affects the length of bone growth and the vertebral development in the lumbar region. One of the few exceptions is the condition of an abnormally heavy muscle development in bovines, usually referred to as 'double muscle'.

At one time it was thought that the muscles from Doppelender cattle were less developed than normal and contained more moisture, but recent research indicates that this is not the case and in spite of the lower quantity of intra-muscular fat, in terms of eating quality, it would appear to be superior.

From the commercial aspect double-muscle development is of considerable interest, but so far it has not been found possible to control this condition and efforts to breed such animals have proved unsuccessful.

The following results were obtained from an investigation carried out at the University of California, in which two related females, one double-muscled and one normal, were compared. The double-muscled beast weighed 1133 lb (514 kg) at 750 days, and the normal 1093·5 lb (496 kg) at 935 days. The chilled carcases were dissected and it was found that the ratios of weights of the double muscled to normal were as follows.

Empty body	1·0
Carcase	1·1
Total muscle	1·4
Carcase fat	0·7
Offal fat	0·9
Viscera	0·9
Hind	0·8

The eye muscle area at the 12th rib was 17·6 sq in (114 cm²), for the double-muscled carcase and 11 sq in (71 cm²) for the normal, whilst the fat cover over the eye was 0·6 in (1·5 cm) and 0·7 in (1·8 cm) respectively.

Based upon the difference in the carcase fat as compared with the offal fat, it was suggested that the operation of more than one factor is involved for the laying down of carcase and of the mesenteric fat.

Muscle colour

In recent consumer-preference investigation it was found that some 60% of the housewives gave colour as being the most important initial consideration in their selection of beef. Should this be representative, the colour of the meat is a very important consideration in sales technique. This is probably more important in the case of the supermarket where pre-packed meat has to sell itself and there is little if any opportunity of explaining to the housewife that a portion of beef well hung and perhaps lacking somewhat in the bright beef colour may be a more satisfactory beef. Basically the chemistry of meat colour is that of one pigment, myoglobin. With the live animal this substance will account for about 10% of the total iron but during the bleeding a very high proportion of the iron is removed as haemoglobin.

In the muscle from a well-bled beast practically all of the remaining iron is accounted for as myoglobin. Myoglobin is a complex protein similar to the blood pigment haemoglobin, as they are both associated with the oxygen requirements of the live animal. The main difference in their function, however, is that the haemoglobin is a carrier of oxygen in the blood-stream whilst the myoglobin is essentially for storing oxygen within the meat cells.

Age and activity appear to influence the myoglobin content of muscle, veal being the lowest, followed by beef and finally old bull beef. As might be expected whale meat is particularly high, since the whale can remain submerged for prolonged periods, without breathing and taking in oxygen.

The range of myoglobin in pork is somewhat similar to that of veal, mutton being somewhat higher.

There is not too much information on all the practical factors affecting meat colour but looking through the literature some general information can be obtained. Over thirty years ago Hammond found that in lambs all the muscle fibres were of the same colour but at 5 months they had differentiated into light and dark fibres, the latter increasing in intensity of colour by the age of eleven months.

As early as 1910 it was established that castration diminished the haemoglobin content of the blood and McCay in 1931, following examination of over 1000 blood samples, established that the blood of bulls has a higher haemoglobin content than that of cows. No difference in colour was found between steers and heifers.

Regarding the influence of breed, Hammond and many other workers have noted differences arising from this source. This, however, has not been fully supported by some other investigations and some workers claim that individual variation within breeds is as important as or even more important than the breed differences which may occur.

Feeding can also play a part, again probably influenced by the iron content. It is well known that calves fed on milk (which is deficient in iron) will produce the typical white milk-fed veal whilst veal from those fed with a mixed diet, containing oatmeal which contains iron, is much darker. It has also been stated that barley gave a lighter beef, with a haemoglobin content of 0·291, than steers fed on maize with 0·325.

The Kansas Station gave the haemoglobin content of grass-fed steers as 0·4584.

Opinion generally appears to be that as a whole the optimum colour was reached at between one and two years in the case of beef.

On cutting and storage, colour changes occurring in beef may be chemical, physical and a combination of the two, the balance being influenced by the temperature and humidity. Freshly cut meat is normally a dull somewhat purplish-red which on exposure to the air becomes more pink and brighter owing to the combination of haemoglobin with oxygen.

Depending upon humidity and temperature, a colour change will also take place owing to the drying of the surface until eventually it may be almost black.

The drying results in the formation of a surface layer which has an increased rigidity and transparency. This change in transparency also increases the depth of light penetration before reflection and this with the increased concentration of the pigment produces an increase in the depth of colour.

Thus it will be appreciated that with wrapped meat two main factors are involved: (a) control of moisture to prevent desiccation of the meat and (b) the passage of oxygen to allow satisfactory colour development. Regarding the latter, temperature is also important as the take-up of oxygen takes place through the surface fluid of the meat and oxygen solubility in water increases as the temperature decreases.

Flavour in muscle is extremely difficult to define, but it depends upon the type and amount of nitrogenous extractives. It is generally agreed that flavour develops with age, and Hammond (1932) found a correlation between high flavour and dark colour in the muscle. In this respect the somewhat insipid nature of veal should be noted. The type of feed would appear to play a part, and the full flavour of Mountain sheep as compared with Down types can be attributed to the type of feed consumed. During storage at temperatures above the freezing-point of meat, in addition to an increase in tenderness, other chemical changes go on which influence the flavour, and should the meat be stored too long the proteins may suffer changes and become denatured. Under good storage conditions the question of flavour changes, owing to bacterial action and/or mould growth, should not arise except possibly in the case of hams and dried sausage.

Tenderness

With the exception of price, tenderness is the most important single factor in the consumer's assessment of beef quality, although flavour and juiciness are factors of considerable importance. It must, however, be admitted, that the many variables which may exert an influence on tenderness have yet to be established. The connective tissues and muscle fibres are constituents, which influence tenderness, and, as their relative proportions vary considerably, differences will occur as between muscles from the same carcase, and even between different regions of the same muscle. The effect of rigor mortis (see p. 254) and the subsequent changes following the resolution of rigor on these constituents is difficult to predict with any degree of accuracy.

Investigations aimed at evaluating tenderness must be very carefully carried out, if they are to have any real meaning. Mechanical tests measuring resistance to pressure or to penetration do not reproduce the action of the incisor and molar teeth or the effect of the salivary juices of the human.

Progress in feeding, breeding, and selection of livestock have resulted in younger animals of an acceptable weight, with a suitable degree of finish. Broadly, meat from high grade carcases will be more tender than those from low grade, but the influence is more pronounced in meat which has been cooked by dry heat (grilling and roasting), than in the less tender cuts in which tenderness is attained by moist cooking (stewing, boiling, and braising).

The traditional method of 'hanging' or conditioning meat (see p. 256) with the object of increasing tenderness and flavour may vary from a few days to three weeks and an increase in tenderness can be achieved by hanging at a high temperature for a short period, or at a lower temperature for a long period. However, other practical considerations are involved. These include loss of weight, discoloration involving trimming, capital investment in holding stock, and the refrigeration costs.

Traditional methods of 'hanging' have little effect on tough collagen fibres and consequently shin, leg of beef, and similar portions will be cooked by the use of moist heat, which tends to change the tough collagen into tender gelatin. This change is accelerated in the presence of dilute acid, and consequently it is influenced by the pH of the flesh, which in turn is affected by the pre-slaughter condition of the animal. Observations indicate that meat cooked before the onset of rigor mortis is relatively tender, whilst that cooked during rigor mortis is tough. Similarly, if rigor mortis is interrupted by freezing, the meat is also tender after thawing and cooking, *provided that the muscle is kept in tension* (as when attached to the skeleton) during the freezing. Although it has been shown that proteolytic activity is associated with hanging, the actual extent to which it is related to tenderness is unknown. Frequently a good quality carcase may fail to become tender after hanging and a low quality carcase become tender in 24 hours to 48 hours after slaughter.

As a safeguard against any possibility of risk of Foot and Mouth disease, the importation of bone-in beef from South America into the United Kingdom, has been prohibited.

Resulting from this action, a considerable trade has developed in chilled boneless primal cuts of beef, and as a further precaution, such cuts must have their appropriate lymphatic glands attached, which can be inspected upon arrival in the United Kingdom.

The primal cuts normally imported include fillets, striploins, topsides, silversides, toprumps, and ponies.

High standards of hygiene are essential in order to ensure a satisfactory commercial life, above the freezing point of meat.

The process involves packing the cuts into cryovac film from which the air is exhausted, followed by sealing, shrinking the film, and packing into cartons. Thus the risk of subsequent surface contamination is eliminated.

During storage and the subsequent marine transport, the temperature is rigidly maintained at between 29°F and 30°F ($-1\cdot7$°C to $-1\cdot1$°C). As sea transport will be about 3 weeks the total maturing period prior to retail sale, will probably not be less than one month.

Thus, the relatively long maturing period, under controlled conditions of vacuum and temperature, result in a marked increase in tenderness and a considerable saving in the labour involved in preparation for retail sale.

A number of wholesale meat processors in the United Kingdom and Eire have now adopted a similar system for cuts from home-killed beef, although in general, the period in film is reduced considerably.

Irradiation brings about changes in the proteins which increase tenderness but which result in objectionable flavours, and adversely affects the colour.

Various mechanical devices have been employed with the object of increasing tenderness, from the more sophisticated mechanically operated metal probes to the somewhat drastic method of mincing, to effect changes in the texture of the meat.

The commercial application of enzymes of the proteolytic variety has received considerable attention. The method of application includes injection in the form of a solution, dipping, spraying, or dusting the surface with a powder containing the enzyme. With the possible exception of some injection techniques, these methods are most effective with steaks or similar thin portions of meat. Usually, a surface application may give rise to discoloration and may produce excessive 'mushy' texture of the surface layers. As this state may not permeate the complete thickness, the underlying layers may present a marked contrast on eating. It has been found that the re-hydration of accelerated freeze-dried meat, using a solution of papain, tends to offset the adverse effects of freeze drying on the tenderness.

As far as meat is concerned, the most important commercial enzymes are papain from the pawpaw, ficin from figs, bromelin from pineapple, and trypsin from the pancreas (gut bread).

In 1961, Swifts, Chicago, developed the technique of introducing minute quantities of enzyme into the circulatory system of the animal prior to slaughter. This accelerates the digestion of protein substances when the heat of cooking is applied. After pre-tendering, the raw meat contains about 4 parts per million of the enzyme introduced. The cooking process largely denatures the minute quantity present, and any residual margin is readily absorbed as a natural protein substance by the digestive processes of the body. A large number of tests indicated that the activation of the papain enzyme begins when heat is applied and that the most active range is within the 140–160°F (60–71°C) region. A test carried out, involving six animals in each test, gave the following results.

	Steaks		Roasts	
Quality Enzyme level	Average	Good	Average	Good
None	5·4	6·8	7·2	8·9
Optimum	6·5	8·1	9·0	9·5

A minimum tenderness level of 7·0 being considered as the ideal.

Tenderstretch process

This system of tenderizing was originally developed in the United States and it is now widely used in Australia. The process aims at maintaining the muscles in a somewhat similar position to those in the live animal, whilst the carcase is suspended following slaughter.

With the normal suspension a side of beef is hung from the hind hock, some of the muscles are relaxed and are consequently more subject to the contraction of rigor mortis, than are those muscles under strain. It is recognized that a decrease in length and consequent increase in muscle fibre diameter, is associated with toughness. Conversely, stretching the length of the muscle fibre will increase tenderness.

The Tenderstretch process involves hanging the side from the aitchbone, instead of the hock, so that the leg drops forward, thus approximating to its position in the live animal.

It is important that this method of hanging is carried out within $1\frac{1}{2}$ hours of slaughter, before rigor commences, and that it is held in this position in the chiller for at least 24 hours.

Owing to the change in the disposition of the muscles, some modifications in the customary method of subsequent cutting is necessary.

In general, it can be assumed that the improvement in the tenderness in the rump, sirloin and topside, is similar to that obtained by maturing for 3 weeks at 34°F (1·1°C). However the silverside is not tenderized to the same extent and the fillet may become slightly less tender, but not sufficiently so, as to affect the consumer acceptability.

From the aspect of production, extra handling is involved in transferring the side from the dressing hook, to suspension in the new position.

In some parts of Australia this technique is being applied to mutton carcases.

Quality

A description of quality of a beef carcase is usually defined in terms of *conformation, finish, and quality*, the latter describing a condition of the muscle. To the butcher the beast with the best conformation is one which will yield a large proportion of valuable joints and a small proportion of bone. The question of bone content is more important in beef than with mutton or pigs, as in the latter cases practically all the bone is disposed of in the various joints, but with beef a very large percentage of the bone is removed prior to sale.

Finish refers to the external covering of fat, and correct finish suggests a smooth covering of creamy white fat distributed over the surface of the carcase.

Quality of the meat is associated with the texture, and this depends on the size of the muscle bundles and the quantity of connective tissue. Intramuscular fat, 'marbling', is a good indication, and the question of sap, or meat juices, must not be ignored.

A large number of factors influence this quality in beef and among the more important are: breed, condition, age, sex, activity, pre-slaughter and slaughter conditions, and finally the methods of storage. A number of these are, of course, interdependent, but they all exert an important influence on the final product.

Beef generally can be divided into the following broad divisions (see Fig. 13).

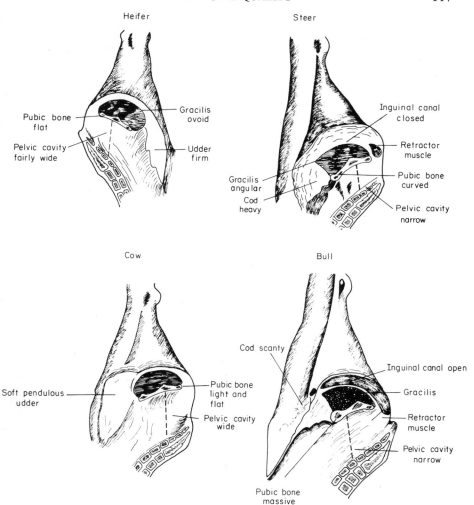

Fig. 13 Hindquarters of heifer, steer, cow, and bull beef. *Note.* Throughout this book the term 'inguinal canal' is employed as it is a common trade term. Anatomically this expression may be open to criticism

BULL BEEF

The age and condition will affect the quality to some extent, but mature bull beef is characterized by the relatively heavy forequarters and massive muscular development, with usually a very poor covering of fat and little kidney fat. In addition to the secondary male features, e.g. pronounced muscle, muscular shanks, etc., the fact that it is an entire male can be ascertained by examining the hind.

The retracter muscle (root of the penis) is broad, the pubic bone, especially the anterior tubercle, heavy, whilst the gracilis muscle is somewhat triangular in shape. The inguinal canal is open (not infiltrated with fat as in the castrated male), the cod fat is poor, and the pelvic cavity from pubic bone to sacrum is narrow.

In the forequarter the crest muscle is very massive and the neck thick. The flesh is usually dark in colour, with coarse texture, and the total fat content is small. This class of beef is used almost entirely for sausage and prepared meats as it possesses exceptional 'binding' qualities, with usually a high percentage of lean muscular tissue in relation to carcase weight.

In the United States, bulls are boned out fresh from the slaughter floor, and the warm flesh chopped down with ground ice. Using this method, good lean meat will absorb up to its own weight of water.

In most of the European countries there has always been a demand for *young* bulls and they attract a considerable price premium, in comparison with other cattle.

At one time, considerable quantities of Yugoslavian beef were sold in Britain and proved to be very suitable for certain types of retail trade. This beef was mainly from intensively fed, young Simmental bulls of about 12 to 15 months, and there is little doubt that the period of transport under controlled temperature conditions, contributed to its eating quality. On account of its light finish, very little trimming was necessary, resulting in a higher yield of prepared retail joints, than from comparable steers.

It would appear that young bull beef may be attractive to the housewife, where lean meat is the major consideration.

An investigation carried out in Canada (Field, Schoonover & Nelms, 1964) involved 19 pairs of Aberdeen-Angus cattle. It was found that the bulls at 16 months provided a greater proportion of best cuts, except from the loin and rib, than did the steers. However the latter were rated better as regards marbling, texture and colour.

Following a ten-day maturing period, the meat was sold in a supermarket, where customers showed a marked preference for the bull beef.

Subsequently they rated 45% of the bull sirloin steaks as good, against 66% of the steer loin steaks and 75% of the bull steaks tender, compared with 85% of the steer steaks.

It is usually accepted that bull beef tends to be dark, but considerable variations can also be found in steers. It would appear probable that at a similar age, although bull beef may initially be darker, after 'blooming' there will be a little difference in the colours.

Cow Beef

The average type of cow carcase available has a low degree of muscular development, and as the proportion of lean meat to bone can be very small, this class of carcase should be purchased with care. There are of course exceptions, and a good, well-finished, one-calf cow can yield flesh of quite good quality, but as a rule, after the third calf, deterioration is particularly rapid. In old cows the flesh is dry, generally with a meagre covering of fat, frequently yellow in colour.

A cow hind can be recognized by the mammary gland (udder), or, if this has been removed, the triangular patch which is left. The pubic bone will be very light, almost flat, forming a bean-shaped gracilis muscle. The pelvic cavity is broad, the angle of the sacrum to rump wide, and the flank is particularly thin. In the forequarters the neck is long and thin, the ribs barrelled, and the crest muscle slight and narrow. A large proportion of cow beef and of bull beef is boned out by wholesalers ready for the small goods manufacturer, though in some areas, where a cheap form of English meat is demanded, cow beef and less frequently bull beef is sold to the butcher.

Ox and Heifer Beef

The vast majority of the meat consumed in this country is obtained from these two classes of animals. The mammary gland of the heifer will be rounder and firm to the touch, and the angle of the rump to loin less wide than in the cow. Should the heifer udder be manipulated, whilst hot, to resemble the cod fat of the ox, the absence of the retractor muscle and the presence of the supramammary lymphatic gland will decide the sex.

In the ox the retractor muscle will be very poorly developed, the inguinal canal infiltrated with fat, and the cod fat heavily lobulated. The pubic bone is much lighter than in the bull, with a markedly smaller anterior tubercle. The general muscular development is much lower than that of the bull, particularly those of the crest and neck.

Heifers mature more rapidly than steers and, although there are regional variations in weight requirements, overweight heifers decrease rapidly in value per lb, as frequently they become excessively fat.

For the retail trade the optimum demand for steer beef is probably within the 450 to 600 lb (200 to 270 kg) range, then decreasing fairly rapidly to the 700 lb (315 kg) and over. With heifers, those around 450 to 500 lb (200 to 230 kg) (correlated with quality) meet a ready demand.

The graph (Fig. 14), based on Smithfield (London), will indicate the respective decreases in values per lb with increasing carcase weight.

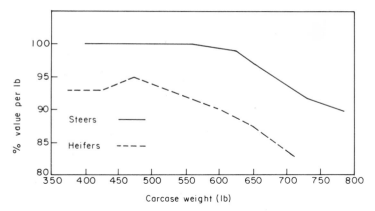

Fig. 14   Weight suitability of English sides (Smithfield, London)

In the case of 'heifers' which are pregnant for the first time, the condition of the udder will provide some indication of the stage of pregnancy. During the early stages no visible changes occur in the mammary tissue; although there may be a few drops of serous secretion present, this may also occur in a maiden heifer.

At around the fifth month, the cells along the milk ducts begin to develop and secrete a sticky fluid, rich in globulin and from then onwards, the fatty tissue becomes replaced by milk tissue. The development of these cells is caused by secretions from the pituitary gland and heifers can be brought into milk without pregnancy by the injection of a hormome extract from this gland.

Spaying is the term commonly used for the removal or destruction of the ovaries and at one time this was practised on the assumption that animals so treated would settle down more placidly and fatten more readily. Cows which have been spayed will continue to produce milk for prolonged periods, in some cases up to four years, without the interruption and disturbances associated with calving.

A freemartin is a heifer born as a twin to a bull calf. In such twins the vast majority of the females are sterile. In about 90% of such twins, the foetal circulations become fused and the male hormones dominate and inhibit the development of the female genital organs. Where such fusion does not take place, the heifers are capable of breeding, but the livestock breeder may not be prepared to risk such odds.

As a general rule it is assumed that heifers, as compared with steers of a similar type, will give better eating quality, smaller bones and will tend to carry more fat. The difference in their relative weights is reflected in the common live weight divisions, as follows:

	Heifers	Steers
Light weight	330–395 kg	380–460 kg
Medium	400–480 kg	465–555 kg
Heavy	over 485 kg	over 560 kg

Influence on yield

Work carried out by G. Harrington and R. W. Pomeroy on some 68 carcases of Aberdeen-Angus cross steers and heifers, resulted in the following conclusions.

Steers were significantly lighter than heifers in the weight of the kidney knob, cod/mammary fat, the flank, forequarter flank, and loin and rump, but they were significantly heavier than heifers in the weight of leg, shin, topside, top rump, and clod and sticking.

The extent of these differences are shown in the table below.

SEX DIFFERENCES

Differences between average weights of corresponding primal cuts from steer and heifer carcases, sides adjusted to 300 lb.

Steer weight (lb) in excess of heifer weight		Heifer weight (lb) in excess of steer weight	
Clod and sticking	2·2	Loin	2·5
Leg	2·1	Rump	2·2
Shin	1·4	Cod/mammary fat	1·9
Steakmeat	1·3	K. Knob	1·7
Topside	1·2	Hindquarter flank	1·6
Silverside	1·2	Forequarter flank	1·0
Thick flank	1·1	Brisket	0·1
Middle rib	0·4		

The above primal cuts were based upon the London and Home Counties method of cutting.

Removal of KKCF (see page 75) would have the effect of modifying the above figures.

The following features are usually looked for in a good side of beef: a thick, full rump and loin, flesh extending well down the legs, ribs nicely covered, and short neck. The general build (conformation) of the carcase depends upon breed, environment, sex, age, and feed. Not only must the proportion of meat to bone be considered, but also the ratio between the more valuable and less valuable portions. The degree of finish or fatness is an important point, and a large quantity of suet and fat is seldom really utilized.

A smooth, even covering of fat is desirable, though it should not exceed ⅜ in (1 cm) over the ribs or loins. As the leg, shin, neck, and flank are usually the last portions to fatten, these parts can be used as an index and the degree of fat inside the flank is another guide. In most beef carcases there is a fairly close relationship between the weight of the kidney suet and the total fat in the carcase.

The colour of the fat should be creamy white, and in the case of Scotch beef a characteristic richness is very noticeable. In the absence of the head, the condition of the bone will provide some indication as to age. The pubic bone (aitch-bone), spinal processes (especially those in the dorsal region), and the size of the pads between the vertebrae should receive attention.

The final test is of course the actual yield on cutting. The following figures (Table 20) are based on a good quality English side of beef of approximately 300 lb (136 kg). It will be noticed that about 60% of the carcase should be prime joints; the so-called coarse cuts, i.e. clod and sticking, flank and brisket, shanks and two-bone steak meat are therefore 40% approximately.

TABLE 20

Cutting yield of good-quality English beef

	%
Round, including cod fat and skirt	16
Thick flank or bed of beef	5·4
Pubic bone	0·7
Rump with suet	9
Loin with suet and kidney	12
Fore-rib	6·7
Middle-rib	10·3
Steak meat	10
Flank and brisket	14
Clod and sticking	8·5
Leg and shin	7·2
Loss	0·2
	100

Suggested scale of points for judging beef carcase

	Max.	Award
GENERAL		
Conformation. Compact, well fleshed, small bone	15	
Finish. Smooth, even cover of firm creamy fat	10	
Quality. Flesh marbled, fine grain, good colour	5	
Internal fat. Suet in proportion to general finish	2	
Weight. According to trade requirements	5	
Soundness. Well dressed, free from bruises and scores	3	
	40	
HINDQUARTERS		
Loin. Well fleshed, not excessively fat	15	
Rump. Full, evenly fleshed to tail head	5	
Round. Full, extending well down hock	12	
Flank. Thick and full of meat	2	
Leg. Fine bone, fat extending well down shank	2	
	36	
FOREQUARTERS		
Ribs. Well fleshed, deep, good eye muscle, smooth finish	15	
Shoulder. Compact, well covered	2	
Neck. Short and thick	2	
Brisket and flank. Short and well fleshed	4	
Shin. Fine bone	1	
	24 Total 100	Total

Bone content

In the earlier stages of animal development the skeleton of the foetus consists of cartilage; later this substance becomes ossified—that is, turned into bone. In some parts of the skeleton this cartilage persists for a considerable period, and the butcher examines the condition of the pubic bone and the spinal processes as an indication of age.

Normally, the percentage of bone, inedible offal, and blood decreases as the animal reaches the fattening stage or maturity. In round figures the percentage of total bone in a bovine animal of 100 lb (45 kg) live weight is about 20%, whilst a really fat beast of between 13 and 14 cwt (660 and 710 kg) might have a bone percentage of under 9%. With an average good beast of about 1000 lb (450 kg) live weight about 12% of bone is a fair estimate.

Bone content in the carcase is probably of greater interest to the average butcher, and as a larger amount of bone is in the carcase than in the offal, the percentage in relation to the carcase is much higher than the percentage in relation to the live animal. This difference will of course be influenced by the dressing percentage. For example, a big framy cow with a large 'fill' might have a moderate bone percentage of live weight, but as it may dress at about 50% or even under, the majority of the skeleton would be concentrated into half the live weight, whereas a well-finished beast might give a dressing percentage of 60% and contain the same weight of bone as the cow but a lower percentage.

As would be expected, the bone content of individual quarters will show variations, and though the average bone content for hindquarters is about 13–14% and forequarters 16–17%, the size and finish of the quarter can produce surprising figures. It must, however, be borne in mind that an abnormally low bone percentage is usually obtained at the expense of excessive fat.

The two examples given below (Table 21) are interesting from the aspect of effect of weight, fat content, and bone on the percentage yield. A, an exceptionally heavy Australian hind, was fairly heavily fatted, with a large frame, and the actual *weight* of total bone was getting on for twice that of B, the meat to bone ratio being approximately 7:1. In B, an Argentine hind, the conformation was very good, the bone small, but the quantity of fat was excessive for modern requirements. In this case the meat to bone ratio was about $9\frac{1}{2}$:1.

Beef grading

It is now generally admitted that the judgement of the live animal in terms of potential beef is a somewhat hit and miss procedure, as compared with judging the dressed carcase. The hidden variables such as hidden fat, eye muscle development, flesh colour, and marbling may each have a marked effect on the subsequent carcase assessment.

Probably one of the earliest forms of grading was incorporated in the

TABLE 21

Cutting yields of Australian and Argentine hinds

Joint	A		B	
	Hind (288 lb)		Hind (209 lb)	
	Weight	Approx. % of H¼	Weight	Approx. % of H¼
	lb oz		lb oz	
Thin flank	19 14	6·9	18 3	8·6
Cod fat	6 10	2·3	5 3	2·5
Goose skirt	1 10	0·6	1 6	0·6
Loin	65 4	22·7	37 0	17·7
Kidney knob	20 4	7·0	23 1	11·0
Rump	41 8	14·4	30 4	14·5
Rump suet	3 4	1·1	3 1	1·5
Thick flank	27 8	9·6	21 8	10·3
Leg	18 0	6·3	13 4	6·3
Topside	29 8	10·1	21 8	10·3
Silverside, long cut	49 8	17·2	31 12	15·3
Pubic bone, part of	4 0	1·4	2 4	1·1
Loss	1 2	0·4	10	0·3
Totals	288 0	100·0	209 0	100·0
Total bone	36 1 (approx. 12·6%)		19 12 (approx. 9·5%)	

Mosaic laws. For sacrificial animals it was required that such animals should not have 'anything superfluous or lacking in his parts' and 'only male animals over 7 days old should be offered'.

Traditionally, the selection of beef carcases was based upon bulls, steers, cows, and heifers, although the definition of the latter was sometimes subjected to some degree of elasticity (for example the Ministry at one time conveniently discarded physiological considerations and created a 'cow-heifer').

Castration was no doubt an advantage when cattle were required to serve for many years as draught animals, before reaching the beef stage. It is possible that castration may have had a world-wide fetish association with the dominance of man over beast.

In carcase grading there is the broad distinction of sex, and, on account of the differing rates of maturity, the weights at which they tend to meet the highest demand and consequently the highest price will vary considerably between steers and heifers. On Smithfield (London) the highest price of heifer sides is at around 475 to 500 lb (215 to 230 kg) and for steers at, say, 550 to 600 lb (250 to 270 kg). There are, however, regional variations in weight demand and in the acceptance of heifer beef.

Beef has generally been described in terms of conformation, finish, and quality. Unfortunately it is extremely difficult to define accurately 'quality'.

Some visual appraisal of finish and internal fat is possible, but it is now suggested that there may be little correlation between conformation and the percentage of prime cuts, the yields being somewhat similar in such widely differing types as the Charolais and the Jersey (Mother Nature appears to be remarkably consistent in her pattern for ruminants).

United Kingdom grades and grading

Definition of classes (Ministry of Agriculture, Fisheries and Food)

Cattle

1. STEERS. Males which have been properly castrated at an early age.
2. HEIFERS. Females which have neither calved nor are sufficiently advanced in pregnancy as to depreciate the value of the carcase.
3. SPECIAL YOUNG COWS. Females which have calved, or pregnant females which have reached a stage of pregnancy which will depreciate the value of the carcase. They must be firm, deep and even in the flesh and not unduly patchy in fat. They must be young and their teeth must show no sign of wear.
4. COWS. Females, other as defined in paragraph 3 above, which have calved or which have reached a stage of pregnancy which will depreciate the value of the carcase.
5. BULLS. Uncastrated males.
6. STAGS (Seggs). Males which, by reason of late or ineffective castration, show some physical characteristic of bulls.
7. VEAL CALVES. Calves which have been fed to produce the distinctive veal colour in the flesh.
8. RUNNER CALVES. Calves which have not been fed to produce the distinctive veal colour in the flesh.
9. 'BOBBY' CALVES. Calves up to about 3 weeks old.
Grades:
    5 grades of steer (bullock) and heifer meat
    5 grades of cow meat
    4 grades for bull meat and for stags (seggs)
    3 grades for young bulls.

MLC beef carcase classification scheme

This system provides a descriptive code to enable buyers to specify their requirements and to provide comparisons of prices quoted for sides/quarters of similar quality. It will also assist in assessing the significance of price differentials for carcases of different qualities.

Trade requirements vary in different parts of the country, and, whereas 'Grading' in its trade sense suggests establishing pre-determined quality values, 'Classification' permits the selection of the most suitable carcase for a particular trade.

Traditional grading tended to consist of 4 or 5 major groups whilst with the Classification scheme there were 5 divisions for conformation and 5 for fat class, providing, at least in theory, 25 different types.

The Beef Carcase Classification Scheme has been based upon five major factors which are applied independently, these consist of:

1. SEX.   S—Steer
         H—Heifer
         C—Cow
         B—Bull

2. WEIGHT. See p. 75 for 'hot weight rebate'.

3. AGE. This is included at the option of the wholesaler and is indicated by differentiating cattle with calf teeth or two permanent teeth erupted, as Y (young); and those with four or more permanent teeth, as T.

4. FAT CLASS. Determined by a visual appraisal of external fat development. Five basic fat classes in which 1 indicates leanest and 5 the fattest. The suffix P may be added for excessively patchy fat, U for excessive cod/udder fat and K for excessive kidney knob and channel fat development (where these are left in the carcase).

5. CONFORMATION. Determined by visual appraisal of shape, taking into consideration thickness of flesh, fullness of round and general blockiness of the carcase. There are five classes. Class 1 indicates the worst shape and class 5 the best shape.

For example, Y H 3 4, would describe a young heifer carcase, average for fatness (3), with above average conformation (4). It has been found that some 50% of all classified cattle fall into Fat Class 3 and many traders found commercially important differences between carcases in the upper and lower halves of this class. It was therefore decided to sub-divide Fat Class 3 into 3L (low or lean) and 3H (high 3) so that the classification grid is now as shown in Fig 15. In addition, a Z class has been introduced for those carcases that are excessively fat.

	Fat class					
	1 (Leanest)	2	3L	3H	4	5 (Fattest)
5 (Very good)						
4						
3						
2						
1 (Poor)						

Confirmation class

Fig 15 Carcase classification 'grid'

ARGENTINA

Exporters from Argentina originally tended to base their standards on conformation, finish, and quality, i.e.

```
A   A   S   SS
N   R   W   S
G   M   I   A
L   O   F   OO
O   Y   T   L
```

In many cases weight classifications were incorporated.

When the Argentine Government took over control of the South American Meat Trade, they substituted in place of the five-letter grading of the various firms, the following:

```
J                   J
U                   U1      chiller quality
        which was  U2
N      subdivided  N
T          into    T1      continental
                   T2      cutters
A                   A      canners
```

Thus they produced six chiller grades.

In 1960 the Argentine Government stated that their existing grades, based on conformation and weight, should be modified to give more emphasis on the degree of finish, in accordance with the changing demands of their markets. As a result, the following experimental scheme was introduced:

Type JJ carcases of milk teeth steers, with grades of fat 1 and 2
Type J   grades of fat 1:2:3
Type U   grades of fat 0:1:2:3
Type U2   grades of fat 0:1:2:3
Type N
Type T
Type A

(With the restriction on the importation of carcase meat (October 1969), boneless cuts will be prepared from beef grades J : U1 : U2, and N.)

AUSTRALIA AND NEW ZEALAND

Both Australia and New Zealand use two general grades, GAQ (good average quality) and FAQ (fair average quality), with weight grading under each heading and colour marked wraps, blue and red respectively.

UNITED STATES

The USDA grades consist of

Prime
Choice
Good
Standard
Utility

Largely based upon conformation and quality as indicated by colour, texture, marbling fat, and maturity. It was appreciated that such a system was not closely associated with the actual yield of boneless, trimmed retail cuts. It was also found that the amount of fat cover was not highly correlated with conformation and that excessive finish and suet could offset the effect of desirable conformation.

Following work covering over 1000 carcases, it was considered that the yield of the major boneless, trimmed cuts could be fairly accurately predicted by the use of only four factors.

(1) Thickness of fat over the eye (12th rib).
(2) Size of the eye muscle.
(3) The amount of kidney and channel fat.
(4) Carcase weight.

In 1965 the USDA instituted the option of a dual grading system consisting of the normal quality grades to each of which is added five 'cutability' grades. The major cuts consist of round, rump, loin, and crop. On the basis of this work, the USDA have produced a slide rule which will give the cutability yield for carcase weights ranging from 300 lb (136 kg) to 1000 lb (454 kg).

It should be emphasized that the usual butchers' beast is a beef type, commonly Hereford, Angus, or their cross, feed lot finished, and in general, pretty consistent in form and weight.

Some continental methods

SWEDEN

Sweden has probably the most complicated grading system. There are six main categories:

Steers	Mature bulls
Heifers	Young cows
Young bulls	Older cows

This sex classification is combined with age, as judged by the dentition. Prior to grading, all the kidney and channel fat is removed and grading is based on a numerical score for assessing fleshing and quality of the lean meat. There are seven classifications plus five classes for the degree of fatness based upon measurement, each indicated by letter grading. Although the graders are trained by the Government, they are actually employed by the slaughterhouse operators.

FRANCE

No nationally applicable grading system is employed. Major meat markets publish prices based on quality. In these cases, four main qualities are quoted, assessed on age, cross section of muscle, and fat deposition. The 'extra' grade is reserved for young heifers and oxen, whilst all other classes and ages may be included in any of the other three grades.

WEST GERMANY

Here the recognized classifications are

Ox and heifer
Bull
Cow
Boneless beef

There are two grades of ox and heifer, two for bull beef, three for cow beef, and one grade only for boneless beef. The main criteria for grading are

Age
Fleshiness
Fat deposition and cover
Colour of bones
Texture of flesh

DENMARK (COPENHAGEN MARKET)

The main classifications are

Ox and heifer
Bull
Old cows
Young cows

Each class is divided into two grades.

SWITZERLAND

Three main recognized classifications are

Ox and heifer
Cow
Bull

There are six grades of ox and of heifer beef, two grades of cow and of bull beef, with a subgrade for bull beef for manufacturing purposes. The criteria for grading are

Age
Fleshiness
Fat deposition and cover

ITALY

Age, as indicated by the dentition is important.

1st quality beef:	from castrated males up to the age of their 6th permanent incisor
2nd quality beef:	from female animals up to the age of the 4th permanent incisor, provided they have not calved or reached the 6th month of pregnancy
Mature ox beef:	from castrated animals from the age of the 7th permanent incisor onwards
Cow beef:	three quality grades

Bull beef:
Criteria for grading are
> Development of muscle
> Physical condition
> Colour of flesh
> Consistency (query—texture)
> Distribution and colour of fat

Future Developments

There has been some practical interest in developing a method for selling beef with a guaranteed minimum standard for eye muscle depth, maximum fat cover, a maximum figure for bone content, and a maximum suet weight (estimated), related to the carcase weight. Such a system was recently tested at the request of a small slaughtering unit in Northern Ireland. Based upon a 550 lb (250 kg) carcase weight, the following standards were suggested:

Fat thickness over eye (10th rib)	max. 9 mm
Eye muscle depth	min. 55 mm
Kidney suet (estimated) per side	max. 6 lb (2·7 kg)
Bone content	max. 72 lb (32·7 kg)

If we disregard that elusive characteristic, quality, the retail butcher is mainly concerned with the amount of lean, boneless meat obtainable from a beef carcase. Many efforts have been made to calculate the lean meat content of a side from a specific sample joint. However, in buying a side of beef, such techniques are not possible. Some indication of fat cover over the eye muscle can be obtained by judicious use of a skewer, and it is possible that the best indication of probable fleshing of the carcase may be obtained from the degree of muscle development of the shin (see p. 274).

In considering the question of carcase evaluation and grading, it is desirable to define the objective, i.e. supreme eating quality irrespective of cost, maximum yield of marketable meat at minimum cost, or, as required by the meat processor, a minimum of fat in relation to protein.

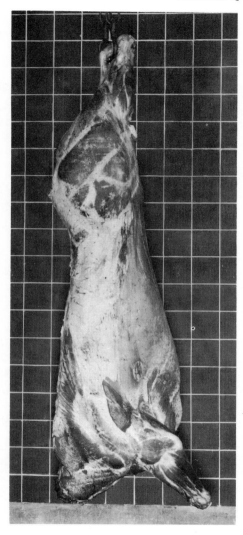

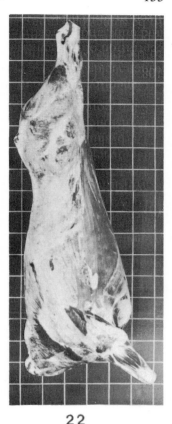

22

13

Plate 25   Under the MLC classification scheme, the factors of most importance to the butcher are fatness and conformation. The scheme is described on page 127.

Originally, one group only for fat class 3, was employed. As it was found that a large number of steers and heifers fell into this class, it was decided to subdivide into 3L and 3H, in order to obtain a finer degree of classification. (The following photographs and figures, by courtesy of the MLC indicate the classification employed for various types of carcases. The first character refers to finish, followed by those for conformation.

13   Very poorly finished, but with reasonable conformation. Average lean meat yield in the carcase ex KKCF 68·8%

22   Light finish, rather poor conformation, somewhat large forequarter. Average lean meat yield in the carcase ex KKCF 64·7%

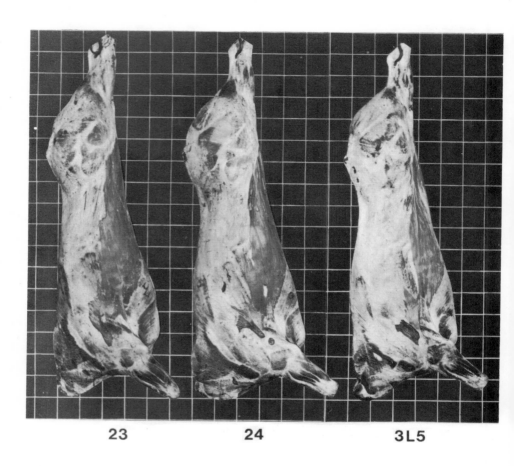

23   **24**   **3L5**

Plate 25 (Cont)   23   Again, reasonable conformation, somewhat lightly finished for a good type of retail trade. Average lean meat in carcase ex KKCF 63·9%
24   Good conformation with somewhat light finish. Average lean in carcase ex KKCF 64·7%
3L5   Excellent conformation and sufficient finish for the normal run of retail trade.

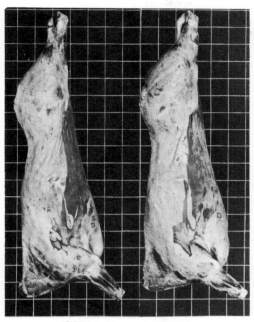

3H3   **44**

Plate 25 (Cont) 3H3   Reasonable conformation and the good degree of finish would meet the demand of many retail shops. The overall average yield of lean meat from carcases ex KKCF from the original fat classification 3, is estimated to be a little over 60%.

44   Very good conformation and well finished but could be in demand for a relatively high class trade where quality rather than yield is the major criterion. Average lean in carcase ex KKCF 55·7%

53   Excessive finish and reasonable conformation, the latter being influenced by the heavy deposition of subcutaneous fat. Average lean in carcass ex KKCF 52.8%

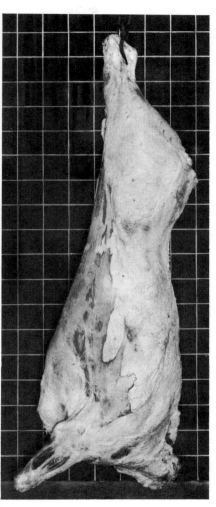

53

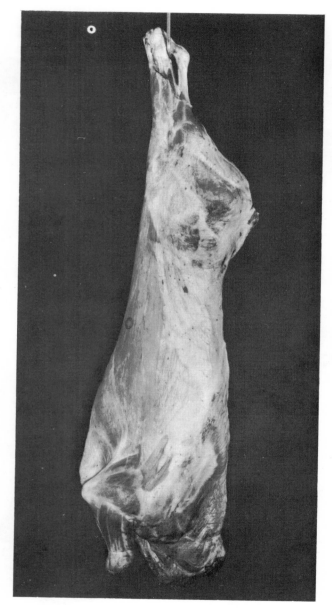

Plate 26   A fine side of a veal carcase (*Meat and Livestock Commission*)

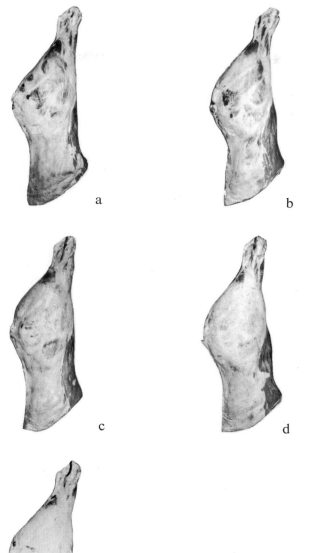

Plate 27 Assessment of conformation
and degree of finish in commercial beef.
(a) poor conformation and poor degree of
finish; (b) good conformation, finish
somewhat light; (c) very good
conformation, finish probably ideal for
demand; (d) excellent conformation,
current degree of finish acceptable for
high-class trade; (e) good conformation,
but degree of finish excessive.

TABLE 22

Analysis of various bovine animals

Sex	Age	Live weight (lb)	Carcase weight cold	Dressing %	% of carcase weight		
					Muscle	Fat	Bone
Male	1 week	85½	46·621	54·5	63·56	9·25	22·92
Steer	13 months	336	159·512	47·5	61·61	10·92	22·38
Steer	17 months	476	221·484	46·7	58·28	14·85	21·50
Steer	2 years	742	371·970	50·0	64·56	13·53	17·47
Steer	12 months	791	419·014	53·0	60·18	21·07	15·80
Heifer	over 2 years	924	510·770	55·0	58·89	25·93	12·79
Steer	2 years	945	534·231	56·5	56·62	27·43	13·17
Steer	2 years	1036	583·523	56·5	57·55	26·89	12·90
Steer	20 months	1064	656·474	61·5	52·92	34·30	10·49
Cow	10 years	1148	558·042	48·5	59·19	20·85	15·71
Cow	12 years	1148	544·588	47·5	61·86	18·09	16·82
Cow	8 years	1372	848·502	62·0	54·31	33·49	10·25
Bull	4 years	1260	743·339	58·5	72·32	9·99	14·63

(From figures kindly supplied by Dr E. H. Callow.)

7 Sheep and mutton

Evolution

The sheep group, know as Caprinae, is a subfamily of the Bovidae group and it includes the closely allied sheep (Ovis) and the goat (Capra). In common with many goats, the sheep possess, between the two front toes, a small sac, the pedal gland, which secretes an oily, odorous substance, and this taints the tracks of the animal, enabling its path to be identified. The main external difference between the sheep and the goat is the presence of the chin beard in the latter. Separating the sheep from the goats may not be such a simple matter if the sheep are of the unimproved type. However, an examination of the carcases will show some points of contrast. In the goat the spines of the cervical processes are longer and more pointed than in the sheep and the spine of the scapula is flat and straight, also the pelvis is smaller. In their wild state the sheep are chiefly inhabitants of Asia, but representatives are also found in North Africa and North America.

They are normally associated with the mountainous parts of the world, but under domestication they flourish in the temperate regions of both hemispheres. Probably the nearest wild relative of our domestic sheep is the Moufflon, which can still be found in Corsica and Sardinia. Remnants of ancient breeds, such as the Soay, Shetland, and the Four-horned sheep, provide valuable comparison with our modern improved meat types. It is thought that the wool breeds fall between the improved mutton breeds and the wild types, and this theory is supported by the long vertical spinal processes of the Merino as compared with the short ones of say, the Hampshire Down. Various authorities use different methods of classifying our modern breeds, e.g. Horned and Hornless, Mountain and Lowland, Longwool and Shortwool, Long and Short Tail, etc. A convenient method of grouping for our purpose is to form three sections: Mountain or Hill breeds, Long-woolled breeds, and Down breeds. As there are almost forty distinct breeds, all possessing their peculiar characteristics, only the more important are selected.

Some British breeds of sheep

Mountain or Hill Breeds

Scotch Blackface	Rough Fell
Cheviot	Swaledale
Welsh Mountain	Limestone
Lonk	Exmoor Horn
Herdwick	Dartmoor
Derbyshire Gritstone	Kerry Hill
Penistone	Radnor
Clun Forest	

Generally this group is recognized by their relatively light build, which yields a carcase of handy size. The flesh is of good flavour owing to the type of feed, though it may be inclined to coarseness in mature types, due to the natural activity of the sheep. The conformation tends to be somewhat 'rangy' with a fair depth of rib. The wool is usually of medium length and texture. The majority of these breeds possess horns, frequently massive in the adult male. As fairly representative members of this group, the Scotch blackface, Cheviot, Welsh Mountain, and Clun Forest will be selected to provide an outline of their individual features.

Scotch Blackface

This breed (Plate 28) is smaller and hardier than the Cheviot and it thrives on moor and heather land. The face and legs are black or mottled, the nose is broad, very prominent, with wide nostrils, black in colour. The horns of the ram are massive, coming out level with the head, curling forwards in line with the cheeks. The horns of the ewe are much smaller and flattened in form. The ears are small and concealed by the horns, whilst the back is broad and the tail naturally short. The wool is loose and shaggy and rather hair-like in texture. It is particularly useful for carpet manufacture.

Cheviot

A mature tup of this breed might weigh up to 200 lb (90 kg) (Plate 29). The head should be of medium length and covered with fine short hairs. The ears are rounded and rather short, with a nose slightly arched and broad. The ribs are well sprung and extend well backwards, legs broad and flat, covered with fine white hair. At one time horns were common in the ram, but this is now rare and their presence is looked upon by some breeders as a sign of lack of constitution. Lambs intended for Lowland pastures have their tails docked short, but in breeding ewes

Plate 28 Blackface tup

Plate 29 Cheviot shearling tup

intended for mountain pastures it is preferred longer, to provide some protection for the udder. In many parts a Leicester × Cheviot is popular to produce a carcase with good quality flesh, much leaner than in the case of the pure Leicester.

Welsh Mountain

From time immemorial a hardy race of mountain sheep has existed on the highest of the Welsh hills (Plate 30). Many unsuccessful attempts have been made to introduce other mountain breeds and consequently the breed has retained its original characteristics to a marked extent. Old ewes are frequently drafted to lower ground, and when crossed with a Southdown they will produce an extremely good butchers' animal, yielding an excellent carcase of a useful size. A pure-bred mountain carcase seldom exceeds 32 lb (14·5 kg), though in the case of sheep reared on much lower ground much heavier weights are obtained. The mutton is of the highest quality, and is comparable with that obtained from the Southdown.

The Welsh have a narrow body, somewhat long and light in the fore-quarters, the wool is short, fine, and thick, the face and legs may be white or tan. The latter colour is thought to be a sign of hardiness and is therefore preferred. The tails are bushy and long, and strong curved horns are present in the ram, whilst the ewes are hornless. Wethers have a modified horn growth a few inches in length, curving backwards.

Clun Forest

Originally these sheep (Plate 31) were a somewhat small speckle-faced breed probably related to the Kerry and Radnor. At one time they were found almost exclusively in the upland areas of south-west Shropshire. There is little doubt that some Shropshire 'blood' has contributed materially to some of the Down-like features such as the tuft of wool on the forehead and the dark brown or black face. Of recent years the breed has become increasingly popular on account of its length and depth of frame and its ability to thrive on the higher pastures and moorland, with a minimum of attention. Many farmers in the West of England have taken up the Clun as an orchard sheep. The breed is prolific and a yield of 150 lambs per 100 ewes is fairly common.

The carcase is relatively lean and therefore popular for the present demand and under good conditions dressed carcase weights of about 45 lb (20 kg) can be obtained in four months. For fat lamb production, young may be produced in February, but the more general rule is to lamb in late March.

Plate 30   Welsh Mountain ram (*Farmer & Stockbreeder*)

Plate 31   Clun Forest tup (*Meat & Livestock Commission*)

Long-woolled Breeds

Leicester   Devon Longwool
Romney (Marsh or Kent)   South Devon
Border Leicester   Wensleydale
Lincoln   Roscommon
Cotswold

Our British Long-woolled breeds have descended from the flocks originally kept for wool production, the flesh being a secondary consideration. As no one breed can combine outstanding qualities in both wool and mutton, the standard of the flesh and fat cannot be compared with that of the Down breeds. In maturity the carcases usually run to fat and this is inclined to be somewhat tallowy. There are, however, many breeds which are valuable for the production of fat lambs and early hoggets, slaughter taking place before these undesirable features have had time to develop. Long-woolled breeds are usually large, with wool long and sometimes lustrous; they are hornless and in the main they belong to the Lowland areas. Practically all the Long-woolled breeds have benefited, at some time, by the introduction of some Leicester blood.

Leicester

Roman nose, wedge-shaped face, covered with short white hair, the lips and nostrils are black (Plate 32). The forehead is covered with wool, the ears are long, thin and mobile, and the neck short. The ribs are well sprung and the loins wide, the feet are neat, the hocks straight, and the form generally rectangular. Their early maturity and rapid fattening qualities make them valuable for crossing purposes, with the object of producing fat lambs.

Romney (Marsh or Kent)

Head is wide, level between the ears, with a thick fore-top (Plate 33). They are white-faced and white-legged, with a very close coat of good wool. The nostrils should be broad and black. Shoulders are wide and level, with the back straight and loin flat, the tail being set almost level with the chine. The chest is wide and deep. They are essentially graziers' sheep, and can normally be fattened on grass alone. The breed is very popular in New Zealand, and in South America they can be found from Brazil to Patagonia.

Plate 32   Leicester shearling ram (*Farmer & Stockbreeder*)

Plate 33   Two Romney sheep (*Romney Sheep Breeders' Society*)

Down Breeds

Southdown	Dorset Down
Suffolk	Shropshire Down
Oxford Down	Dorset Horn ⎱ Associated with the Down breeds
Hampshire Down	Ryeland ⎰

The Down breeds can be recognized by their fleeces of short to medium length, with fine close wool, their thick compact conformation, and the absence of horn growth. Originally they were confined to the chalky and sandy areas in the southern part of England, but they have shown a tendency to spread north, the rams being in great demand for crossing purposes. The quality of the flesh and fat is unsurpassed, and the carcase will yield a high proportion of valuable joints.

Southdown

The head is level between the ears and fairly short from eyes to nose, the eyes are large and prominent, ears covered with short wool (Plate 34). The chest is deep and the back wide and flat, the rump long and wide, whilst the tail is thick and almost level with the chine. The legs are well fleshed, short and straight, and appear to be set on almost outside the body. For rapid maturity it has no rival, and unless handled carefully it may lay down too much fat. Thus the value of the Southdown carcase will decrease more rapidly, as the weight increases, than is the case with the Blackface.

Suffolk

As with the other Down breeds, the Suffolk owes a great deal to Southdown blood, and the breed developed as a result of crossing the old Norfolk horned ewe with the Southdown ram. Thus from a relatively rough heath sheep a very fine butchers' animal has been evolved (Plate 35). The black face, legs, and length of head has been retained, horn growth has been lost, whilst the body form and flesh qualities of the Southdown have persisted to a very marked degree. The head is black, fairly long and hornless, and usually free from wool; ears black and moderately long. The legs are covered with black hair below the knees. The fleece is short and fine, well covering the belly. The carcases have a high reputation for quality and leanness of the flesh, and the Suffolk usually shows up very well in the carcase competitions of the Smithfield Show. A good ewe flock can be expected to yield 5 to 7 lb (2·25 to 3 kg) of wool each.

Plate 34 Southdown two-shear ram (*Farmer & Stockbreeder*)

Plate 35 Three Suffolk rams

Oxford Down

This breed is probably the largest of the Down breeds and it is thought to have been produced from the original Cotswold breed crossed with the Southdown or Hampshire ewes. The head is carried high and posses-ses a tuft of wool on the poll (Plate 36). The face is a dark colour as are the legs, which are short and well set apart. The back is full and level, with ribs well sprung. The breed is highly thought of in the United States, and in this country the rams are frequently crossed with Border sheep. The flesh is lean and of good quality.

Plate 36   Oxford Down shearling ram (*Farmer & Stockbreeder*)

CHARACTERISTICS APPLICABLE TO MOST BRITISH BREEDS OF SHEEP*

(1) A graceful carriage and springy style of walking.

*Farm Livestock of Great Britain, Robert Wallace, 1923.

(2) A characteristic head, with good depth and strength of jaw, and breadth across the bridge of the nose, and full bright eyes, indicating docility and courage.

(3) The neck thick towards the trunk, tapering to the head, arching slightly, and not too short.

(4) The chest broad, deep, projecting well in front of the fore legs and descending from the neck in a perpendicular line.

(5) The back level, broad behind and before (except in the Cheviots and the Lonks, which have sharp shoulder-tops or withers), with a uniform covering of flesh, not boggy to the touch but firm and muscular; under and upper lines straight.

(6) The ribs well sprung, rounded, and deep.

(7) The shoulders well laid and covered with firm flesh. The regions immediately behind the shoulders filled up.

(8) Thighs and gigots and also the arms and the fore flanks fleshed well down.

(9) The rump (or part near the dock) well developed, though not too fat and large, as is sometimes the case in Cotswolds, Border Leicesters, and on heavy-fleshed breeds.

(10) The quarters long and not drooping behind, and the spaces between them and the last ribs short and well filled.

(11) The legs straight and set wide apart, not too long; the bone clean and fine, and neither coarse nor deficient: the hocks are much better slightly turned outwards than at all inwards or 'cow-hocked'.

(12) The characteristic wool of the special breed covering well the body, and particularly the belly; also the scrotum of the ram.

Skeleton

HEAD

Without entering into great detail, the head can be considered as follows.

(1) The lower jaw, containing 8 incisors and 12 cheek teeth.

(2) Cranium, or brain-case, the frontal bone, and 12 cheek teeth of the upper jaw.
('Dentition', see p. 153.)

VERTEBRAE

(1) Cervical vertebrae	7 bones
(2) Dorsal vertebrae	13 bones
(3) Lumbar vertebrae	6 bones
(4) Sacral vertebrae	1 bone (5 segments, fused)
(5) Coccygeal vertebrae	Very variable: up to 18 bones

(Variation in the number of vertebrae is common, except in the cervical region.)

RIBS

13 pairs, but 14 pairs are not uncommon.

STERNUM

Breast bone   1 bone (7, sometimes 6, segments)

PELVIS

Pelvic bones

HIND LIMB

Femur and Patella
Tibia–fibula
Tarsals
Cannon and Foot bones

FORE LIMB

Scapula
Humerus
Radius and Ulna
Carpals
Cannon and Foot bones

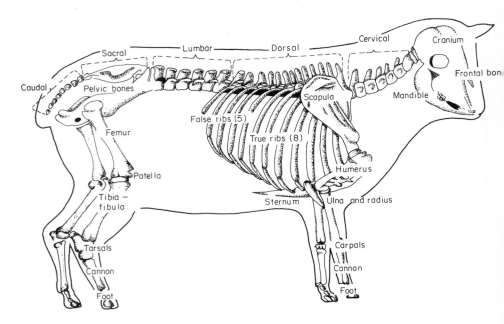

Fig. 16   Skeleton of ovine animal

Organs

Generally speaking, with one or two minor exceptions, the organs of the sheep are similar to those of the ox. In the sheep the kidneys are simple and the spleen is somewhat circular in shape. The upper lip is cleft, permitting much closer grazing than in the case of the ox, and the palate is deeply grooved. The intestine is relatively longer, being about 26 times the body length, whereas in the ox it is approximately 20 times the length of the body. The pancreatic and bile ducts join to form a common bile duct. When present, the horns are triangular in section and the sheep possesses a scent gland between the toes. The females have two teats as against four in the cow, though the females of some breeds having 4 horns possess 4 nipples.

Nomenclature

There is some variation in the names applied to sheep in various parts of this country, and though one might accurately define a 'lamb' as an ovine animal that has not acquired its first pair of permanent incisors, this definition might not meet with universal approval. Particularly in the case of the carcase, the line of demarcation is hard to fix; weight plays an important part, and different breeds of sheep will show considerable variations in weight at the same age. The following terms are the expressions most commonly employed.

ENTIRE MALES

Ram lambs, hoggets or hogs. From weaning to first shearing.
    Shearing tups or rams. After first shearing.
    Two-, three-, or four-shear rams or tups. According to the number of times they have been shorn.

CASTRATED MALES

Wether or wedder (in some parts teg). From weaning to first shearing.
    Shearing wethers or wedders. From first to second shearing.
    Two-shear wether or wedder. From second to third shearing.

FEMALES

Ewe lamb, gimmer, or chilver. From birth to weaning.
    Ewe tegs, gimmer hogs, ewe hogs, maids. From weaning to first shearing.

Shearing ewes, shearing gimmer, gimmer, or theave. From first to second shearing.

Ewe. Has produced young.

Crone. An old ewe past breeding.

General Features

Frequently the dentition is incorporated to provide an indication of age, such as the two-tooth gimmer or a four-tooth wether. Culls or shotts are sheep which are inferior and have been rejected for breeding. 'Rigs' are imperfectly castrated males, whilst the term 'pallies' is applied to lambs which are deformed.

The New Zealand specification for export lamb is meat derived from ovines of either sex under 12 months of age at date of slaughter. (In practice, lamb exported is usually from between 4 and 6 months.)

Hogget is meat derived from ovines which are wethers or maiden ewes, showing not more than two permanent incisor teeth at time of slaughter. Carcases exceeding 56 lb (25 kg) are classified as ewes or wethers, whichever is applicable.

United Kingdom Classes

The various Classes as defined by the Ministry of Agriculture, Fisheries and Food, are as follows:

Sheep

1. LAMBS. Lambs will be classified as such only when marketed in the calender year in which they are born except that lambs born in October, November or December of one year will continue to be classified as such until 31 December (or such other date thereabouts as may be announced) of the following year.

2. HOGGETS (i.e. Fat Hoggets or Hoggs or Tegs or Wethers). Will be classified as such when marketed in about the first six months of the year after the one in which they were born, but lambs born in October, November or December will be classified as hoggets in the first six months of the second year after the year of their birth.

Note: The actual date on which lambs and hoggets will be classified as such, will be notified at the beginning of each fatstock year.

3. OTHER CLEAN SHEEP. Clean sheep other than lambs and hoggets as defined above. Females must neither have lambed nor have reached a stage of pregnancy which will depreciate the value of the carcase. Males must not possess ram characteristics.

4. EWES. Females which have lambed or have reached a stage of pregnancy which will depreciate the value of the carcase.

5. RAMS. Uncastrated males which have matured sufficiently to affect the value of the carcase or males which, by reason of late or ineffective castration, show some physical characteristics of rams.

There are certain features which are desirable in sheep intended for the butcher, and though there will, of course, be distinguishing characteristics with different breeds, the following broad principles will apply. The body should have a rectangular outline, with the belly and back parallel, the back level and broad throughout its length, and the ribs well sprung and deep. There should be no depression immediately behind the shoulders, and the legs set straight, wide apart, and not too long. The neck should be broad, tapering slowly from the body.

When handling sheep the points usually considered of most value are as follows:

(1) *Loin.* Which is tested by placing the hand across the sheep to estimate the width and firmness.

(2) *Tail.* Grasp at the root, to obtain an indication of finish.

(3) *Rump.* There is a depression along the centre of the rump and loin which is a valuable guide as to the fatness of the animal.

(4) *Scrotum.* In the case of castrated animals the quantity of fat laid down in the scrotum is a good indication of the probable quantity of internal fat.

(5) *Brisket.* Some buyers will insist on turning one or two sheep, to check up the amount of fat on the breast bone.

(Some mountain breeds will *not* possess a level back, as there is a rise at the withers.)

Teeth as an indication of age

The dental formula for a 'full mouth' is the following.

	Molars	Premolars	Incisors	Premolars	Molars	
Upper jaw	3	3	0 | 0	3	3	} 32 teeth
Lower jaw	3	3	4 | 4	3	3	

The formula of the *deciduous* teeth is as follows.

	D. Premolars	D. Incisors	D. Premolars	
Upper jaw	3	0 | 0	3	} 20 temporary
Lower jaw	3	4 | 4	3	teeth

Under normal commercial conditions the incisor teeth are examined as an indication of age. Some variations will occur, depending on breed and feed, but the following standard will give a good general guide.

These teeth are erupted in pairs from the centre outwards. Each pair is referred to as the centrals, middles, outers, and corners respectively.

APPEARANCE OF INCISORS

	Temporary	Permanent
1 pair (centrals)	At birth or 1st week	1 year
2 pair (middles)	1st or 2nd week	$1\frac{1}{2}$ years
3 pair (outers)	2nd or 3rd week	$2\frac{1}{4}$ years
4 pair (corners)	3rd or 4th week	3 years

(In some cases the corners will appear later, but the centrals and middles would be heavily worn.)

Below are the standards of the Smithfield Club Show regarding the dentition in sheep.

'Sheep having their central permanent incisors cut will be considered as exceeding 10 months.

'Sheep having their central permanent incisors fully up will be considered as exceeding 12 months.

'Sheep having their third pair of permanent incisors cut will be considered as exceeding 19 months.'

Growth in sheep

'When a cell increases in size its volume enlarges at a greater rate than its surface, and so the metabolism, or exchange of energy, which can only occur at the surface, is inhibited and further growth becomes impossible. It therefore divides into two, and each daughter-cell repeats the process. As the organism increases in size sets of cells become specialized and take over different functions: once the cells have become specialized for a particular purpose they lose their power of division, and so the growth of the animal as a whole becomes slowed down. Thus growth consists essentially of two things, increase in size and differentiation of tissues; or, in other words, as an animal grows up it not only increases in size, but it also changes in its shape or conformation.' (*Elements of Agriculture*, 12th edition, Fream, 1932, p. 623.)

The increase in size will, within limits, determine the quantity of meat, but the disposition of this weight (conformation) will decide the quality, and consequently its value per weight unit. At birth the lamb is all head and legs, with a very short loin, lacking in depth. As the lamb develops, the body lengthens and deepens so that the proportion of valuable parts increases, whilst the ratio of bone, head, and legs decreases. In early maturing breeds developmental growth takes place

more rapidly than in slow maturing types. In un-improved breeds the
extent of these changes is less marked than in the case of, say, the
Southdown. Expressed in another fashion, our present improved breeds
of sheep have been developed from more primitive types by breeding
from animals which showed the greatest changes in their proportions
at a given age. What these changes mean to the butcher are well brought
out in the findings of Hammond, based on Suffolks. Thus at birth each
100 lb (45 kg) of live weight contains 31 lb (14 kg) of edible muscle and
fat, increasing to 54 lb (25 kg) at 11 months, whilst the amount of bone
decreased from 17 lb (8 kg) at birth to 5 lb (2·27 kg) at 11 months per
100 lb (45 kg) of live weight. The proportions of fat, muscle, and bone
in a mutton carcase, coupled with the gross weight, are the main factors
in deciding the value of a carcase. Regarding this latter point, the old
question of 'when does lamb become mutton?' is possibly one rather of
size than actual age, and certainly, commercially, lamb from the smaller
breeds remains lamb longer than those from the larger breeds. Even
within the lamb class, size is very important, and in the case of imported
meat one will often find that light lambs of poor quality will fetch a
higher price than first-class heavy lambs. The butcher is probably not
so interested in bone, as the majority of carcase is sold with the bone in,
but the deposition of fat is rather a different matter, and for this reason
a Southdown will decrease fairly rapidly in value as the weight increases.

8 Slaughter

Pre-slaughter care

As in the case of cattle and pigs, a period of rest and fasting is necessary to obtain a good carcase. The undigested food putrefies rapidly, and muscular fatigue will retard efficient bleeding. Care should be taken in handling the sheep, as grasping the fleece will cause inflamed or bloody spots which detract from the appearance and adversely affect the keeping qualities. As a general rule a fasting period of 24 hours is suggested as ideal, except in the case of suckling lambs which should be killed as soon as possible after removal from the ewe.

Slaughter

STUNNING

The animal is rendered unconscious by either an electrical appliance or a mechanical instrument. (For greater details see p. 67.) Methods of dressing will vary considerably in different parts of the country but the following is a general summary of the operations.

STICKING

The animal, lying on its left side, is stuck immediately below and behind the ear with a pointed knife. The jugular vein is severed and the head is jerked backwards, breaking the neck. This can be managed by grasping the lower jaw with the left hand and placing the right hand over the poll, and by an upward movement the neck is broken. (In some cases the spinal cord is severed by inserting the finger between the skull and the vertebrae.) The sheep is then left to bleed for a short period.

LEGGING

The animal is turned on to its back and the fore leg is 'knuckled', a cut is made from the knuckle down the front of the leg. The neck and side of the cheek is skinned off and a portion of the shoulder. This operation is then repeated on the other fore leg. The throat is opened up, the sweet-bread removed, and the food-pipe (oesophagus) tied off, to prevent contamination of the flesh. The hind legs are 'knuckled' and a cut made to the root of the tail. The legs are skinned and the sheep is hoisted by a gambrel inserted into the hocks.

DRESSING

A rip is made down the centre of the loose skin covering the belly and the skinning proceeds over the flanks. The more fist and the less knife at this stage the better the pelt will be. Following this, the pelt is pulled down over the backbone to the base of the head. Any subcutaneous blood vessels can be 'wiped back' and the carcase may be sprayed with clean hot water at about 122°F (50°C), using a fan type jet.

EVISCERATION

A small cut is made in the belly-wall, just above the brisket, and the fingers of the left hand are inserted to protect the viscera as the knife opens the belly wall to within about 2 inches (5 cm) of the cod fat or udder. Following this the caul (omentum) is carefully removed, the rectum is loosened, the bladder taken out, and all of the intestines and stomachs are withdrawn, the foodpipe being pulled up through the skirt (diaphragm). The breast bone is split and the pluck (trachea, lungs, heart, spleen, and liver) removed.

LINE DRESSING

As in the case of beef, the modern method of dressing sheep and lamb whilst the carcases are hanging on the rail is rapidly extending.

A recent development takes the form of a mechanized moving 'cratch'. Thus the carcases are dressed whilst situated in a horizontal position, the height being adjusted to ensure the best working position for the operative.

VARIATIONS IN DRESSING METHODS

Although there appears to be a tendency to standardize dressing methods, there are still great variations as between slaughter centres, and even the time of year will play its part in the system employed. The following indicate the main types of dressing.

Plain dressed carcases. In this method the carcases are ex shanks and the shoulders may or may not be strung back by string passed round the neck.

Backsets. Single or double diagonal backsets are frequently used for lamb or small mutton.

Spring lamb is sometimes dressed with the feet on and the caul wrapped round the legs. In a few cases the feet, head, pluck, and caul are left on the carcase.

(The practice of leaving the feet on the carcase is hardly hygienic, and caul and plucks are more easily transported if they are packed separately. The inside of a carcase, smeared with blood from a pluck, will prove an ideal breeding-place for putrefactive organisms.)

The following specifications provide a valuable guide as to the recognized standard for dressing.

Dressing specifications

MLC specifications for dressing the carcases of Lambs, Hoggets and Sheep.

A. The following parts shall be removed before weighing:

(a) Skin.

(b) Head, including tongue. The head shall be removed at the junction of the skull and spinal column, leaving the entire spinal column on the carcase. The ears will be left naturally attached to the carcase until the carcase has been identified by the person responsible for weighing, after which the ears may be removed; where they are not so removed, their weight will be included in the carcase weight.

(c) The forefeet shall be removed at the knee joint and the hindfeet at the hock joint.

(d) Paunch and guts (but the fleshy or muscular part of the diaphragm ('skirt') shall be left intact).

(e) Caul and gut fat.

(f) Liver, melt, heart and lungs, i.e. the 'pluck' or 'race'.

(g) Heart or breast fat.

(h) Sweetbreads.

(i) Genito-urinary organs (excluding kidneys and kidney fat).

B. Carcases shall be weighed:

(a) If weighed 'hot', within 1 hour of slaughter. When carcases are weighed 'hot', the 'cold' weight will be ascertained by making rebates as follows:

Hot weight (lb)	Rebate (lb)
56 and under	1
57 and over	2

(b) If weighed 'cold', within 24 hours of slaughter, except when prior approval for an extension of this period has been given. If weighed in lots, the lots must not contain more than six carcases, and must be level i.e. they must consist of carcases of animals of one category and of approximately equal weights.

It is permissible for a carcase:

(a) to be back-set and/or dressed with caul on, but the weight of the back stick and/or caul must be deducted from the weight of the carcase.

(b) to be dressed with the head on and pluck in, but a deduction must be made for the weight of the head and the weight of the pluck.

N.B. The adoption of these Specifications for sheep is a necessary condition if stock are to be certified deadweight under the Fatstock Guarantee Scheme.

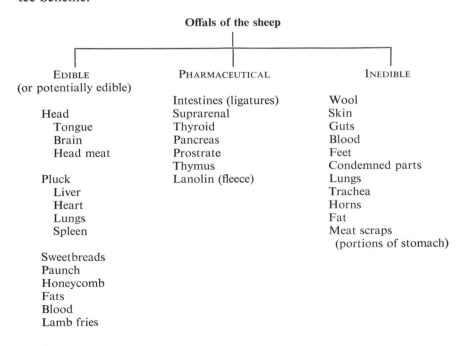

Offals of the sheep

EDIBLE (or potentially edible)	PHARMACEUTICAL	INEDIBLE
Head	Intestines (ligatures)	Wool
Tongue	Suprarenal	Skin
Brain	Thyroid	Guts
Head meat	Pancreas	Blood
	Prostrate	Feet
Pluck	Thymus	Condemned parts
Liver	Lanolin (fleece)	Lungs
Heart		Trachea
Lungs		Horns
Spleen		Fat
		Meat scraps
Sweetbreads		(portions of stomach)
Paunch		
Honeycomb		
Fats		
Blood		
Lamb fries		

Offals

As a brief definition we can classify offals as all the products obtained from the sheep except the dressed carcase. This statement must be modified, as will be seen (p. 157) when carcases are 'fancy dressed', in which case the head and feet, and occasionally the pluck and caul fat as well, may be left on or in the carcase.

Offals can be considered under two main sections, edible and inedible, and a minor classification for pharmaceutical products. In the case of English mutton and lamb the value of the edible offals is roughly represented at about 10% of the total value.

Edible

HEAD

The head, unlike that of the ox, possesses a cleft lip. After skinning, it is normally used for boiling.

The tongue can be identified by the presence of a depression running along its centre. It can be used to form an attractive meat pack after salting, boiling, and pressing.

The brain is a common item of diet and can be used for normal cooking purposes or in the preparation of brain sauce.

PLUCK

This consists of the lungs, windpipe (trachea), heart, melt (spleen), and the liver. In some cases the head is left attached to the pluck.

The lungs are similar to the ox in miniature and much tougher than those of the pig. They can be used in some manufactured goods or sold for animal feed.

The liver consists of one large lobe partly divided and a small 'thumb piece'. Usually it is grilled or fried.

The heart is somewhat pointed and the fat is hard and white. The muscular tissue is much firmer than that in the heart of the pig. Though it is generally used stuffed and baked, it is sometimes employed as pie meat.

In dressing the carcase the spleen or melt is left attached to the pluck; it is useful for flavouring stews.

SWEETBREADS

These are highly prized delicacies of diet.

PAUNCH

Tripe obtained from the stomach of the sheep is common in the Midlands and in Scotland; the fore-stomach is used as a container for haggis.

Caul Fat

This fat (omentum) is frequently placed on legs and shoulders of lamb, as in the cooking it compensates for any deficiency of fat and exerts a basting effect.

Blood

This can be used in blood sausage, and blood and barley loaf, though pigs' blood is generally preferred.

Lamb Fries

These are usually obtained from ram lambs of 2–3 months.

Kidneys

With lamb carcases the kidneys are usually left attached to the loins, but in the case of mutton they are sometimes removed and sold separately.

Inedible

Wool

The value of the wool obtained from sheep in this country is estimated to be about one-sixth of the value of the mutton and lamb production. The yield will vary from about 12 lb in the case of the Lincoln to approximately 4–5 lb in the Scotch Blackface. Normally the highest prices are obtained for wool from Southdowns and the lowest for that from Blackfaced ewes. The best wool is obtained from the shoulders, followed by the loin, legs, and finally that from the breast and belly. A fleece is usually examined for fineness, length, and density. Fineness is due to the fineness of the fibre and the number of serrations. In the Merino these serrations may number 2700 per inch; in the Cheviot 1400 per inch.

Skin

The skin is the most valuable by-product. It is usually disposed of to fellmongers or direct to the hides and skin merchants. After de-woolling, the pelt is passed on to the tanner and the wool to the wool merchant. The skins may or may not be salted at the slaughterhouse, depending on the method of disposal.

CASINGS

The treatment of intestines for sausage containers is usually carried out by specialist firms of gut scrapers. In the case of tennis rackets, strength is the main requirement, lamb gut being used. It is said that eleven animals are necessary to contribute to the stringing of one racket. They are also used for the strings of musical instruments.

BLOOD

In its dried form it forms a valuable animal feeding stuff or fertilizer. As it contains over 80% of moisture, the amount of dried blood per head for sheep is just under half a pound.

FEET

These can be rendered down and treated for the extraction of glue, tallow, bone meal, etc.

CONDEMNED PARTS

Compared with pigs and cattle, sheep are particularly free from disease and condemned portions are rendered down for inedible purposes.

LUNGS AND TRACHEA

These are generally cooked for animal feed.

HORNS

These can be ground down and used as a valuable fertilizer.

FATS

Mutton tallow is much harder than beef tallow and it is more prone to rancidity, consequently its use is somewhat limited. It cannot be used in butter substitutes or the highest class soaps and its use is chiefly confined to the preparation of commercial greases, glycerol, and soap.

MEAT SCRAPS (PORTIONS OF STOMACH)

Trimmings are rendered for meat meal, and pelt trimmings for gelatine or glue.

Pharmaceutical

In this country, owing to the large number of small slaughter units, the collection of glands is seldom practised. Immediate handling or rapid freezing is necessary, and their location and collection is a rather skilful operation if it is to be efficiently carried out. The preparation of surgical ligatures is a highly technical operation, necessitating rigid bacteriological control. Lanolin is extracted from wool and is used as a basis for ointments.

Dressing percentages

It is usually assumed that lambs give a higher dressing percentage than sheep. To a certain extent this is due to the fact that, breed for breed, sheep will carry a higher ratio of wool, and probably dirt and moisture. Another important factor is the intestinal content—this loss will vary, depending upon the period of fasting and the amount of the last feed. Thus the stomach and intestinal content of a sheep slaughtered within about 4 hours of the last meal might be in the region of 20% of its live weight, whilst a similar animal fasted for 24 hours would probably give about half this figure. Therefore the method of stating the dressing percentage on the *empty live weight* is more scientifically satisfactory for purposes of comparison.

The only figures readily available are usually obtained from show animals, which have probably been shorn. The ordinary run of commercial sheep cannot, of course, be compared with such figures. The loss due to evaporation following slaughter will depend to some extent on the type of carcase and storage condition, and the trade practice of 'bating' 1 lb (0·45 kg) on a hot lamb carcase represents a fair average figure, assuming a lamb carcase is about or under 50 lb (23 kg) in weight.

In some parts of the country lamb carcases are 'fancy dressed', i.e. the head, feet, caul, and in some cases the pluck as well, is left on the carcase (see p. 157).

Commercial sheep will generally dress out at about 50%, although a poor specimen in lean condition may dress as low as 40% and a very fat animal may yield up to 60%. In the case of the show type of sheep, an average dressing percentage of about 56% could be obtained, while in the case of lambs a slightly lower figure might be anticipated.

An analysis based on twenty Suffolk wethers of 7 months* provides Table 23.

Sheep and lambs purchased for slaughter are usually sold on the basis of price per lb 'estimated dressed carcase weight' (e.d.c.w.). An

---

Growth and Development of Mutton Qualities in the Sheep, Hammond.

Table 23

Carcase, organs, etc., as a percentage of the 'empty live weight'
Live weight, 100·2 lb; carcase % on actual live weight, 52·6

	%		%
Carcase	60·6	Loss on cooling	1·3
Caul fat	2·0	Stomach contents	11·3
Gut fat	1·3	Intestinal contents	3·9
Skin and feet	11·2		
Head	4·1		
Pluck	4·8		
Stomachs	3·9		
Small intestine	2·1		
Caecum	0·7		
Large intestine	1·0		
Blood	5·1		

experienced buyer will be able to judge this with a high degree of accuracy. However, some variations can arise and their effect can be calculated as follows: Example—price of live lamb 35p with e.d.c.w. 42 lb. Actual dressed carcase weight 41 lb. Then $\dfrac{35 \times 42}{41}$ = approx 36p per lb as the true cost.

MLC Sheep Classification Scheme

This provides a standard definition of four primary factors which affect sheep carcase value. These are: weight, category, fatness and conformation. The scheme does not describe the many secondary carcase factors which may influence carcase meat buyers.

1. WEIGHT. As now defined for fatstock guarantee purposes.

2. CATEGORY (age/sex group). As defined for fatstock guarantee purposes: L = lamb

          Hgt = hogget

          Shp = sheep

3. FATNESS. Determined by visual appraisal of external fat development. There are five classes, ranging from 1 (very lean) to 5 (very fat). In addition, the letter K is used to denote carcases with excessive kidney knob and channel fat development.

4. CONFORMATION. Based on four classes: extra, average, poor and very poor. The conformation class is determined by visual appraisal of shape, taking into account carcase thickness and blockiness and fullness of the legs. Fatness plays its part in influencing overall shape and no

Slaughter Record

SHEEP

Breed.............. Sex........ Remarks.............. Date..............

£ p

Grade........ Weight..............kg at........per kg =

Transport, etc. =

Cost at slaughterhouse =

Live weight at slaughter...........kg   Shrinkage........%

Carcase weight, hot........lb   Carcase weight, cold........lb

Cold carcase weight of live weight as purchased........%

Offal	Weight		% of live weight	Offal	Weight		% of live weight
	lb	oz			lb	oz	
Skin				Head			
Feet				Pluck			
Blood				Caul fat			
Stomach contents				Mesenteric fat			
Stomachs empty				Breads			
Intestinal contents				Miscellaneous			
Intestines empty				Miscellaneous			
Trimmings, etc.				Miscellaneous			
Total				Total			

£ p

Cost at slaughterhouse
Add slaughter and storage cost

Less value of offals

Net cost of carcase   Carcase cost per lb

attempt is made to adjust for fatness. Most carcases fall in fat classes 2, 3 and 4. Carcases of very good conformation in these fat classes are identified by the letter E (Extra) following the fat class number. Any carcase of poor or very poor conformation, regardless of fat level, is classed as C or Z respectively and there is no subdivision between average and extra in fat classes 1 and 5.

The sheep classification scheme is, therefore, based upon the ten class combinations shown in Fig. 17 on page 167.

The French Sheep Grading System

Weight		Condition	Conformation
Lambs kg	**Ewes** kg		
below 13 13–16 16–19 19–22 Over 22	below 22 22–27 over 27	Lean lightly covered covered fat very fat	Excellent (F) Very Good (R) Good (A) Average (N) Mediocre (C)

Trade classes for sheepmeat, Western Germany

The regulation for statutory trade classes for sheepmeat in Western Germany came into force in 1971, but it is only applied in Northern Germany. Frozen sheepmeat or meat imported in a frozen condition is excluded.

Classification Categories

Category	Marking	Characteristics
Milk-fed lambs	M	Carcases of milk-fed lambs, not more than 6 months old. Maximum weight: carcases without head 22 kg., carcases with head 23·5 kg.
Fat lambs	L	Carcases of indoor and pasture-fed fat lambs, not more than 12 months old.
Clean sheep	H	Carcases of female animals, not used for breeding and of castrated male animals, not more than 2 years old in either case.
Mutton	S	Carcases of castrated male animals, more than 2 years old and of female animals.
Rams	B	Carcases of uncastrated male animals, more than 12 months old.

Carcases of these categories will be classified into trade classes E, I, II and III in accordance with the table below.

Trade Classes and the symbols used for each trade class

Trade Class		Characteristics	
Compulsory Symbol Mark 1	Permitted Additional Symbol Mark 2	Conformation of parts of the body, such as leg, back, shoulder and middle neck 3	Proportion of fat and surface fat (evaluated according to category) 4
E	g m s	very good	Low Medium High
I	g m s	good	Low Medium High
II	—	average	—
III	—	Do not conform to the requirements of E, I and II	

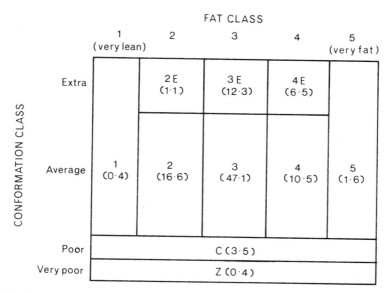

Fig. 17 Carcase classification grid. Figures in brackets show the percentage of all classified carcases in each class during one year of the experimental scheme, when approximately 10% of total clean sheep slaughtered were classified (MLC)

9 Carcase quality

It is an extremely difficult matter to define actually what is understood by the term 'quality' as applied to a carcase of mutton or lamb. One's judgement is naturally coloured by personal experience, both geographical and as biased by contact with the various classes of consumer demand. It might be qualified as the effect of the cooked flesh on a normal human palate. The cooked flesh will contain lean, fat, meat juices, and varying amounts of connective tissue. A normal human palate is not such a simple matter, as persons connected with tasting panels will readily agree. The lean meat will contain the characteristic extractives which supply flavour, and this will be influenced by age, feed, and sex. A mature Scotch Blackface wether, having fed on rough feeding, possesses a fuller flavour than say a milk-fed lamb, whilst ram mutton has too much flavour for the average taste. The fat would be responsible for fat soluble flavours and probably those attractive odours, so important and yet intangible. The setting-point of the fat is also important, as fats which solidify at about blood temperature will produce a 'furry' effect on the palate, which is usually associated with cold mutton from a tallowy carcase. The meat juices present will influence the texture, and will probably contain some soluble protein. Tenderness depends not only on the portion of the animal from which it is obtained, but also the age, activity, and general condition of the muscle at the time of slaughter, and the period of 'hanging'.

The experienced buyer of carcases will look for certain external indications of *probable* quality. He might find it very difficult to classify these many features, but consciously or subconsciously it is the following points which guide his judgement.

Indications of quality

Size

The size or weight of a carcase is not a direct indication of the age. An adult Welsh Mountain carcase might scale 32 lb (14·5 kg), whilst some

Long-wool breeds might yield a carcase of three times this weight. Market requirements are greatly affected by two factors, size of joints and deposition of fat. In the case of imported lambs, third-grade *light* carcases are as valuable per lb as *heavy* first-grade carcases. In some breeds there is a tendency to lay down excessive fat as the weight increases, and a combination of these two results in a rapid reduction in the value of the carcase. Hammond states that the value decrease as weight increases is most rapid in the Southdown, less rapid in the Suffolk, and the Scotch Blackface almost retains its value.

Age

In the absence of the head, the degree of ossification of the bone will provide some indication of age. In this respect the most valuable point is the 'break-joint'. In lamb this joint will exhibit well-defined ridges, with a moist surface. As the animal ages, the bone becomes whiter in colour and the surface is rough. In old sheep it will fail to break. The colour of the ribs in young animals, particularly those of the Down type, are a bluish-pink, and as the animals age the ribs turn white and opaque, loosing their semi-translucent appearance. In the cut carcase the gristle end of the blade bone and the surface of the aitch bone should be examined; the former should present a smooth pearly touch and the latter should have a generous covering of cartilage.

Conformation

From the commercial aspect the form of the animal is extremely important, for it will determine the cash value of the carcase to the butcher. A high ratio of the more valuable joints is required. From the sale aspect the bone content is not of such great importance as in beef, because practically all of the mutton carcase is purchased by the consumer with the bone in. On a reasonably good carcase the legs, loins, and shoulders should represent about 73% of the total weight. Therefore what the butcher requires is a fairly short rib and light neck, which will give a small 'target'. It is difficult to obtain a smooth deposition of fat on long shanky legs; this can be observed in the mountain type of carcase; also the loss on cooking and drawing-up of the shank meat is less in a thick, plump leg. A rectangular form with well-sprung ribs and flesh extending well down short stocky legs should be the aim. Breed, age, sex, feed, and environment all contribute their quota to conformation.

Finish

There is little demand for mutton-fat trimmings; a small proportion can be used in dripping, but it has not the value of beef or pork fat to either the butcher or the housewife. In the sheep, fat is first laid down round the intestines and the kidneys. Deposition on the carcase starts at the root of the tail, extending forwards over the back towards the shoulders, and round the ribs and flanks, under the breast and scrotum, and then extending down the shanks. The fat should have a firm consistency, be creamy in colour, not oily or yellow. A maximum thickness of $\frac{3}{16}$ inch (5 mm) over the loin is sufficient for present-day requirements.

GENERAL

A cherry-red bark usually goes with a flinty bone and dark harsh flesh. If a cut surface is available, the colour should be light and the texture smooth with plenty of 'sap'. Gristle will develop with age, and the degree to which the gristle at the eye muscle has extended is a valuable point. Some mountain breeds have a characteristic dark flesh, and females slaughtered on heat are said to 'cut dark'.

Indications of sex

RAM

As in other entire males, the muscular development is heavy, the neck thick, the forequarters forming a relatively large proportion of the carcase. Usually there is a pronounced crest. The pizzle 'string' is very big in section, and if the legs are split, the development of the retractor muscle will supply conclusive evidence.

WETHERS

The cod fat is lobulated and usually fairly heavy. The muscular development in general is much lower than in the ram, the neck is relatively light, with a bigger proportion of hindquarter than in the ram. The retractor muscle is poorly developed and the pizzle should not exceed the thickness of a normal pencil.

FEMALES

Here the condition of the udder will indicate whether or not the animal has been used for breeding. In the gimmer the mammary organ will be smooth, oval, and consist of firm fat. With lactation the fatty tissue will be replaced by spongy, brown, milk tissue, and in an old ewe the organ consists almost entirely of this substance, which will never 'set'. With the production of lambs the pelvic cavity will become wide, and the belly lining, which has adjoined the uterus, may show a number of small veins. The neck is long and light, the ribs barrelled, and the belly-wall thin. The back passage will be relatively large, owing to the removal of the anus *and* the vagina.

Types of carcase

RAMS

The ratio of rams to ewes is small, usually in the ratio of about 1 ram to 50 ewes; thus the number coming on to the market annually is relatively low. In maturity the flesh is dark in colour, coarse in texture, and possesses a very strong flavour.

EWES

Great variation will occur in the quality of ewe carcases, from a good class animal which has produced one lamb, to an old ewe past breeding. At the present time ewe mutton is practically the only mutton readily obtainable which has the full mature flavour, though such carcases would require 'hanging' to make the joints tender. When ewes begin to lose their teeth they are usually fattened for the butcher; this will, of course, vary with the type of feed. In sheep fed on roots this would probably be after the production of three or four crops of lambs.

OLD WETHERS

It is considered that the finest mutton flesh is obtained from a three-year-old wether, and many famous eating-houses specializing in grills and roasts built up their reputation on such carcases. The portions required for these purposes would be hung for a considerable period and would acquire tenderness with excellent flavour.

YEARLING SHEEP

This category supplies some of our best mutton, the flesh is of good flavour and the age does not permit the excessive development of toughness. In addition to wethers, a certain proportion of barren ewes must be included; in fact in some cases there is a decided preference for the latter, as it is contended that the flesh is more mellow and the bone is usually less massive.

LAMBS AND HOGGETS

As previously mentioned, weight has a very important bearing on value. It is safe to assume that any carcase over 60 lb (27 kg) in weight is too

Table 24

Summary of sources of supplies: Home-killed mutton and lamb, London

	Jan.	Feb.	Mar.	Apr.	May	Jun.	Jul.	Aug.	Sep.	Oct.	Nov.	Dec.
Lamb Christmas; Milk-fed lambs, West of England												- - -
Dorset-horn, Dorset and Hamp., Down and other breeds from Dorset, Somerset, Hants, Sussex and Isle of Wight	----	----	---									
Easter; Down and D × Long-wool from South and South-West Counties and Oxford, Suffolk, Cambridge; Milk-fed lambs from Ireland				--								
Regular trade of fat lambs from South and South-West Counties; Grass-fed lambs from Ireland				----	----	----	----	----	--			
Scotch hill or border lambs, chiefly Blackface							--	----	----	----	----	---- ---
Mutton Root-fed sheep from upland areas in South and East of England	----	----	----	----	--					--	----	---
Scotch hoggets and North of England	----	----	----	----	----	--				--	----	---- ---
Small Irish supplies	----	----	----	----	---							- - -
Grass-fed Lincoln and Yorkshire tegs						---	----	---				
Kentish tegs, Romney and Pevensey Marshes						---	----	----	---			

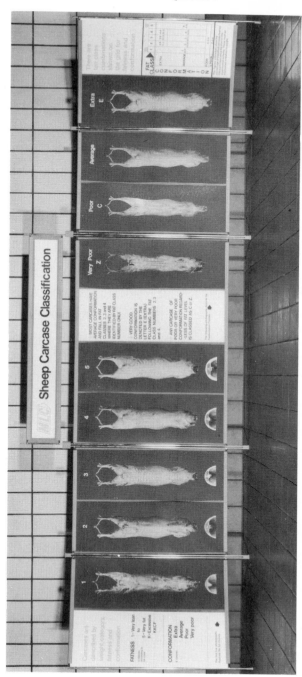

Plate 37 Sheep carcase classification (*Meat & Livestock Commission*)

large for modern requirements. In fact, for the London trade hoggets of 45 to 50 lb (20 to 23 kg) and lamb carcases of 28 to 40 lb (13 to 18 kg) are in greatest demand. To the breeder the lamb carcases should not present any great difficulty, as practically any breed, or, as many prefer, a cross-breed, will produce a reasonably good lamb carcase. With mutton, however, such is not the case, as many of our breeds are too heavy, and with development some of them acquire the tendency to lay down a tallowy fat.

MILK-FED LAMBS

These represent only a very small proportion of our production and they can be considered as a luxury article, though at certain times of the year there is a ready demand. With this class of product, the ewes require special attention regarding feed, and the weather is an important factor, particularly in the early part of the season.

Imported supplies

The killing season in Australia begins in the late spring (about September) and usually extends over about six months. This, however, can be influenced by the vagaries of the Australian climate. The first consignments of lamb and mutton arrive in this country in November, and, at this period, command relatively high prices. The New Zealand killing season follows the Australian, and usually begins in the North Island about November and in the South Island roughly a month later. Thus the 'new season's' lamb and mutton usually reach this country in December, or early January. With their good and long seasons, there is always some overlapping on the English market, as New Zealand killing may go on into August and lamb and mutton of that season may be reaching this country as late as December. From January to the end of March lamb and mutton from both countries are arriving.

The U.K. is dependent on imported supplies for over 50% of our lamb/mutton, New Zealand normally providing almost 90% of these imports. Consequently their grading system is of importance to the butcher. New Zealand meat enjoys a high reputation for the standard and consistency of the grading.

New Zealand lamb carcases for export are graded into classes, see page 175.

The Australian grading of export lamb tends to follow closely that of New Zealand regarding weight grades. The quality grading is based upon age; colour and appearance of the bones, flesh and fat; conformation and fat cover.

Grade Mark	Weight range lb	Colour Code
PL	17·5–27·5	Blue
PM	28·6–35·5	Blue
PH	36·5–56·0	Blue
YL	17·5–27·5	Red
YM	28·5–35·5	Red
YH	36·5–56·0	Red
OL	17·5–27·5	Brown
OM	28·5–35·5	Brown

The 'Blues' are prime carcases with good flesh content and finish.

Australian quality grades are identified by the tag colour and/or marking on the wrapper or container:

1st Quality = Blue
2nd Quality = Red
3rd Quality = Black

Table 25

Analysis of various breeds and crosses

Breed	Age (months)	Live weight (lb)	Carcase weight (lb)	Dressing % cold	Muscle	Sub-cutaneous fat	Inter-muscular fat	Total fat	Bone	Tendon and loss
B.L. × Blackface	13	116	56·53	48·7	52·2	19·5	14·4	33·9	11·9	1·4
B.L. × Cheviot	13	113	57·84	51·2	58·9	15·5	11·4	26·9	12·0	1·6
Cheviot	13	109	58·40	53·6	53·5	18·8	13·7	32·5	12·0	1·4
Oxford × B.L. Cheviot	13	112	55·70	49·7	58·1	11·7	13·4	25·1	14·4	2·1
Suffolk × B.L. Cheviot	13	—	61·60	—	56·6	18·5	10·4	28·9	13·0	1·6
Southdown × B.L. Cheviot	4½	75	37·00	49·3	58·8	17·3	11·1	28·4	11·8	1·6
Suffolk × B.L. Cheviot	4½	79	39·34	49·8	61·4	12·8	10·9	23·7	13·9	1·8
Oxford × B.L. Cheviot	4½	76	38·00	50·0	55·4	15·3	12·8	28·1	15 4	2 2
Blackfaced	4½	76	36·20	47·6	54·3	15·2	14·8	30·0	13·0	2·1
B.L. × Cheviot	4½	80	37·72	47·2	59·1	13·8	10·5	24·3	14·3	2·0
B.L. × Blackfaced	4½	75	37·24	49·6	56·9	15·9	11·8	27·7	13·7	1·8
Cheviot	4½	71	36·80	51·8	58·9	13·6	13·5	27·1	12·8	2·0
Uruguay Southdown × Romney	4½	—	35·04	—	51·7	16·9	14·1	31·0	14·5	2·4
	4½	—	40·44	—	47·4	21·0	17·0	38·0	10·1	1·5
B.L. × Iceland	4½	84	37·42	44·5	58·2	13·1	10·9	24·0	14·5	1·6
Iceland	4½	90	38·75	43·0	58·3	11·2	10·5	21·7	14·5	1·9

(Compiled from *Meat Qualities in Sheep*, Palsson.)

Suggested scale of points for judging U.K. mutton carcase

	Max.	Award
GENERAL		
Weight. According to trade requirements	10	
Conformation. Compact, well-filled legs and loins	10	
Condition. Smooth covering of white fat; well fleshed	10	
Quality. Flesh sappy and good colour; fine grain	10	
	— 40	—
CARCASE. Well dressed, clean, free from cuts and bruises	10	
Shoulders. Neat but well fleshed; smooth finish	7	
Ribs. Well barrelled, short and well fleshed	6	
Loins. Eye muscle broad and long;* correct cover of fat;† kidney fat not excessive	20	
Legs. Thick, plump‡ uniform layer of fat, extending well down shank	15	
Neck. Short and meat	2	
	— 60	—
Total	100	—

Judging

AUSTRALIA

To simplify judging, the scale is applied only to the main external features and points are entered in the score card of every carcase in the competition for leg, loin, and fat covering.

Although a good twist of meat is essential on all four quarters, no points need be allotted for shoulders, neck, etc. This is because, in the case of shoulders, they follow the leg. If the bones in the leg are short, those in the shoulder will be found to be short also; similarly, the depth of flesh in the shoulder is related to the depth of flesh in the leg. If there is too much fat on the loin, there will be too much on the shoulder. For similar reasons no points are allotted for type, conformation and 'fullness of meat'.

There are *three* variables to be looked at in a carcase—meat, fat, and

---

*A good eye muscle should measure about 1·4 in (3·5 cm) in depth on a carcase of about 45 lb (20 kg) at nine months old or under.

†The optimum thickness of fat over the eye muscle is about 0·25 in (6 mm).

‡In a good leg the width across is equal to or greater than the length of the bone (Hammond).

bone. If in carcases of equal weight there is a greater proportion of one, there must be less of one or other of the two remaining and it is the relative proportions of the three which determine value from the butchers' point of view. It follows that a carcase of faulty type is un-likely to be up to show standard and it is hardly possible that a carcase of the desired conformation, *with no excess of fat*, will be anything but 'full of meat'. Nevertheless, any abnormality such as, for example, the heavy shoulder characteristic of some breeds, is taken into account in judging.

To score the maximum number of points, the following conditions should be met.

Legs (maximum 35 points) should be short in the bone and fully fleshed. The space between them should be in the form of a U rather than that of a V.

In a good pair of legs, the width across (at the widest point) is equal to or greater than the distance from the base of the tail to a line running across the top of the opening between them (from hock to hock). This ensures a joint yielding a thick cut of meat over the bone and one which will not dry and shrivel on roasting as does the meat of a leg with long bones.

Loin (maximum 35 points). This is a part of the body which does not come to full maturity until comparatively late and it is most important, therefore, to examine the development of a part of the carcase which plays an important part in determining quality. In judging both live animal and carcase this point can be assessed by seeing how far the loin fills up the spread between thumb and second finger when the loin is grasped in the hand.

One of the most valuable parts of the carcase, the loin should be wide, well filled with no excess of fat covering.

Fat Covering (maximum 30 points). There should be a smooth cover-ing of 'creamy' fat to denote a proper distribution throughout the whole carcase. The covering, which is thickest on back and sides but thins out towards the extremities, is essential on the lower parts of the legs, particularly of light-weight carcases.

It has a bearing on the all-important point of appearance and an adequate covering of fat serves to protect the legs; the meat of which, when held for long periods in cold storage, would otherwise tend to become dry and hard—conditions which become more marked on roast-ing. The importance of short legs is thus seen, since by shortening the bones the fat covering is brought further down.

On the other hand there should not be too much fat over the loins or elsewhere and this is a common fault in some of the early maturing breeds of today.

There remain only the colour and texture of the meat and with these, in the well-shaped well-finished carcases of the early maturing breeds, there is unlikely to be much wrong.

New Zealand

The New Zealand Meat Producers' (N.Z.M.P.) Board has approved a judging system for lamb competitions, based upon measurement, as well as visual appraisal.

Basically, the system covers three main weight classifications for wether or ewe lamb carcases.

(1) 20–28 lb.
(2) 29–36 lb.
(3) 37–56 lb.

(Dressed carcase weights less $4\frac{1}{2}\%$).

Entries must be for export as defined by the N.Z.M.P. Board.

Judging procedure consists of two sections.

Section A

(1) Length of bone: maximum 10 points. Is measured in centimetres from the tibia–tarsus bone to the protrusion just above the stifle joint (see Fig. 18). Points are awarded as in the scale below.

The carcase is split and the right side only quartered between the 12th and 13th rib.

Scale of points for length of bone

in centimetres (Maximum points = 10)

Points	Carcase weight (lb)		
	20–28	29–36	37–56
0	19·5 and over	20·5 and over	21·5 and over
1	19·0	20·0	21·0
2	18·5	19·5	20·5
3	18·0	19·0	20·0
4	17·5	18·5	19·5
5	17·0	18·0	19·0
6	16·5	17·5	18·5
7	16·0	17·0	18·0
8	15·5	16·5	17·5
9	15·3	16·3	17·3
10	15·0 and under	16·0 and under	17·0 and under

(2) Size of rib eye: maximum 35 points. Measured in millimetres as indicated in Fig. 18 and points awarded according to the scale below.

(3) Depth of fat: maximum 55 points. Is taken in millimetres as shown in Fig. 19 and points awarded according to the scale shown.

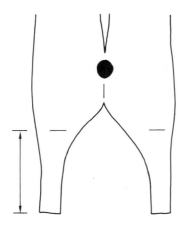

Fig. 18   Length of bone measurement

Scale of points for the size of the rib eye

in millimetres (Maximum points = 35)

Points	Carcase weight (lb)						
	20–25	26–28	29–32	33–36	37–42	43–50	51–56
1	18	19	20	21	22	24	26
5	19	20	21	22	23	25	27
9	20	21	22	23	24	26	28
12	21	22	23	24	25	27	29
14	22	23	24	25	26	28	30
16	23	24	25	26	27	29	31
18	24	25	26	27	28	30	32
20	25	26	27	28	29	31	33
22	26	27	28	29	30	32	34
24	27	28	29	30	31	33	35
26	28	29	30	31	32	34	36
28	29	30	31	32	33	35	37
30	30	31	32	33	34	36	38
32	31	32	33	34	35	37	39
35	32	33	34	35	36	38	40

Scale of points for depth of fat over rib eye

in millimetres (Maximum points = 55)

Points	Carcase weight (lb)	
	20–36	37–56
0		under 1
20	under 1	1
40	1	2
50	2	3
55	3	4
50	4	5
40	5	6
20	6	7
0	7 and over	8 and over

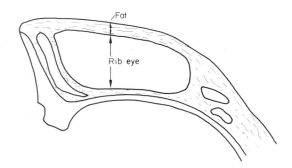

Fig. 19   Rib eye and fat measurement

Section B

(1) The top ten (or so) entries which score the highest points under Section A, may have further measurements taken for fat depth at other positions on the cut surface (these presumably would be chiefly applied to excessive fat deposition over the barrel).

(2) From the selected top carcases the right side is cut into the following.

(a) Long cut leg:

> Loin (including the 6th rib).
> Full 5-rib fore.
> Breast removed from the loin and fore on a line 3 in (7·6 cm) from the outer edge of the rib eye muscle.
> Offcuts, which include breast, kidney, and internal fats.

(b) The above portions are individually weighed and each divided by the side weight. The resultant answers are then multiplied by 50, to produce a unit value per 50 lb (23 kg) of lamb.

(c) The following unit values shall be used:

> Leg weight × 6·5
> Loin weight × 5·0
> Fore weight × 3·0.
> Offcuts weight × 1·0.

(d) The winner shall be the entry with the highest aggregate of points, based upon the sum of the measurements and unit values.

All other entries shall be ranked according to the points scored.

Provision is made for penalty deductions. Up to 20 points may be deducted from each entry, for such faults as yellow fat, abnormal muscle texture or colour, stagginess, bruises, and scars.

The Ideal Carcase. On this basis the perfect carcase at 30 lb (14 kg) carcase weight would presumably be as follows:

Section A

	Pts.
(1) Length of Bone 16 cm or under	10
(2) Rib Eye 34 mm	35
(3) Fat Cover 3 mm	55
	100

Section B

Based upon the following assumed yield for a good carcase.

$$\text{Leg} \quad \frac{3\cdot75}{15} \times \frac{6\cdot5}{1} = 1\cdot625$$

$$\text{Loin} \quad \frac{4\cdot75}{15} \times \frac{5\cdot0}{1} = 1\cdot583$$

$$\text{Fore} \quad \frac{4\cdot75}{15} \times \frac{3\cdot0}{1} = 0\cdot95$$

$$\text{Offcuts} \quad \frac{1\cdot75}{15} \times \frac{1\cdot0}{1} = 0\cdot117$$

$$4\cdot275 \times 50 = 213\cdot75$$

$$\text{Total } \overline{213\cdot75}$$

With this system the final evaluation of the top carcases is strongly influenced by the carcase yield in terms of retail values.

10   Pigs and pork

Evolution

The Pig family (Suidae) belongs to the even-toed ungulate mammals. It forms a group with Peccaries and Hippopotami. The true pigs (*Sus*) are found in Asia, Europe, and Africa, showing a preference for bush country. They consume vegetable or animal food, though normally they appear to show a distinct inclination towards roots. In the wild state they are as a rule exceedingly fierce. They vary considerably in size, from the large Indian wild hog to the pigmy hog of the Himalayas, which is a little larger than a good-sized hare.

The common wild boar (*S. scrofa*) existed in England in the Middle Ages and probably it is the progenitor of the British domestic pig. Sanders Spencer refers to the wild boar of Europe as 'of a russety grey colour when young, deepening as the pig reaches maturity, and becoming a dark chestnut brown, with its hair tinged with grey at the extremities, as old age crept over it'. The Chinese pig made its appearance in this country previous to 1800, and Youatt, in 1846, states: 'Most of our smaller breeds are more or less indebted to the Asiatic swine for their compactness of form, readiness with which they fatten on a small quantity of food, and early maturity.' In 1830 Lord Weston imported a grey-black boar and sow from Italy, and it appears that the black breeds owe a good deal to this stock, whilst the white breeds have been greatly influenced by their Chinese white ancestry.

There is very little authentic information on the development of our British breeds of pigs, and type changes can be very rapid with such a prolific animal, which reaches sexual maturity at a comparatively early age. It is usually accepted that the Tamworth is the most direct descendant of the aboriginal pig of this country, or at least, if the Neapolitan and Chinese pig have been used, their influence has not been so marked as in the other cases.

Pig Testing

Pig recording and testing has been used in various forms for over 50 years. Testing may be aimed at determining the transmission of a number of factors, such as food conversion, litter size, weight gain for age and carcase quality, etc., but frequently the relative importance of these many factors may be difficult to assess in the general summing-up.

With the traditional progeny testing, the boar to be tested may be used on four or five sows and although this would reproduce commercial conditions it is difficult to assess the influence of the sow.

Inherent differences in the sows and variations in management and the ever-present risk of disease may make it difficult to accurately measure the true influence attributable to the boar.

A technique developed by the British Oil and Cake Mills can ensure that many of these variables are eliminated. It is based upon the mating of the sow with semen obtained from two boars, the one to be tested and the control, mixed together and injected by the usual A.I. procedure. Thus each litter will contain piglets sired by each boar and subjected to similar maternal influences.

The identification of the parentage of the piglets in each mixed litter is made possible by a system of blood classification. The piglets are then grouped to identify the sires. Two teams of equal sex distribution and weight are selected from each litter, one representing the boar under test and the other the control.

The figures in Table 26, taken from a preliminary trial, indicate the type of information it is possible to obtain. The test boars are assessed by comparison with a standard progeny-tested control boar, whose performance is rated at 100.

Our improved British breeds may be conveniently considered as white, black, red, belted, and spotted.

WHITE BREEDS

Large White, or Large Yorkshire
Middle White
Small White (now extinct)
Lincoln Curly-coated (now extinct)
Cumberland
Welsh Lop-ear
Large White Ulster
Long Lop-eared White (Devonshire White)
British Landrace

Table 26

Analysis of pig progeny test

	Standard A	Test boar B	Performance A = 100
Birth to 50 lb			
Birth weight	3·2 lb	3·8 lb	119
Age at 15 lb	22 days	21 days	105
Food conversion, 15–50 lb	1·3	1·4	94
Daily live-weight gain, birth–50 lb	0·77 lb/day	0·82 lb/day	106
Test period			
Daily live-weight gain for period	1·57 lb/day	1·51 lb/day	96
Food conversion for period	3·82	4·0	95
Carcase results			
Killing-out percentage	77·38	76·33	99
Dead weight	156 lb	156 lb	
Eye-muscle area	3·50 in²	3·28 in²	94
Weight of lean	64 lb	63 lb	98
Percentage lean dead weight	41	40	98
Weight of fat	52 lb	51 lb	102
Percentage fat on dead weight	33	33	100
Distribution of lean			
Percentage lean in leg	28	26	
Percentage lean in middle	37	38	
Percentage lean in shoulder	35	36	

BLACK BREEDS

Large Black
Berkshire
Suffolk Small Black (now extinct)

RED BREEDS

Tamworth or Staffordshire
Dorset Gold-tip (now extinct)

BELTED BREED

Essex
Wessex Saddleback

SPOTTED BREED

Gloucester Old Spots

Skeleton (Fig. 20)

SKULL

Occipital bone   Lachrymal bone
Temporal bone   Maxillary bone
Parietal bone   Mandible (lower jaw)
Frontal bone

TEETH

4 canines
12 incisors
16 premolars
12 molars
—
Total 44 (adult)
—

VERTEBRAE

Cervical vertebrae   7 bones
Dorsal vertebrae   14–15 bones
Lumbar vertebrae   6–7 bones
Sacral vertebrae   4 bones (fused together)
Coccygeal vertebrae   20–26 bones (frequently 23)

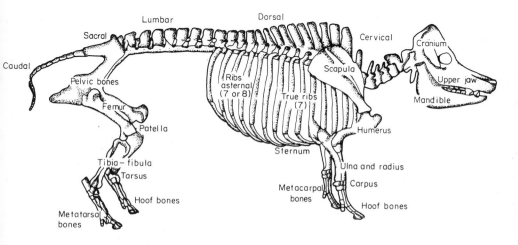

Fig. 20   Skeleton of porcine animal

RIBS

14 or 15 pairs (7 pairs sternal; 7 or 8 pairs asternal). The 15th rib, when present, may be completely developed, its cartilage entering into the costal arch, or it may be only about an inch long.

STERNUM

6 segments which are fused.

PELVIC GIRDLE

Ilium
Os pubis
Ischium

HIND LIMB

Femur
Patella
Tibia–Fibula
Tarsus (7 bones; hock)
Metatarsal (4 bones)
Hoof bones

FORE LIMB

Scapula
Humerus
Radius and Ulna
Carpus (8 bones; hock)
Metacarpus (4 bones)
Hoof bones

Organs

DIGESTIVE SYSTEM

The lower lip is slight and pointed, the upper lip being short and very thick. The mucous lining of the cheek is smooth. The hard palate is narrow with a central cleft and on each side of this cleft there are about 20 transverse ridges.

Dentition (see p. 185).

The tongue is long, narrow, and thin, and there is no central depression as in the sheep. There are 2 or 3 vallate papillae towards the root of the tongue, also a large number of soft, long-pointed papillae directed towards the epiglottis.

The pharynx is situated between the muscles of the head and the beginning of the oesophagus.

The oesophagus is short and nearly straight. It is usually stated that the stomach end is funnel-shaped.

The stomach is relatively large and in the adult has a capacity of about $1\frac{1}{2}$ gallons (7 litres). The larger curved surface is related to the skirt (diaphragm), spleen, liver, and the floor of the abdomen, whilst the other surface is in contact with the intestines.

The intestine is about 15 times the body length. The *small intestine* is 50 to 60 ft (15 to 18m) in length and it receives the pancreatic and bile ducts; the *large intestine* is about 12 to 15 ft (3·5 to 4·5 m); and the *caecum* is cylindrical, about 3 in (7·5 cm) wide and between 8 and 12 in (20 and 30 cm) in length.

The rectum is usually covered with a quantity of fat.

The liver is comparatively large and in the adult may reach a weight of about 4 lb (1·8 kg); there are four principal lobes, and a small lobe formed by a fissure in the right top lobe. It is thick in the central portions but tapers sharply to a fine-pointed circumference, and the surface has a 'nutmeg-like' appearance. The surface in contact with the viscera is deeply concave, and the *gall bladder* is mainly on the right central lobe.

The pancreas is situated at the back of the stomach just below the left kidney; it is a somewhat triangular flattened body containing a good proportion of fat. The pancreatic duct passes into the duodenum.

The spleen is a long, tongue-shaped organ and its position in the live animal will vary with the distension of the stomach, with which it is in contact and lightly attached to. It appears to vary considerably in size, and in a bacon hog is about 6 oz (170 g) in weight. It is red in colour, with a rib of fat on its visceral surface.

Respiratory System

The nostrils are small and situated at the extremity of a disc-like snout covered with a thin skin, which is highly sensitive and possesses small fine hairs. The nasal cavity is long and narrow, whilst the turbinate bones are similar to those of the ox. The *larynx* is long and mobile, the cartilages being very loosely attached.

The trachea consists of 32 to 35 rings which overlap at the back. As in the ox, there is a special bronchus detached for the top lobe of the right lung.

Lungs. The left lung has two or three lobes, whilst the right lung has four. The lung tissue is less tough than in the ox or sheep and is easily punctured by finger pressure. The lungs, not including the trachea, weigh about 1½ lb (0·7 kg) (bacon pig).

Heart

Is very small in relation to the body-weight, especially in the case of fat pigs, and seldom weighs more than 1 lb (0·45 kg) (bacon pig). It is short and blunt and has two longitudinal grooves running across its surface.

In some cases a third smaller groove may be present. The fat is softer and more greasy to the touch than in the case of the sheep's heart.

KIDNEYS

Are somewhat flattened, bean-shaped, and smooth. They are usually situated below the first four lumbar vertebrae, though occasionally the left one is slightly farther forward. The weight of the kidneys (two) is about $\frac{1}{2}$ to $\frac{3}{4}$ lb (0·25 to 0·34 kg) in a bacon pig.

Main lymphatic nodes of the pig

SUBMAXILLARY

Situated behind the angle of jaw, in *front* of the salivary gland.

PRECRURAL

In the fold of the groin; examine from *inside* the belly-wall.

INGUINAL

In lower belly-wall, just below leg.

POPLITEAL

Very small, just beneath the surface of the leg.

HOCK

Very small, situated near hock joint.

SUPRASTERNAL

Near the first segment of sternum.

ILIAC

In chump end of loin, along the line of the iliac artery.

PRESCAPULAR

As in the ox. Sometimes cut when removing the blade bone from the spare-rib (difficult to find in large fat pigs).

Dentition

Following is the standard for the dentition of pigs, as laid down by the Smithfield Club Show.

The following is the state of dentition which will be considered as indicating that they exceed the ages specified below.

'Pigs having their fourth molar up will be considered as exceeding $4\frac{1}{2}$ months.

Pigs having their corner permanent incisors cut will be considered as exceeding 6 months.'

Nomenclature

There is some variation in different parts of the country, but the following definitions are usually accepted.

BOAR

A male entire.

BRAWNER OR STAG

An entire male which has been castrated after having been used for service. In some parts the term 'brawn' is applied to a young, entire male.

CLEAN HOG, HOG, SHOTT, BARROW

Male pig castrated at an early age, usually at about weaning-time. (In some parts 'clean hog' is applied to a female before mating.)

SOW

A female which has produced young.

BROOD SOW

A female which is in young.

YELT, GILT, YILT, HILT

These terms are usually applied to the female pig until they have been covered, though in some parts one hears of the term yelt or gilt in pig.

Speyed Hog

Females which have been cut to prevent them breeding. (This practice is now practically obsolete.)

Stores

Are young weaned pigs.

Shoots
Small stores.

Sucking Pig

An unweaned pig (pigs are usually weaned at about nine weeks).

Dolly, Anthony, Runt

A non-thriving small pig of a litter.

Rig

An imperfectly castrated pig.

11   Some British breeds of pigs

Large White

The Large White or, as it is sometimes referred to, the Large Yorkshire is numerically the strongest of the British breeds (Plate 38). It is a large pig, and though primarily of great interest to the bacon curer, it can also produce good porkers at about 16–18 weeks. The sows of this breed are prolific, easy to handle, and good mothers. Their general hardiness is evidenced by the demand for them under such differing conditions as are met with in Northern Scandinavia and Malaysia. It is probable that one of the finest butchers' pigs was obtained by crossing the Large and Middle White.

CHARACTERISTICS

White in colour, free from black hairs, and bluish spots on the skin. The head should be fairly long, only very slightly dished, with a broad snout, light jowl, and wide between the ears. A longish neck, full to the shoulders, chest deep and wide, shoulders neat and not too wide. The legs straight and well set, level with the outside of the body and possessing flat bone. Pasterns short, with the feet strong and wide. A long back, level and wide from neck to rump, particularly broad across the loin. Tail set high, long, with a tassel of fine hair. Deep sides, ribs well sprung, the belly full without being flabby, and a straight under-line. The ham should be full and deep to the hocks, the skin free from wrinkles, and the coat fine and fairly long.

As the development of the young pig is inclined to be somewhat slow, it is at times difficult to judge a Large White at an early age.

Middle White

This breed (Plate 39) is a popular pork pig and it is thought to have been developed from the Large Yorkshire and the Small White (now extinct).

191

Originally the distinctions between these three were extremely fine, and we are told of a White pig which started its career by winning a prize as a Small White and gaining an award at two years old as a Middle, and finally heading the Large White class. There is an increasing demand for small pigs at Smithfield Market (London), and carcases of about 80 lb (36 kg) will fetch the top price. The early maturing characteristics of this breed will ensure a good muscle development in proportion to bone, at this carcase weight.

CHARACTERISTICS

Compared with the Large White, it is shorter, thicker, and rather stocky. The legs are short, the ears cocked, the face dished, with a good quantity of fine, soft hair.

Colour white, head dish-faced and short, broad turned-up snout, light jowl, wide between the ears, ears cocked forward and fringed with fine hair. The neck rather light, deep wide chest, shoulders sloping moderately wide. The legs should be straight, with short pasterns, the feet strong, and flat bones. The back long and level, tail high with a tassel of fine hair. The ribs well sprung, sides deep, the flank well let down, with a straight under-line. Hams to be broad, with flesh extending well down the hocks. The skin should be fine, and free from wrinkles and black spots. Strong objections are inbent knees and a coarse crooked jaw.

Berkshire

Other than its colour the general features of the modern Berkshire (Plate 40) are somewhat similar to that of the Middle White. It is fairly widely distributed, though its stronghold is the south and south-west of England. It was one of the first breeds of pigs to be improved, having been registered over eighty years ago. It has proved popular in warmer countries owing to its protective coloration. It has shown up particularly well in the carcase competitions at the Smithfield Show, not only in the pork but also in the bacon classes. The carcase usually yields a good percentage of lean meat at an early age with a high ratio of valuable cuts, coupled with a low offal yield.

CHARACTERISTICS

Black in colour with white marks on the feet, tail, and face. The head should be short, dish-faced, with large cocked ears inclined forwards and fringed with fine hair. Back long and straight, level loin, wide with plenty of depth in the body. The tail should be set high, legs short, and

Plate 38   Two Large White heavy pigs

Plate 39   Middle White sow (*Farmer & Stockbreeder*)

Plate 40   Two Berkshire gilts (*Meat & Livestock Commission*)
Plate 41   Wessex sow (*Farmer & Stockbreeder*)

Plate 42   Essex sow (*Farmer & Stockbreeder*)

Plate 43   Large Black sow and litter (*Meat & Livestock Commission*)

the hams well fleshed to the hocks. A straight under-line with a thick belly and plenty of depth through the heart. There should be plenty of fine, long hair with an absence of mane. A fine skin, free from wrinkles.

Wessex Saddleback

It seems evident that this hardy grazing pig (Plate 41) originated in the West Country and it may have received a slight infusion of Neapolitan blood. Certain it is that this English Forest Pig was exported to America over a hundred years ago and its descendants are now known as the Hampshire. The Wessex Saddleback has a reputation for a sound constitution and the ability to resist disease whilst living under adverse conditions. It enjoys a good record for fecundity, the sows being excellent mothers.

CHARACTERISTICS

Black in colour except for a continuous belt of white hair extending over the shoulders and forelegs. The head is very slightly dished with a long, straight snout. Ears are medium size, carried forward close to the face, with plenty of fine hair. Neck fairly long and muscular, shoulders wide, and the ribs well sprung. The tail should be stout and long, set high, with a good tassel of black hair and the hams broad and well fleshed. The following features are considered undesirable: curly coat; coarse mane; crown on back; short or turned-up snout; over-heavy shoulders; wrinkled skin; inbent knees; hollowness at back of shoulders; white colour on any part but the saddle and fore legs; and prick ears or ears unduly floppy.

Essex

This breed (Plate 42), sometimes referred to as the 'Essex Half-black' or the 'White-shouldered', bears a very strong resemblance to the Wessex Saddleback. It has been bred in the Eastern Counties for well over one hundred years, and having been bred in a fairly harsh climate, it has developed a reputation for extreme hardiness. It is a good forager and, when penned, will fatten readily, with early maturity. It is popular for both bacon and pork production, and, for the former, a Large White × Essex produces an excellent carcase.

CHARACTERISTICS

It is a rather large-framed pig, black in colour, with a white belt covering the shoulders and fore legs, the hind legs white up to the hocks, and a white nozzle and tip to tail. The head is of medium length and broad, with fair-sized ears, carried well forward but not flopped. The tail should be well set on, fine and curved. The hair to be fine and silky. The bone is fine and it usually yields a high percentage of carcase in relation to the live weight. The sows are noted for their deep milking propensities and their fecundity.

(The Essex and the Wessex are now grouped together as 'British Saddleback'.)

Large Black

Although the Large Black breed (Plate 43) is one of the oldest, there is very little authentic information regarding its history. Originally it appears to have been confined to Devon, Cornwall, Suffolk, and Essex. Such a wide distribution naturally resulted in widely varying types, and as a general rule they were a large coarse pig, with great length. The herd book was instituted in 1899, and since then there has been a steady elimination of the undesirable features and a grading up of the poorer classes of stock. There is now a demand for good-class Large Blacks for crossing purposes, and crosses with a Large White—either way—are very successful.

CHARACTERISTICS

The colour should be black or a blue-black, with a fine skin having a good quantity of straight fine hair. The head is broad, of medium length, with a straight snout. The ears are long and thin, and inclined forward and slightly inwards over the face. The back should be long and level, tail set high and well developed but not coarse. Short straight legs set well apart, and the body with plenty of depth. They are hardy and docile and their colour protects them from sun-scald.

Tamworth

This breed (Plate 44) is usually considered as the oldest pure breed in the world and, if it does contain any Neapolitan or Chinese blood, it shows very little evidence of it as compared with our other breeds. It is found chiefly in the Midlands, particularly Warwickshire, Staffordshire, Northamptonshire and Leicestershire. They have always been recognized as an active prolific breed, capable of attaining great weights, somewhat slow in maturing, but producing good quality lean bacon. In New Zealand a Tamworth–Berkshire cross was extremely popular for the production of pork pigs for export.

The coat should be golden red or sandy colour, free from black hairs. The head fairly long, wide between the ears, and the face slightly dished. The ears large, carried rigidly, sloping slightly forward, and fringed with fine hair. The neck is fairly long and muscular, evenly set on the shoulders, which should be fine and slanting. A chest wide and deep, loins broad, and a tail set high with a good tassel, sides long and deep, well-sprung ribs, the hams full and broad.

Lincoln Curly-coated

It is perhaps unfortunate that this breed no longer exists. It was claimed to be equally good as a pork or bacon pig, although it tended to lay down rather too much fat. As a general rule, the breed was noted for its hardiness and for the ability to attain great weights rapidly.

Gloucester Old Spots

A spotted breed of pigs has existed in the West of England for a very long period (Plate 45). This breed is noted for its fecundity, hardiness, and docility. Previous to 1914 it was confined almost entirely to Somerset, Wiltshire, and Gloucestershire, but since then its popularity has become widespread and a boar has been sold by public auction for 600 guineas. The breed has been exported to many European countries, also to the United States and India.

CHARACTERISTICS

The skin should be light or dark, and should not show coloured patches other than beneath the spots of the coat. The coat fairly thick, hair long, not curly, with an absence of mane bristles. The head of medium length, nose wide and slightly dished, plenty of width between the ears, which should be rather long and drooping. The neck fairly long and muscular, thick belly and flank, large hams, well fleshed to the hocks. Tail set high and carrying a good brush.

Welsh

This breed is of extremely ancient lineage and was at one time known as the Old Glamorgan Pig. It almost faced extinction about fifty years ago, when the Old Glamorgan Pig Society was formed. As there were similar types of pig in other parts of Wales, this Society was amal-

Plate 44   Tamworth boar (*Meat & Livestock Commission*)

Plate 45   Gloucester Old Spot sow (*Farmer & Stockbreeder*)

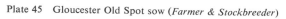

Plate 46   Welsh pigs, under 4 months

Plate 47   Cumberland boar (*Farmer & Stockbreeder*)

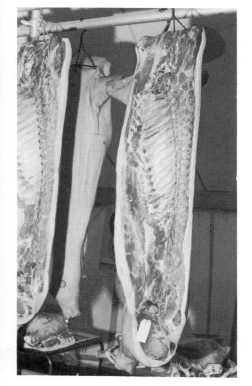

Plate 48 British Landrace boar (*Thorpe Willoughy Centre*)

Plate 49 A prize-winning side of English bacon

gamated with the Welsh Pig Society in 1922. Swedish Landrace blood has been introduced since 1953. A typical Old Welsh Pig is white in colour with a fair quantity of straight silky hair (Plate 46). The head is of medium length with lop ears, long and thin, extending over the face as far as the nose. The eyes may be of two colours, blue or brown, the former being preferred. The body is long and deep with the legs short and straight, whilst the tail is unusually long. It is a hardy, grazing pig, prolific, and yielding a good bacon carcase. In many respects its general appearance resembles that of the German Landrace.

Cumberland

This breed of pig (Plate 47) was well known over a hundred years ago, and in 1813, in the *Survey of Durham*, John Bailey makes reference to 'the breed of swine in this county was formerly a large white kind, with broad ears hanging over the eyes'. It was popular with both the pork butcher and bacon curer in this area, and it enjoyed a reputation for fecundity and its outstanding qualities as a good feeder. Today very few of this breed remain.

CHARACTERISTICS

The colour should be pure white, though blue spots may appear as the animal matures. Black spots, pink ears, and black hair will disqualify a pig for show purposes. The head is rather short, with a dished face, broad snout, and wide between the ears. The jowl is heavy and the ears broad and long, falling forwards. The skin is smooth with a light covering of hair, which should be fine and silky. The back lengthy and level, with only a very slight droop. The tail set high and free from coarseness, and the legs straight, short, and strong.

British Landrace

This breed, now forms an increasing part of our pig population, and due credit must be paid to its valuable contribution to pork and bacon production (Plate 48).

Denmark might be considered as the leading centre of pig breeding and their policy aims at producing a long lean pig suitable for the Wiltshire type of bacon. In some strains the breeding for extreme length appears to result in some loss of conformation in the hams.

Work carried out by the Pig Industry Development Association in 1960, covering over 15,000 Landrace bacon pigs with average carcase weights of 152 lb (69 kg) at 196·5 days, gave the best grading results of

any of the breeds or crosses tested. Of the recorded Landrace pigs 77%
were in the quality premium grades (AA × and AA) and with the cross-
bred pigs Large White/Landrace and Landrace/Large White crosses
had the highest proportion in quality premium grades. Standards of
excellence for the British Landrace are given on p. 207.

Other lesser known breeds include the Large White Ulster, at one
time extremely popular in Northern Ireland for the production of
rolled bacon on account of its fine skin; the Long Lop-eared White pig,
originally the 'Devonshire White'. The Small White which was thought
to have originated by crossing with the Chinese, is now extinct, as is
also the Suffolk Small Black, which in general form it very much
resembled. According to the librarian of the Rare Breeds Survival
Trust, the Lincoln Curly-coated became extinct in 1971 or 1972.

12 Growth and quality points

It is probable that greater difficulty will be experienced in judging the live pig than either cattle or sheep. Pigs which may appear similar from external appearances can vary markedly in their carcase quality. Feed is of the utmost importance, particularly if the pig is intended for bacon.

Sir John Hammond, Cambridge, conducted extensive investigations in growth, and it is evident that entirely different body proportions can be obtained by varying the type and method of feeding. A porker at 16 weeks can be compared with, say, a child of 5 years, and the breeder and feeder have attempted to produce a balanced animal with relatively small head and legs long before the animal has reached maturity. In the case of the wild boar the relative proportions as between the foetus and the adult vary but little, but as we get towards our improved types the greater the variation becomes. In early maturing types the point at which the proportions become balanced takes place rapidly; for example, in the case of the Middle White this point might be reached at 110 lb (50 kg) live weight, whereas with the Large White 200 lb (90 kg) will probably be the figure. An approximate list of the breeds in order of early maturity would be Middle White, Berkshire, Essex, Wessex, Large Black, and Large White. The growth of the bone is closely followed by, and is related to, the muscular development; not so in the case of the fat. The fat starts at the shoulder and extends along and over the loin. It would appear that the Danish method of high-level feeding from birth to about 16 weeks, followed by controlled feeding up to bacon weight, produces the best results. It is during the initial stages when the bone and muscle is being developed that the animal should receive the best food, and after this the amount of fat laid down can be regulated by controlled feeding. Conversely, poor initial feeding followed by good feeding will result in the laying down of much fat on the carcase. It is therefore evident from the foregoing that there is an optimum slaughter-point for each breed, which will be influenced by the feeding methods employed. (For greater detail the student is recommended to read *The Body Proportions of Different Breeds of Bacon Pigs,* J. Hammond and G. N. Murray.)

The live weights required vary considerably in different parts of the country. At Smithfield, London, a good pig of 80 lb (36 kg) carcase weight will usually fetch the top price; such a carcase would be obtained from a pig of about 120 lb (55 kg) live weight. Throughout the South of England there is a ready demand for this small porker type (Fig. 21).

Figure 22 indicates the relative values of the various cuts of the pig, and it can be seen that the length of loin, fullness of hams, and lightness of the shoulders and head will have an important bearing on percentage of profit obtained. Even though the general conformation may approach the ideal, an excess of fat will necessitate wasteful trimming, and a soft fat depreciate its value as bacon. In this respect a knowledge of the feeder will prove of great value.

The judging of the live animal should be based upon a definite scheme, and the 'standards of excellence' laid down by the National Pig Breeders' Association and the British Landrace Society are given hereunder as applied to the Large White, Middle White, Berkshire, Wessex Saddleback, and British Landrace.

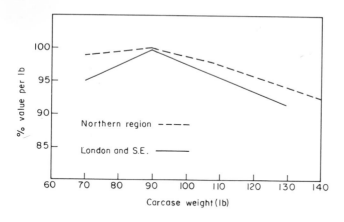

Fig. 21   Weight suitability of pork pigs

Standards of excellence

LARGE WHITE

Principal characteristics. In outline the ideal Large White pig resembles the ideal baconer. The standard of excellence laid down by the National Pig Breeders' Association emphasizes such important points as long,

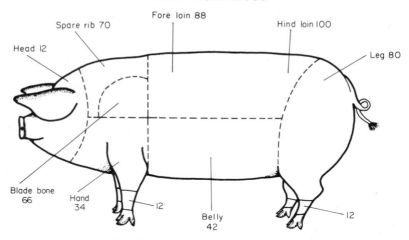

Fig. 22   Relative values of a pork carcase

level back, long and wide quarters, broad and deep hams, light shoulders, and a white skin free from wrinkles. Here is the complete standard.

Head. Moderately long, face slightly dished, snout broad, not too much turned up, jowl light, wide between the ears.

Ears. Long, thin, slightly inclined forward, and fringed with hair.

Neck. Long, fine, and proportionately full to shoulders.

Chest. Wide and deep.

Shoulders. Level, obliquely laid, medium width, free from coarseness.

Back. Long, level, and wide from neck to rump.

Loin. Broad.

Quarters. Long and wide.

Hams. Broad, full, and deep to hocks.

Tail. Set high, stout and long, but not coarse, with tassel of fine hair.

Ribs. Well sprung.

Sides. Deep.

Belly. Full, but not flabby, with straight under-line and with at least twelve sound, well-placed teats.

Flank. Thick, and well let down.

Legs. Straight and well set, level with the outside of the body, with flat bone.

Pasterns. Short and springy.

Feet. Strong and even.

Action. Firm and free.

Skin.   Fine, white, free from wrinkles, black hairs and black spots, and as free as possible from blue spots.

Coat. Long and silky.

Wessex Saddleback

Colour. Head and neck black, white over shoulders and fore legs. Continuous belt of white hair over fore legs and shoulders. Body, hindquarters, and hind legs black.

Head. Fairly long, snout moderately long and straight, face very slightly dished, medium width between ears; under-jaw clean-cut and free from jowl; nose black, and velvety in appearance.

Ears. Medium size, with forward pitch, setting well on to face, but not obscuring view, furnished with plenty of fine hair.

Neck. Fairly long and muscular.

Chest. Wide and deep.

Shoulders. Fine, sloping, and well set.

Legs. Strong and shapely, with good bone, well set on each corner of the body.

Pasterns. Strong and sloping.

Feet. Strong and of fair size.

Back. Long and straight.

Loin. Strong and broad.

Tail. Stout and long, with tassel of long black hair.

Sides. Long and deep.

Ribs. Well sprung and extending well up to flank.

Belly. Deep, with straight under-line, and with at least twelve sound, well-placed teats.

Flank. Full and well let down.

Quarters. Long and wide.

Hams. Broad and full, deep to hocks.

Coat. Abundant, long, and straight.

Action. Firm and free.

Boars. Should have masculine appearance and strong points.

Objectionable features. Curly coat, coarse mane, crown on back, short or turned-up snout, over-heavy broad shoulders, wrinkled skin, inbent knees, hollowness at back of shoulders. Prick ears, slouch, floppy, or papery ears.

Colouring: White on any part but the saddle.

British Landrace

Head. Light, medium length and fine with minimum jowl and straight nose (slightly concave with age).

Ears. Medium size, neither coarse nor heavy, drooping and slanting forward with the top edges as near as possible parallel to the bridge of the nose.

Neck. Clean and light, of medium length.

Shoulders. Light, firm, free from coarseness, medium width and well laid on to body. Not deep through the shoulder.

Back. Great length, slightly arched along length. Breadth uniform throughout. No dip at shoulders or loin.

Sides. Firm, compact, and not deep.

Ribs. Well sprung throughout.

Loin. Should be strong and wide with no deficiency in muscle, no dip in front of hams.

Hindquarters. Medium length, broad, straight, or very slightly sloping to the tail.

Tail. Set reasonably high.

Hams. Very broad and full, rounded both from the back and sides. Deep to hock and wide between legs with good inner thigh.

Belly. The line of the underbelly should be straight or slightly sloping down to the rear. At least twelve sound, well-placed teats starting well forward.

Legs. Medium length, well set, and square with the body. Bone adequate, but fine rather than coarse.

Pasterns. Strong and springy, not too long.

Action. Firm and free, but, owing to very wide hams and above average length, tendency to walk with a decided swing.

Skin. Soft, springy, and slightly pink. (Black or blue spots are permissible if small and few in number but the hairs growing on them must be white.)

Hair. Fine and white. 'Roses', while not encouraged, are of minor importance.

General. The Landrace pig has been developed to furnish long, lean sides, with the greatest proportion of the dearer cuts and the minimum of the least valuable parts, whilst preserving stamina and strong constitution.

Although the butcher eventually reaps the benefits of careful selective breeding, he is probably less directly concerned with pedigree points than with the general external signs in the live animal, which will probably indicate suitable carcase characteristics. His chief considerations are quality, without excessive fat necessitating trimming, and a large proportion of the valuable cuts at a figure allowing him a reasonable profit. Provided that the animal carries the right quality of meat, in the correct quantities in the right places, actual breed purity fades into insignificance. There appears to be very little difference in the qualities of flesh obtainable from pure and cross-bred animals of similar finish, and in some cases, owing to the varying rates of maturing, a cross can be a definite advantage. For example, a Large White/Middle White cross will produce an almost ideal porker carcase, though it must be remembered that even within these breeds great variations of type occur. The following standard of points is tentatively suggested for judging a pork pig from the butcher's standard, the ultimate carcase being the prime object. By using a somewhat similar allocation of points to the carcase, it should be possible for the student to form a fairly accurate opinion of his judgment of the live animal as compared with his estimation of the carcase.

Suggested scale of points for judging pork pigs

GENERAL	Max.	Awards
Weight. According to trade requirements	10	
Form. Long, compact, level back and neat shoulders	10	
Condition. Well fleshed and suitable quantity of fat	12	
Quality. Fine skin, free from wrinkles, fine silky hair, and fine in the bone	8	
	— 40	—
Quarters. Long and wide	10	
Loin. Broad and long	10	
Ribs. Well sprung	8	
Flanks. Deep and full	6	
Shoulders. Neat and level	6	
Neck. Well developed	4	
Head. According to breed: wide, light jowl	3	
Fore legs. Straight and well placed	5	
Hams. Wide and well fleshed to hocks	8	
	— 60	—
Total	100	

I am indebted to Mr David Geary for the following figures obtained from six very good pure Welsh pigs, which were bred and cut by him.

Live weight, approx. 775 lb; cold carcase weight, 557·4 lb; average carcase weight, 92·9 lb; average KO%, approx. 71·9%; weight range of carcases, 89 lb to 100 lb.

	Average % primal cuts	Range
Legs	23·1	21·5–24·0
Loins	26·4	24·5–29·5
Neck ends	14·35	13·8–15·2
Hands and bellies	28·15	26·7–29·5
Heads	8·0	7·7– 8·3
	100%	

Average fat thickness over legs, 10 mm; average fat thickness over loins, 12·5 mm.

Best eye muscle length, 80 mm; poorest eye muscle length, 70 mm; best eye muscle depth, 50 mm; poorest eye muscle depth, 32·5 mm.

13   Slaughter

Pre-slaughter care

As domestic pigs are by nature less active than cattle and sheep, the question of resting prior to slaughter is most important, particularly if the pig is intended for bacon. It appears probable that the pig will recover less rapidly from the effects of fatigue, and after slaughter this would result in a low acidity in certain of the muscles, with a consequent deterioration in the keeping qualities of the carcase.

The pigs should be rested, at least overnight, and fasted, though, if they are particularly restless, it might be desirable to allow a small quantity of food. A plentiful supply of clean water should be available and when they are driven to the killing floor they should be carefully handled to avoid excessive excitement and bruising. In some American packing houses, pigs intended for immediate slaughter, without a rest period, are sprayed with lukewarm water to accelerate cooling.

Slaughter

STUNNING

The electrical method, whereby tongs are applied to either side of the neck, uses a high-frequency current with a moderately low voltage, the electrodes being kept moist in a 20% saline solution. A current is switched on and an application of 5 to 10 seconds is sufficient to produce complete unconsciousness. Should the pig be left for 2 or 3 minutes it will recover and in approximately 5 minutes be completely normal, exhibiting no indications of pain or fear. This method is particularly suitable for dealing with pigs, and independent investigations have shown that 'splashing' is practically eliminated. As the voltage employed is between 60 and 80 volts only, in the event of a short circuit no serious shock could be transmitted to the operator. The upkeep and maintenance has been found less than that of guns and cartridges.

Reference has already been made to captive and loose bullet pistols, and where these methods are employed the muzzle is applied just above the level of the eyes, in the centre of the forehead. In the case of bacon pigs it is absolutely essential that sticking must immediately follow shooting before reflex movements start, and even with pork pigs it is important to ensure perfect bleeding. With pigs up to 10 score, a $1\frac{1}{4}$-grain (yellow label) cartridge is used with a captive bolt, above this weight a 2-grain (blue label). When a gun is employed, it is desirable to make an incision over the snout of the pig to permit the blood to escape.

Under some circumstances it may be necessary to secure the head of the pig by passing a loop round the upper jaw.

In some overseas packing-houses, stunning is not normally resorted to, the pig being shackled by a chain passing round the hind leg, the animal then being hoisted by a wheel to be transferred to the sticking rail. With this method the pig must be hoisted carefully to avoid undue twisting of the hindquarters, which would cause bruising.

STUNNING BY ANAESTHESIA

The Slaughter of Pigs (by Anaesthesia) Regulations of 1958 sanctioned the use of CO_2 for the stunning of pigs.

As compared with electrical stunning it was found that using a concentration of about 65–70% of CO_2 to air the pigs were completely relaxed, the respiratory rate being reduced to about 5 to 7 per minute.

The pigs do not react to subsequent shackling so that the person 'sticking' the pig could concentrate on the job and the stick cut is accurate and the risk of 'shoulder sticking' reduced. A higher blood yield is obtained, giving improved keeping qualities in the carcase. This method has not been widely popular, probably on account of the fact that it may be somewhat slower than using the electrical apparatus.

STICKING

Blood is an ideal media for the growth of putrefactive organisms and it provides a vehicle for their distribution throughout the animal system. It has been proved that organisms introduced at the time of sticking may subsequently be found in the deep-seated tissues. In addition to this, the temperature of the body will prove favourable to their multiplication. For this reason it may be desirable to scrape away any dirt and hair from breastbone to throat.

A long sticking knife is unnecessary and most slaughtermen prefer a knife of 6 to 8 in (15 to 20 cm), in some cases sharpened on either side of the point. Frequently, a hilt guard is fitted. The point of the knife is inserted at an angle of about 45°, about 2 in (5 cm) in front of the breastbone, immediately over the middle line (the point of the breastbone can easily be felt). An incision is made down towards the jaw with the knife penetrating to a depth of 5 to 6 in (12 to 15 cm), depending on the size of the pig. If carried out properly, the carotid arteries and the jugular vein will be cut. The first two ribs of the pig are very close together and unless the knife is kept dead central there is a grave risk of the knife penetrating the shoulder, giving rise to 'shoulder-stuck hogs'. The blood clot resulting from this will have to be trimmed away, causing loss and affecting the appearance. If the pig is stuck whilst hoisted, there is little risk of the blood entering the chest cavity. Under some circumstances it may be necessary to stick the animal on the ground, and in this case some slaughtermen prefer the pig lying on its back, though many experts prefer to stick whilst the pig is on its side, claiming more thorough bleeding. With either of these methods it is desirable to raise the hind end of the pig for a short period, moving the carcase to assist the 'bleeding'.

BLEEDING

Bleeding must be thorough, and in this respect the United States Bureau of Animal Industry specifies that a hog shall hang on the bleeding-rail for at least 6 minutes. During this period the muscles will relax and the hair will be more readily removed. If the blood is intended for blood sausage or similar products it must be stirred *immediately* it is collected to remove the 'fibres'. Where it is to be dried, care must be taken to keep it free from water, as this retards coagulation.

DE-HAIRING

The ideal temperature for scalding is between 140 and 145°F (60 and 63°C). On large plants this temperature is thermostatically controlled, the water being heated by steam. About 5 minutes is sufficient to loosen the hair and make its removal with the scurf a reasonably simple operation. Some variation will occur, depending on the breed of pig and the rearing conditions. Scalding tanks are usually equipped with a cradle, which enables the pigs to be removed prior to scraping.

Some of the smaller establishments depend upon scalding tubs, and a mixture of 3 parts boiling water to 1 of cold is considered to provide the correct temperature. Here, however, the ratio of the weight of the pig or pigs to the water, and heat losses due to the difference in the atmospheric temperature, all play a part. It is sometimes considered that a temperature sufficient to change the colour of blood from red to brown is satisfactory, whilst some operators dip their finger into the scald twice and the second dipping should sting the finger. In this class of slaughterhouse it is very rare to see a thermometer employed. Should the temperature be too high, the hair will become 'fixed' and extremely difficult to remove.

Where hard water is employed it is sometimes the practice to add a small quantity of slaked lime.

Scudding or the removal of the hair can be carried out in de-hairing machines in which the pigs revolve and beaters remove the hair, or it may be carried out by hand. A method of de-hairing in one operation is by immersing the pigs in a hot, adhesive mixture, and on removal from this bath the coating is permitted to become semi-plastic. This substance is then peeled from the surface of the pig, removing with it the hair, including the roots. This produces a very clean skin with a minimum of labour. After use, the adhesive is melted, strained to remove the hair and scurf, and returned to the de-hairing tank. It is stated that over a period of 9 months' operation $1\frac{1}{4}$ oz (35 g) of adhesive per hog had to be replaced.

Although the average butcher is not concerned with bacon curing, this section would be incomplete unless singeing is mentioned. With farm-house curing the hair is frequently burned off, usually by placing the carcase on clean straw, which is lit. It is claimed that a better flavoured product is obtained, and under farm conditions it may prove easier than scalding. In most bacon factories the normal practice is to scald and then to singe the pig by passing it through a singeing furnace, the object being to dry and harden the skin, and possibly the fat immediately beneath it. An oil fuel is generally employed, and the operation is carried out in under half a minute and is followed by washing down.

Dressing specifications

MLC Specifications for dressing Pig Carcases.

A. The following parts shall be removed:
    (a) Hair (but see conditions of weighing below).
    (b) Liver, melt, heart and lungs, i.e. the 'pluck' or 'race'.
    (c) Guts.
    (d) Caul and gut fat.
    (e) Genito-urinary organs, excluding kidneys.

B. The following parts shall not be removed:
    (a) The head and tongue.
    (b) The feet and tail.

(c) The fleshy or muscular part of the diaphragm ('skirt').

(d) Kidneys, kidney fat and flare fat.

(e) Ear roots and eyes.

(f) There shall be no trimming of the neck beyond cutting off ragged edges and cleanly removing the blood vessels.

C. Carcases shall be weighed:

(a) If weighed 'hot', within 6 hours of slaughter. When carcases are weighed 'hot', the 'cold' weight will be ascertained by making rebates as follows:

Hot Weight	Within one hour of slaughter	Thereafter but within 4 hours of slaughter	Thereafter but within 6 hours of slaughter
	lb	lb	lb
5 score 12 lb and under	2	1	–
5 score 13 lb to 7 score 3 lb	3	2	1
7 score 4 lb to 9 score 9 lb	4	3	2
9 score 10 lb to 10 score 15 lb	5	4	3
10 score 16 lb to 12 score	6	5	4
12 score 1 lb to 14 score	7	6	5
14 score 1 lb to 16 score	8	7	6
16 score 1 lb to 18 score	9	8	7
18 score 1 lb to 20 score	10	9	8
Over 20 score	11	10	9

(b) If weighed 'cold', within 24 hours of slaughter, except when prior approval for an extension of this period has been given.

It is permissible for carcases which will be skinned to be weighed with the hair on, but in such cases a deduction must be made for the weight of the hair.

N.B. The adoption of these Specifications for pigs is a necessary condition if stock are to be certified deadweight under the Fatstock Guarantee Scheme.

Offals

In the pig the ratio of offal to live animal is much less than in the case of the sheep and ox, as the skin, head, feet, and tail form part of the carcase. Also, as the pig consumes a more concentrated type of food, omnivorous rather than herbivorous, it is provided with a simple stomach, which is small as compared with the ruminant. In fact, very little indeed of the live pig need be considered as valueless material. The offals can be conveniently considered under the headings 'Edible' and 'Inedible', with a small section for the portions which may be used for pharmaceutical purposes. There is of course overlapping, as some of the organs may be used as edible or inedible products.

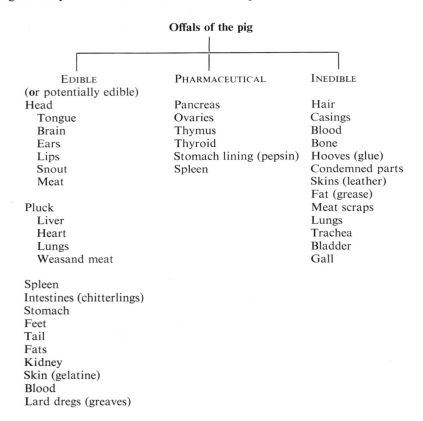

Offals of the pig

EDIBLE (or potentially edible)	PHARMACEUTICAL	INEDIBLE
Head	Pancreas	Hair
Tongue	Ovaries	Casings
Brain	Thymus	Blood
Ears	Thyroid	Bone
Lips	Stomach lining (pepsin)	Hooves (glue)
Snout	Spleen	Condemned parts
Meat		Skins (leather)
		Fat (grease)
Pluck		Meat scraps
Liver		Lungs
Heart		Trachea
Lungs		Bladder
Weasand meat		Gall
Spleen		
Intestines (chitterlings)		
Stomach		
Feet		
Tail		
Fats		
Kidney		
Skin (gelatine)		
Blood		
Lard dregs (greaves)		

Edible (or potentially edible)

PLUCK

This consists of the trachea, lungs, heart, and the liver. The oesophagus is usually attached to it. Some bacon factories also leave the tongue on. The liver is of course the most valuable portion, though it is less tender than that of the sheep on account of the large proportion of connective tissue, which gives it the characteristic 'nutmeg' appearance.

The heart contains a good quantity of protein but seldom more than about 5% of fat. This latter substance is oily to the touch, and this fact, with its rather round, blunted point, will help in differentiating it from the heart of the sheep.

Lungs are frequently used in the preparation of faggots and similar made-up products, and those from an average good pig may contain over 10% of fat, so that they are a relatively valuable product.

The muscular coat forming the outer covering of the oesophagus can be used as normal meat tissue.

Pigs' fry usually consists of the liver, heart, spleen, with the caul and frequently mesenteric fat.

CHITTERLINGS

These are made from the large intestine and the stomach. They should be handled immediately after slaughter and thoroughly cleansed and well cooked.

STOMACH

In some parts the stomach is used as a container for comminuted meats, somewhat similar to the American 'head cheese'.

FEET AND TAIL

At one time it was the custom to sell the feet, or trotters, attached to the hand or leg. If they are to be sold separately, they should be placed in a mild brine for a day or two. They will, of course, provide a good jelly stock for brawn, this also applies to tails.

FATS

Some fats, as already mentioned, can be sold with pigs' fry, but the flare fat is generally preferred for the preparation of leaf lard.

KIDNEYS

In the porker type of carcase these are left attached to the loins, but in baconers the kidney, fat, and fillets are trimmed out when preparing the side.

SKIN

Rind trimmings will yield a good proportion of gelatine, and they can be included in some types of brawn, after thorough cooking and mincing. Their use in the preparation of rind emulsions for use in sausage and similiar products, is common practice.

BLOOD

This can be used in blood sausages, blood and barley loaf, and similar products.

LARD DREGS, GREAVES, SCRATCHINGS, OR CRACKLINGS

These residues of lard rendering are sometimes eaten, with the addition of salt, without any further preparation. They contain a good percentage of protein and sometimes a fair quantity of fat. Provided they are ground down finely on a mincer, a proportion can be included in meat loaves and similar made-up products.

HEAD

Though this forms, strictly speaking, part of the carcase, it is probably as well to mention it in this section, and details of its preparation will be found on p. 299.

Inedible

HAIR

Our domestic breeds of pigs do not produce a sufficient quantity of the type of hair suitable for making into bristles, and it is only in the larger establishments that the pigs' hair is collected and passed on for manufacturing into upholstery stuffing.

CASINGS (Fig. 23)

Specialized firms carry on the trade of gut cleaning and in the larger killing centres they have their premises in the vicinity of the abattoirs. Where smaller numbers are handled, the uncleaned runners are collected by these firms from the butcher.

Casings

Trade term	Anatomical term
Bung	Rectum
Middle, chitterlings, or black gut	Large intestine (colon)
Cap	Caecum
Small casings	Small intestine (duodenum, jejunum, and ileum)
Stomach	Stomach

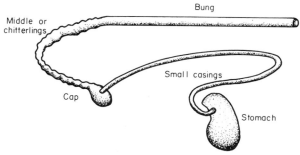

Fig. 23   Hog casings

BLOOD

If not employed for edible purposes it is sometimes dried and utilized as fertilizer and animal feeding stuffs. Pharmaceutical preparations and pigments can also be obtained from it.

BONES

These are rendered down to obtain their constituent materials, mineral matter, fat, and gelatine. The bone meal is used as fertilizer and bone charcoal.

HOOVES

From the hooves meal is prepared which is a very useful fertilizer, normally in much demand by hop growers.

CONDEMNED PARTS

Organs, carcases, and parts thereof, in the larger establishments are rendered down at high temperatures and disposed of for inedible purposes.

SKINS

The majority of the pigs cured in England do not have the skins removed, therefore the industry of tanning pig skins is confined chiefly to Scotland, where there is a trade for skinless rolled bacon. A good skin will average about 4 ft × 3½ ft (1·2 × 1·1 m). Sows will give a larger skin but the grain is less fine. Considerable skill is necessary to flay a pig efficiently.

FAT

Secondary fats are usually disposed of for preparation into tallow, etc.

MEAT SCRAPS, LUNGS, AND TRACHEA

These can be either steam or dry rendered and utilized in the preparation of animal feed or fertilizer.

Pharmaceutical

In the American packing-houses the majority of the larger endocrine glands are collected and treated for the extraction of pharmaceutical products. In this country it is probable that only a very few slaughter establishments are normally handling a sufficient number of animals to justify the expense of their collection.

Dressing percentages

In the case of the pig the loss as between the live weight and dressed carcase weight is much less than in the case of our other food animals, as the carcase of the pig includes the head, feet, skin, and tail. In round figures, the average run of commercial sheep will lose about 50% of their live weight on dressing, cattle about 45%, and pigs roughly 25%. As a general rule, the dressing percentage increases as the live weight of the pig increases, though breed and the intestinal content will, of course, influence this figure. A very high percentage might prove to be a distinct disadvantage, as it might be obtained at the expense of excessive fat, which would necessitate drastic trimming. When the internal organs of the pig have attained their maximum size any weight increase must arise from the carcase. As a rough rule this point is reached at about 200 lb (90 kg) live weight, though it will be modified according to the early or late maturing characteristic of the breed.

Another important factor is the intestinal content. A pig weighed immediately after feeding may lose as much as 5% of its weight whilst fasting overnight prior to slaughter. This figure is extreme, and probably 2–2½% loss might be reasonably expected under normal conditions. There appears to be little information regarding the loss of weight during transport, but it would appear that, provided it is carried out efficiently, losses from this source should not prove excessive. Figures relating to rail transport in the United States give a loss of 1·48% for journeys up to 100 miles (160 km) and 2·10% for distances between 250 and 300 miles (400 and 480 km).

The difference between the hot and the cold carcase weight will be greatly influenced by the temperature, humidity, and the rate of the air circulation to which the carcase is submitted after slaughter. Normally about $2\frac{1}{2}\%$ over 24 hours would be a reasonable loss, and a great deal of the cooling effect is obtained by this evaporation. Therefore, dressing percentages should always be calculated on the *cold* carcase weight.

The dressing percentage for show pigs will range between approximately 75% and 82% for pigs between 100 lb (45 kg) and 300 lb (135 kg) live weight. For the average run of commercial pigs the percentage will be considerably lower, and the graph shown in Fig. 24 will indicate the general trend.

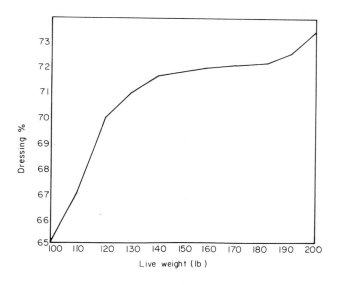

Fig. 24   Dressing percentages for commercial pigs

The suggested scale opposite depends upon experience and visual judgment. To obtain more accurate comparisons, it is desirable that actual measurements should be employed. Considerable work on New Zealand carcases was carried out by Davidson, Hammond, Swain, and Wright* along these lines, and a standard was evolved for judging pork and bacon carcases. The diagram below (Fig. 25) will indicate the ideal measurements found for pigs with a carcase weight from 60 to 100 lb (27 to 45 kg).

*A Method for Judging Pork and Bacon Carcases, H. R. Davidson, J. Hammond, J. B. Swain' and N. Wright.

The body length from the symphysis pubis of pelvis to the junction of the first rib with the sternum.

The leg length from the symphysis pubis of pelvis in direct line to the toe.

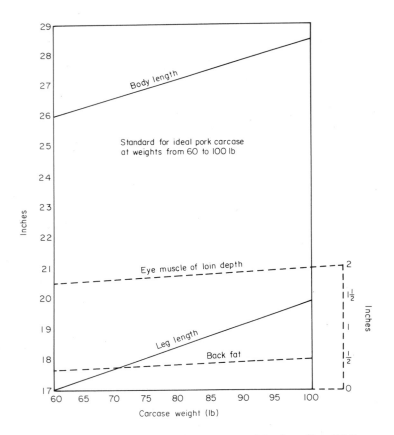

Fig. 25   Standard for ideal pork carcase, at weights from 60 to 100 lb

The eye muscle of the loin is measured at its thickest depth through the centre of the eye when the loin is sectioned at the last rib.

The back fat measurement is measured at the same cross-section $1\frac{1}{2}$ in (4 cm) from the middle of the back (chine).

It should be remembered that these measurements represent the *ideal* carcase, and very few commercial pigs will attain *all* these measurements.

Suggested scale of points for judging pork pig carcase

	Max.	Award
GENERAL		
Weight. According to trade requirements	10	
Form. Long level back, neat shoulders, short legs	10	
Condition. Well fleshed, suitable quantity of fat	12	
Quality. Small bone, fine skin free from wrinkles; kidney fat smooth, white, and firm	8	
	— 40	—
Side. Long and deep, well fleshed and firm	15	
Shoulder. Compact, not excessively fat.	5	
Loin. Long, well fleshed, even thickness of fat throughout	15	
Ham. Short and plump, firm, correct covering of fat	12	
Belly. Thick and lean	6	
Head. Light	3	
Carcase. Well dressed, free from hair, scores, and bruising	4	
	— 60	
Total	100	

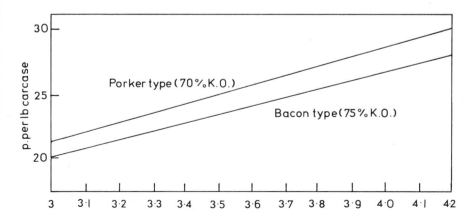

Fig. 26 Pigs' price (£) per score live to price (p) per lb carcase

Live pigs

These are usually now sold on the basis of p per kg. In order to arrive at the equivalent carcase value (sinking the offals), the following calculation is necessary:

$$\left(\frac{\text{cost p per kg}}{1} \times \frac{100}{\text{dressing }\%} \right) = \text{carcase p per kg}$$

Example: a live pig costing 50p/kg and dressing out at 72%:

$$\left(\frac{50}{1} \times \frac{100}{72} \right) = 69{\cdot}44 \text{ p per kg (31}{\cdot}49 \text{ p per lb) carcase price}$$

With the object of eliminating the dressing out calculation, the method would be:

$$\left(\frac{\text{cost p per kg}}{1} \times \frac{\text{live weight kg}}{\text{carcase weight kg}} \right) = \text{Carcase p per kg}$$

Example: the pig's live weight is 54 kg, the carcase weight is 39 kg and the cost is 50 p per kg:

$$\left(\frac{50}{1} \times \frac{54}{39} \right) = 69{\cdot}23 \text{ p per kg (31}{\cdot}40 \text{ p per lb) carcase price}$$

SLAUGHTER RECORD

Pigs

Breed........ Sex........ Remarks.................... Date..............

Grade........Weight..................kg at......per kg

Transport, etc.

£ p

=

=

Cost at slaughterhouse =

Live weight at slaughter..............kg   Shrinkage............%

Carcase weight, hot..........lb   Carcase weight, cold............lb

Cold carcase weight percentage of live weight as purchased........%

Offal	Weight		% of live weight	Offal	Weight		% of live weight
	lb	oz			lb	oz	
Stomach content				Pluck			
Stomach empty				Melt			
Intestinal content				Caul fat			
Intestines empty				Mesenteric fat			
Trimmings, etc.				Miscellaneous			
Blood				Miscellaneous			
				Miscellaneous			
				Miscellaneous			
Total				Total			

£   p

Cost at slaughterhouse
Add slaughter and storage cost

Less value of offals

Net cost of carcase   Carcase cost per lb

14 Carcase quality

Carcase quality in the case of the pig is somewhat difficult to define, and the requirements of the various traders differ according to their class of trade and, to some extent, local preferences. The real pork butcher, dealing chiefly in pork, is usually prepared to accept a larger carcase than the butcher who also deals in beef and mutton. On Smithfield Market, where the latter predominate, there appears to be a maximum price for the pork carcase of 80 to 100 lb (35 to 45 kg), though the firms specializing in cuts reserve larger carcases for this purpose. The usual points considered by the average buyer when purchasing a carcase can be briefly summarized as follows.

(a) A long pig, as the loin is the most valuable portion of the carcase. In small pigs where the joints are retailed whole, usually with the bone in, the size of bone and the plumpness of the legs are not very important factors.

(b) The quantity of fat is important, as an excess will necessitate trimming, particularly from the most valuable part, the loin. The probable fatness is usually judged by inserting the fingers in the vent and feeling the quantity of fat laid down over the spine; by pressing the fingers or knuckles into the fat over the spinal processes, particularly over the shoulders; by grasping the hand to check the quantity of underlying muscle; and by the quantity of flare fat on the belly.

(c) The muscle is thought to be indicated by the quantity of muscle shown at the cut surface of the sternum, and a large kidney is considered as a good sign as it usually goes with a well-finished, well-muscled carcase.

(d) With a smaller carcase, age is not of great moment, but ribs pinkish in colour, and knuckle surfaces showing a bluish tinge, are preferred.

With the exception of the work carried out on New Zealand pork carcases, it would appear that bacon pigs have received most attention from the aspect of standardization. Considerable work has been done

226

on growth in pigs by Hammond and McMeekan, illustrating growth characteristics. Remarkable results were obtained by varying the method of feeding. It was, for example, found that fast growth up to 16 weeks followed by slow growth, controlled by feeding, produced a carcase at 200 lb (90 kg) live weight with a good development of frame and muscle, and, as during the latter period too much fat did not develop, the right proportion of fatness was obtained. On the other hand, in animals which had been restricted up to 16 weeks the early developing parts, bone and muscle, were stunted, and on increased feeding after 16 weeks a short, thick carcase with excessive back fat was obtained at the same live weight. These experiments show that for a pork carcase rapid growth from birth to slaughter will produce the best results, and that for a good bacon carcase the same growth rate should be followed up to about 16 weeks, and subsequently reduced to control the quantity of fat laid down. The worst type of pig, except from the American angle of lard production, is one in which early rapid growth is retarded, followed by heavy feeding and rapid growth.

Fig. 27* will illustrate the age growth changes in the composition of a carcase.

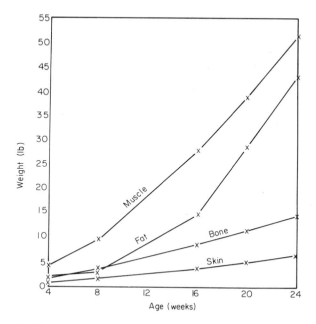

Fig. 27   Age changes in composition of pig carcase (Large White)

*Compiled from *Growth and Development in the Pig*, C. P. McMeekan.

Bone content

As the pig matures, the percentage of bone in the carcase decreases whilst the muscle increases and is eventually exceeded by the total fat. It has been stated* that the average thickness of the back fat in mm $\times 0.691 + 22.45$ will give the percentage of fat in the edible portion of the carcase. This should prove of value to the manufacturer, who is greatly concerned with the proportions of lean and fat in meats intended for sausage, etc. The quantity of bone loss with carcases from manufacturing pigs, under normal commercial conditions, is shown in Fig. 28.

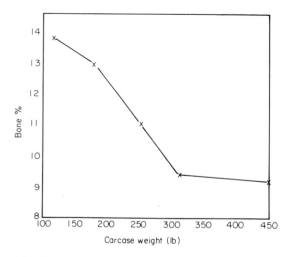

Fig. 28   Bone percentage in carcase of manufacturing pigs

Pork from young boars

At one time there was a marked prejudice against the use of boar meat' on account of the risk of alleged 'Boar Taint'.

The typical smell of the live boar, which arises from the preputial fluid, has now been isolated, but these substances are not present in the meat from boars. However, it has been recognized for many years that the salivary glands, when boiled in water, will give off a musty smell and recent work indicates that of the salivary glands it is the submaxillary only, which has a particular sexual function in stimulating the female whilst on heat.

Work carried out at the Meat Research Institute has proved that the

*Hammond.

prejudice against boar meat has no factual foundation in the case of boars raised rapidly to normal bacon or pork weight.

Consumer tests were also carried out using green bacon slices from 200 lb (90 kg) boars and gilts and anatomically identical pork joints from 200 lb (90 kg) boars and gilts.

'These results showed that overall the difference between the odour of cooked bacon or pork from 200 lb (90 kg) boars and gilts could not be significantly differentiated by cooks in their own kitchens or by consumers in the normal domestic situation even though their discriminatory facilities were probably heightened by the focusing effect of the questionnaire.'

When it is realized that such boars may produce as much as 30% higher yields of lean meat, per unit of feed, than hogs and that it is more expensive to produce animal fat than lean, coupled with the time/labour saved in castration, it is difficult to understand why these prejudices should persist.

Only slight modifications are necessary in the dressing procedure to remove the genital organs, as compared with the dressing of castrates.

In general, as compared with hogs and gilts, young boar pigs usually possess a high degree of muscle development, little if any excessive fat, well-developed legs and relatively light bellies.

The following figures were obtained from a Landrace boar of 135 lb (61 kg) live weight, a carcase weight of 93 lb (42 kg), giving a killing-out percentage of 69% at approximately 16 weeks.

Landrace Boar

	% cold carcase weight
2 legs	25·9
2 loins	26·0
Neck ends	14·8
Hand and spring	11·1
Belly	14·0
Head	7·6
Loss	0·6
	100%

MLC pig carcase classification

The purpose of pig classification is to identify carcases with common characteristics, such as weight and fat thickness. The scheme is based on the following five factors:

1. COLD CARCASE WEIGHT.

2. BACKFAT THICKNESS.

3. VISUAL ASSESSMENT. Applied to certain carcases: scraggy, deformed, blemished, pigmented, coarse skinned, soft fat, pale muscle, partially condemned. These are classed as Z.

4. LENGTH at the option of the trader.

5. CONFORMATION. At the option of the trader; carcases with poor conformation (particularly of the leg, but not poor enough to be scraggy) are classed as 'C'.

Measuring and Marking

There are two main methods of measuring backfat and marking carcases:

METHOD 1. Is used mainly by the pork, cutter and heavy pig trades. Backfat measurements are taken in millimetres with an optical probe (intrascope) at two fixed points over the loin—$4\frac{1}{2}$ cm (P_1) and 8 cm (P_3) from the midline of the back at the last rib. The measurements are added together to describe the degree of fatness, and recorded in a triangle on the trotter (Fig. 29, left).

METHOD 2. Is used for bacon pigs. A probe measurement of backfat thickness is taken at $6\frac{1}{2}$ cm (P_2) from the midline of the back at the last rib. And this measurement, together with measurements of visible back-fat at the shoulder and loin, indicates the degree of fatness. The probe measurement is marked in a triangle on the belly or the foreleg (Fig. 29, right).

METHOD 2a. Sometimes used for checking unsplit pigs, consists of Method 2 without loin and shoulder measurements.

With 'Z' or 'C' class carcases, the letter Z or C is marked outside the triangle and, at the trader's option, the cold carcase weight is also indicated.

Fig. 29 Examples of measurement markings on pig carcases (MLC)

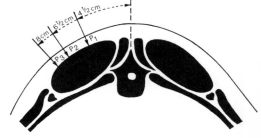

Fig. 30 Position of measurements taken with an optical probe at the level of the head of the last rib for MLC pig carcase classification

TABLE 27

Test on Middle White pig (98 lb)

Excellent butcher's animal

	Weight lb oz		Approx. % of live weight
Blood	4	12	
Hooves and hair, estimated	1	8	
Thymus		3	
Heart		6	
Diaphragm		8	
Lungs and trachea	1	6	
Oesophagus		2	
Stomach, empty		15	
Intestines, empty	4	4	
Caul fat		2	
Mesenteric fat		14	
Fat trimmings		8	
Liver	1	14	
Gall bladder		1	
Spleen		3	
Bladder, etc.		6	lb oz
Total viscera	——		18 0	18·4
Stomach and intestinal content	6	0	6 0	6·2
Carcase, hot	73	0		
Carcase, cold	72	0	72 0	73·4
Loss			2 0	2·0
			98 0	100%

TABLE 28

Test on Large White pig (200 lb)

Fair average quality

	Weight lb oz		Approx. % of live weight
Blood	6	0	
Hooves and hair	1	4	
Thymus		5	
Diaphragm		14	

TABLE 28 *continued*

	Weight lb oz		Approx. % of live weight
Heart		9	
Lungs and trachea	1	7	
Oesophagus		2	
Stomach, empty	1	1	
Intestines, small ⎱ Intestines, large ⎰	5	8	
Caul		5	
Mesentery	2	5	
Liver	4	12	
Gall bladder		1½	
Spleen		3½	
Pancreas		4¼	
Kidneys		13	
Leaf and kidney fat	3	6	
Bladder, etc.		4½	
Total viscera	29	8¾	14·75
Two sides and head	148	0	74·0
Head, ex tongue	13	12	
Tongue		12	
Fillets	1	8	
Bones	4	12	
Feet	3	0	
Trimmings, tail, rough fat	3	4	
Total	27	0	13·5
Two sides prepared	121	0	60·5
Two sides cured			
14 days and drained	116	0	58·0
Smoked 24 hours	108	0	54·0
One side			% of side
Gammon	13	4	24
Fore end	14	4	26
Streaky, whole	11	4	20·5
Back, whole	16	0	29·5
Total	54	12	100%

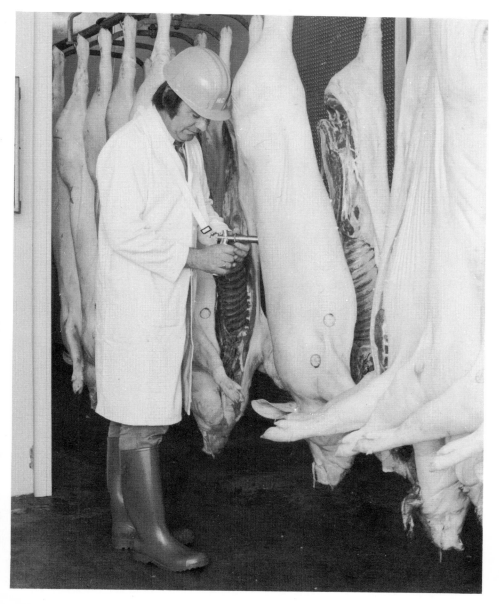

Plate 50   Measuring the fat depth over the eye muscle at the head of the last rib using an optical probe (*Meat & Livestock Commission*)

15 The bacon pig

At the present time, roughly 45% of our bacon consumption is produced within the British Isles. To compete with Danish supplies the emphasis has been on the production of a fairly lengthy, relatively lean side, with well-developed gammon and loin, not too much weight in the belly and a neat fore end.

To produce this type of carcase the Landrace or Landrace/Large White crosses and the Welsh have been found very suitable. The carcase weights in most demand run between 135 lb (61 kg) and 155 lb (70 kg) and under favourable conditions this carcase weight can be attained with good livestock at about 6 months.

Preparation of Wiltshire bacon

In order to obtain a good-quality cured side considerable control is necessary from pre-slaughter care through to maturing the pickled sides.

The following Code of Practice for the production of tank-cured Wiltshire bacon has been recommended by the British Bacon Curers' Federation.

SLAUGHTERING AND DRESSING

(1) *Transport and penning of pigs.*

(a) The vehicle in which pigs are transported to the slaughterhouse should be provided with a thick layer of absorbent straw and ventilated to ensure that the animals have an adequate supply of air. Pigs from different producers should, where possible, be penned separately in the vehicle and in the factory lairage. Sows and boars, if carried in addition to bacon pigs, must be penned separately in the vehicle.

(b) During loading, transporting, unloading, and penning, the pigs should be handled with care and should not be exposed to any treatment

Grading measurements of Clean Pigs from 130 lb to 170 lb Deadweight (1974)
(Courtesy of F.M.C.)

Grade	Weight	Length (minimum)	Backfat Shoulder/Loin (maximum)	'P2' Probe Measurement (maximum)
A1	135–160 lb*†	775 mm	42/22 mm	20 mm
B1	135–160 lb*† or	775 mm —	45/25 mm 42/22 mm	22 mm 20 mm
2	135–160 lb* or or 166–170 lb	775 mm 775 mm — 775 mm	48/28 mm 45/25 mm 45/25 mm 45/25 mm	22 mm 24 mm 22 mm 22 mm
C	135–170 lb	Other pigs not falling in the above grades		

*Pigs with grade A1, B1 or 2 measurements weighing between 161 lb and 165 lb inclusive will be paid for at the amount payable for a pig weighing 161 lb at the grade A1, B1 or 2 price as the case may be.

†Pigs with grade A1 or B1 measurements weighing between 130 lb and 134 lb inclusive will be paid for at the amount payable for a pig weighing 130 lb at the grade A1 or B1 price as the case may be.

In the case of pigs graded with 'skin-off', the backfat and 'P2' probe measurements will be 5 mm less than the above.

The 'P2' probe measurement will be taken at the last rib 6½ cm from the centre-line of the carcase and will be taken on the day of slaughter except in the case of pigs graded with 'skin-off' when such measurement will be taken not later than the day following the day of slaughter.

The loin measurement will relate to the thickness of fat over the top of the rump muscle.

The shoulder measurement will relate to the thickness of fat on the shoulder at the fattest part.

The length measurement shall be taken from the indentation of the first rib to the anterior edge of the aitch bone.

The above measurements (other than that for weight) shall apply whether the carcase is hot or cold.

TABLE 29

Influence of plane nutrition on carcase composition of Large Whites
(at approximately 200 lb (90 kg) live weight)

Nutrition	Age (days)	Carcase (lb)	Percentage of carcase (less kidneys and head)					
			Bone	Muscle	Total fat	Skin	Tendons, etc.	Loss
H.H.	159	143	10·7	38·6	39·5	5·2	3·2	2·3
H.L.	211	146	10·9	41·5	38·1	4·9	3·6	1·1
L.H.	203	147	8·9	33·9	48·2	4·4	3·0	1·6
L.L.	317	143	12·2	48·9	28·4	5·4	4·1	1·0

The above are average figures compiled from the work of C. P. McMeekan at Cambridge.

The pigs were fed at a high protein level:

H.H. pigs were fed at a high level of nutrition throughout their life.

H.L. pigs were fed on a high plane of nutrition until the age of 16 weeks, when they changed over to a low level of feeding.

L.H. pigs were fed at a low plane for 16 weeks followed by a high plane.

L.L. pigs were maintained at a low level of nutrition throughout.

likely to impair their quality. An unloading platform is recommended to lessen the steepness of the vehicle ramps.

(c) On arrival at the lairage pigs should be dealt with in accordance with the Slaughter of Animals (Prevention of Cruelty) Regulations No. 2166 of 1958. These require that wholesome drinking water must be available always, and that when pigs are kept beyond a specified number of hours they must also be fed. It is recommended that pigs should be slaughtered as soon as may be practicable after their arrival at the lairage. Pigs arriving from a farm situated within easy reach of the factory, which have not been fed on the day of their arrival, may be slaughtered on the same day. But pigs which have been transported some considerable distance should be rested overnight before they are slaughtered. To avoid shrinkage, pigs should never be detained unnecessarily at factories before slaughter.

(2) *Slaughtering.* Pigs must be anaesthetized as required by law. It is recommended that an electrolethaler, used at approximately 80 V, or CO_2 gas, should be employed.

(3) *Shackling.* The pig should be shackled on the leg nearest the hoist and always on the foot.

(4) *Sticking.* The knife should be inserted at the bottom of the neck and the operation completed by severing the carotid artery. The jugular vein also is sometimes severed but, if this is done, care must be taken *not* to over-stick the pig, as this will cause damage to the carcase. Care should be taken when withdrawing the knife to ensure the minimum damage to the carcase. The carcase must be left on the bleeding-rail and allowed to bleed until it is completely drained of blood.

(5) *Scalding.* The temperature of the water in the scalding tank should not exceed 140°F (60°C), and thermostatic control is desirable. Better results can be obtained if the temperature of the water is kept below this and if the carcase is allowed to remain in the water for a correspondingly longer period. The scalding tank should be long enough for a lower temperature to be effective. The carcase must be completely immersed in the hot water to ensure that all bristles can be steadily removed by the roots.

(6) *De-hairing.* After de-hairing, where done by machine or by hand-scraper, the carcase should be completely devoid of hair. The carcase should be hung by the hind legs on a gambrel and hoisted to the bar ready for singeing.

(7) *Singeing.* All carcases for Wiltshire bacon should be so singed that any hairs which may remain after de-hairing, and all wrinkles, are removed from the skin, and the skin is drawn taut by the heat to make it stand up more easily to the knife of the slicing machine. It is essential that all the black on the carcase should be removed, either by machine

or by hand scraping, and adequate water sprays should be available. Particular attention should be given to the forehocks.

Note. The processes set out in Sections (8)–(11) must be carried out, but not necessarily in the order stated.

(8) *Opening.* This must be done straight down the centre of the carcase, with the cut carried from the centre of the aitch bone down the centre of the breast bone to the sticking-hole. The aitch bone is now cut through, care being taken not to cut the fat end. The breast bone must be cut through with a strong knife or removed in such a way as to leave the two sides identical, care being taken not to damage the pluck or other offal. The meat is then trimmed back from the bone to the carcase.

(9) *Eviscerating.* This operation must be carried out without cutting the ribs or damaging the carcase in any way. When the fat end is dropped, care must be taken to ensure that it is not cut and is left with as small a crown as practicable.

(10) *Marking down.* The carcase must be carefully marked down over the top of the backbone and then on both sides of it, leaving as little meat on the bone as possible. Back finning is recommended.

(11) *Splitting.* The carcase must be split and the backbone removed, care being taken not to cut through the back muscle of the carcase. The backbone remains with the carcase for weighing. The carcase is now ready for weighing, grading, and final veterinary examination. It is recommended that the removable offal, i.e. fleck or flare (peritoneal fat), skirt, and kidney be removed while the carcase is warm. The inside of the carcase should be thoroughly washed with a high pressure water spray to clear blood from the ribs and neck. A revolving brush with spray attachment may be used to clean the neck of blood and the inside of the carcase of fragments of flare fat. Where the backbone has been sawn out, special care must be taken to ensure the removal of all bone and meat particles. The carcase should then be put into the chill. The fillet is removed after the carcase has been chilled.

(12) *Jowl crook.* It is permissible for a small jowl crook to be attached from the front foot to the head or jowl to set the forehock in a line with the neck of the carcase in order to improve the appearance of the fore end.

CHILLING AND BUTCHERING

(13) *Chilling.* Carcases must be put into chill and chilled as quickly as possible as an aid to keeping surface contamination to a minimum and to get them into a firm condition ready for trimming. The temperature of the chill room should be sufficiently low to ensure that the tempera-

ture of the carcases is reduced to 38–40°F (3–4°C). Carcases should be spaced in the chill room to ensure that no two sides touch at any point in a way that would interfere with adequate cooling.

(14) *Cutting and trimming.* Before curing, sides of bacon should be trimmed as follows.

(a) Loin and ham: The aitch bone must be sawn through so that the whole of its crest is removed. It must be sawn level so that the remaining part of the bone does not protrude beyond the cushion of the gammon. The oyster bone must be sawn through so that the part remaining is flush with the surrounding meat and that meat is undamaged. The chain bone must be removed, with the saw held at the correct angle, to avoid damaging the loin muscle by cutting into the back. Care must be taken to avoid leaving too much chain bone on the carcase. The 'buttons' which remain should not touch each other. The remaining part of the tail bone must be cut away, care being taken not to gouge out the meat with it. The mirror (the retractor ani muscle) must be scraped clean and must not be damaged. Any blood spots or stained tissue remaining and any loose sinews in the abdominal cavity must also be removed. Soft fat remaining after removal of the fat end and excess fat must be trimmed to leave a neat, even surface.

(b) Neck: The neck must be cut in a straight line to leave an even and unbroken cut surface on the fore end.

(c) Shoulder: The neck bone is removed by cutting round it with the point of the knife, lifting it as far as the first rib and severing it at the joint. The shoulder blade, glands, blood clots, and the discoloured fat at the stick-hole must be trimmed or removed. The incision to remove the blade bone should be made with the knife at an angle, rather than upright, so that a flap of meat is left over the pocket-hole. The incision must be as small as possible, preferably less than three inches long and the blade bone must be removed clean of meat and without damage to the surrounding flesh. Discoloured skin and fat around the stick-hole and exposed glands, tattered flesh and blood clots must be neatly trimmed.

(d) Belly: Where necessary, protruding fat on the belly edge must be removed and the belly edges of all hog pigs must be trimmed to an even line. All nipples must be removed.

(e) Feet: The fore foot must be cut off at the upper of the two joints. The hind foot must be sawn off through the middle of the heel bone.

(f) Finish: Fragments of flare fat, loose tatters of meat and the remains of the diaphragm must be neatly removed. The membrane on and between the ribs must remain intact.

(15) *Weight of trimmed sides.* The weight of the trimmed sides prior to curing should not on average exceed 78·5% of the original carcase

weight. An average figure of 78·5%, consistent with good butchering, is possible with a very high average quality of pigs, but for the normal run of pigs a lower figure may be found necessary. If the general level of quality shows marked improvements it will be possible to raise the figure.

PUMPING AND CURING

(16) *Tank curing*. Because sides vary the brine injections should also vary, from 23 to 32 injections per side, according to weight. They should be made at a minimum pressure of 80 lb (36 kg) into the thicker muscles. Only sufficient brine to cure the side adequately should be injected. An excessive quantity would make the bacon too salty and too wet. Only fresh brine should be injected and it must be composed as follows.

(a) A saturated (or almost saturated) solution with a salt content of 30–31% w/v sodium chloride, which is equivalent to 41–41·5° on the Twaddell Hydrometer Scale at 41°F (5°C).

(b) Saltpetre 3% w/v (potassium nitrate).

(c) Sodium nitrite, if added as such, 0·05% w/v (i.e. 500 parts per million) as a maximum.

The injection brine prepared as above should read 44–45° on the Twaddell Hydrometer Scale at 41°F (5°C).

(17) *Shoulder pockets*. The shoulder pockets must be stuffed with $3\frac{1}{2}$ to 5 oz (100 to 140 g) of salt, the quantity varying according to the size of pig and season of the year. To be effective, this salt must reach the extremities of the pockets. The addition of a small percentage of saltpetre to the salt used in the shoulder pocket is permitted subject to thorough mixing of the saltpetre with the salt prior to use.

(18) *Stacking of sides in brine*.

(a) The whole side may be washed over with a soft brush dipped in pickle.

(b) The sides should then be stacked in the tank, cut face upwards, and sprinkled lightly with salt/saltpetre mixture sufficient to compensate for the amount taken up by the sides, so that the strength of the brine remains reasonably constant.

(c) When the tank is full it should be battened down sufficiently firmly to keep the sides submerged, but not so tightly as to prevent the free access of brine between each two contiguous sides. Sufficient immersion pickle should be added to cover all the sides.

(d) The constituents of the cover brine are to some extent controlled by the temperature of the curing room. The composition of the cover brine for curing at temperatures between 40–42°F (4·5–5·5°C) should be maintained within the following figure ranges:

salt 24–26% w/v
saltpetre 0·2–1·5% w/v
sodium nitrite 0·03–0·1% w/v

If the temperature of the curing room can be maintained at 38–40°F (3·5–4·5°C) the salt content may be raised to 27% w/v (or even slightly above this figure). Although in some factories the layout of the cellars may make it difficult, particularly in summer, to ensure that the temperature does not at any time rise above 40°F (4°C) (which may involve some risk of producing slightly salty bacon) this practice nevertheless has the merits of checking nitrite development and of virtually eliminating any possibility of the bacon being wet.

(e) The sides should remain in this brine for not less than 96 hours and not more than 120 hours.

(f) The sides when removed should be stacked, rind upwards and not more than eight high, for maturing at an even temperature for at least *seven* days before despatch. If the bacon is to be stoved, a minimum of 12 days is essential. The temperature chosen for this purpose should lie between 40 and 44°F (4·5 and 6·5°C).

(19) *Treatment of brine*.

(a) All brine must be strained, the scum and any sediment removed.

(b) The salt concentration and saltpetre content of the immersion brine may be controlled by adjustment of the amount of salt *or* salt/saltpetre mixture employed in sprinkling the sides, or by addition of the required amount of salt and saltpetre to the brine in a storage tank fitted with a suitable mixing device. Any sodium nitrite required should be added by the latter method and always as a solution of the calculated quantity of sodium nitrite in water or in some of the brine.

(c) In addition to complying with the provisions of paragraph (19) (b) tests of the brine should be carried out by a qualified analytical chemist at intervals of not more than one month. (This service is provided by the Food Manufacturing Industries' Research Association.)

The weight of each cured side should be not less than 50 lb (23 kg) and not more than 65 lb (30 kg). When sides are packed in bales they should be all of approximately the same weight, and the maximum variation within a bale should not exceed 5 lb (2·3 kg).

Analysis of elite and accredited carcases

For purposes of comparison, the figures shown in Table 30 have been abstracted from the extensive tests carried out by the Meat and Livestock Commission on elite and accredited herds (1968–9).

Obviously the figures do not represent the results which would normally be obtained under average commercial conditions, but they do provide a standard against which other carcases may be judged.

The heavy hog

In contrast with the baconer carcase of about 150 lb (68 kg), there is considerable interest in the 'heavy hog' of about 200 lb (90 kg) carcase weight or over, particularly by the larger organizations dealing with pre-packing and the preparation of sausage and other meat products.

The thinking behind this type of production is to spread the high initial costs over a heavier carcase weight. High-protein feeding, much of which goes into bone and offal, is required for a larger proportion of the shorter life of the lighter pig.

TABLE 30

Test on pigs from elite and accredited herds

	Large White		Landrace		Welsh	
Age at start (days)	84·2		82·4		82·0	
Days on test	87·9		90·2		92·9	
Food conversion	2·84		2·97		3·06	
	Hogs	Gilts	Hogs	Gilts	Hogs	Gilts
Daily gain (lb)	1·61	1·59	1·57	1·55	1·52	1·50
Cold carcase (lb)	155	156	155	155	156	156
Killing out (%)	77·6	78·0	77·6	77·7	78·2	78·4
Length (mm)	812	819	816	823	814	819
Depth (mm)	317	318	312	311	315	313
Shoulder fat (mm)	45·3	41·8	42·3	39·4	45·9	42·1
Midback fat (mm)	22·0	18·0	21·7	18·3	23·1	19·3
Loin fat (mm)	24·8	20·7	23·5	20·4	25·8	22·7
'C' (mm)	19·9	15·2	21·3	16·4	24·0	17·7
'K' (mm)	26·4	19·8	26·2	19·9	29·1	21·5
Eye muscle area (sq cm)	28·6	32·5	29·2	32·7	29·3	33·1
Eye muscle width (mm)	77·8	83·0	80·8	86·1	80·3	85·2
Eye muscle depth (mm)	51·4	55·4	51·2	54·1	51·8	55·7
Trim						
Head weight (lb)	13·1	13·2	11·9	12·0	12·1	12·2
Chine weight (lb)	3·4	3·5	3·4	3·5	3·1	3·2
Flare weight (lb)	1·5	1·2	2·0	1·6	2·1	1·7
Fillet weight (lb)	0·83	0·91	0·72	0·86	0·79	0·86
Kidney weight (lb)	0·29	0·30	0·32	0·33	0·31	0·32
Trimmed yield (%)	82·9	83·1	83·3	83·5	83·6	83·7

Loin fat is the minimum over the rump muscle.
Shoulder fat, maximum depth in the region of the shoulder.
'C' and 'K' are fat measurements taken at standardized points from the cut surface of the back rasher.

The heavier carcase will usually have a greater weight of lean meat, but it will also have more fat. The latter may not prove to be a serious problem to the food processor, as, for example, up to 45% of the meat content of a pork sausage may be fat.

TABLE 31

Test on Large White × Saddleback pig (316 lb (143 kg))

	Weight lb oz		Approx. % of live weight
Blood	9	0	
Hooves and hair, estimated	2	8	
Heart		14	
Diaphragm		8	
Lungs, trachea, and oesophagus	3	11	
Stomach, empty	3	2	
Intestines, empty			
Large	4	3	
Small	3	14	
Caul fat	1	4	
Mesenteric fat	2	8	
Liver	5	0	
Gall bladder		1	
Spleen		7	
Bladder, etc.	1	2	lb oz
Total viscera			38 2 12·0
Stomach and intestinal content	12	0	12 0 3·8
Carcase, hot	269	8	
Carcase, cold	262	0	262 0 83·0
Loss			3 14 1·2
			316 0 100%

In the case of pre-packed bacon, the larger area of 'eye' muscle forms an attractive rasher and in addition it is probable that the flesh from the larger carcase will possess a more mature, full flavour.

Work carried out by Unilevers indicated that with suitable feeding during the fattening stage, the production of lean meat was most economical within the live weight range of 240 lb to 260 lb (109 kg to 118 kg). It was estimated that the difference in the production cost of

EEC Pig Carcase Classification Scheme

Commercial Grade	Subgrade	Carcase Weight		Maximum Backfat Thickness (mm)	Description	Required Meat Content (%)
		kg	lb			
E Extra	E AA	35– 49·9 50– 59·9 60– 69·9 70– 79·9 80– 89·9 90– 99·9 100–119·9 120–139·9 140–159·9 160 and over	77–109 110–131 132–153 154–175 176–197 198–219 220–263 264–308 309–352 353 and over	12 15 15 20 25 30 35 45 50 55	Showing exceptional muscular development in all principal parts of the carcase	55 or more
I Very good proportion of meat	I A	35– 49·9 50– 59·9 60– 69·9 70– 79·9 80– 89·9 90– 99·9 100–119·9 120–139·9 140–159·9 160 and over	77–109 110–131 132–153 154–175 176–197 198–219 220–263 264–308 309–352 353 and over	15 18 20 25 30 35 40 50 55 60	Showing very good muscular development in all principal parts of the carcase	50 or more
II Good proportion of meat	II A	35– 49·9 50– 59·9 60– 69·9 70– 79·9 80– 89·9 90– 99·9 100–119·9 120–139·9 140–159·9 160 and over	77–109 110–131 132–153 154–175 176–197 198–219 220–263 264–308 309–352 353 and over	19 22 25 30 35 40 45 55 65 70	Showing good muscular development in all principal parts of the carcase	45 or more
	I B	Weight of carcase and thickness of backfat as for I but defective in one principal part of the carcase				
III Average proportion of meat	III A	35– 49·9 50– 59·9 60– 69·9 70– 79·9 80– 89·9 90– 99·9 100–119·9 120–139·9 140–159·9 160 and over	77–109 110–131 132–153 154–175 176–197 198–219 220–263 264–308 309–352 353 and over	24 27 30 35 40 45 50 60 70 75	Showing average muscular development in all principal parts of the carcase	40 or more
	II B	Weight of carcase and thickness of backfat as for II but defective in one principal part of the carcase				
	I C	Weight of carcase and thickness of backfat as for I but defective in two principal parts of the carcase				
IV		All carcases not falling within the above grades				
S	1	Sow carcases with a very good proportion of meat				
	2	Other sow carcases				
V		Boar carcases				

one pound of lean meat from a 140 lb (63 kg) live weight pig and one of 260 lb (118 kg) was at that time 2·7 old pence per lb.

It was found that an increase in live weight resulted in an increased killing-out percentage, greater eye muscle area, and a higher percentage of meat and fat in the carcase, whilst the percentages of lean, kidney, bones, and head decreased. In terms of carcase conformation, the proportion of middle increased, with a consequent decrease of the other portions of the carcase.

16   Preservation of meat

Principles

The principles underlying the normal commercial methods of preserving meat usually involve one or more of the following factors.

TEMPERATURE

By placing the meat in a temperature range unsuitable for the development of putrefactive bacteria. In the case of frozen meat their growth is inhibited, and even at chilling temperatures (28 to 30°F, or −2 to −1°C) their rate of growth is retarded, to extend considerably the commercial life of the product. At the other end of the scale, efficient sterilization, as in the case of canning, aims at the destruction of such germs by the application of heat.

ABSENCE OR REDUCTION OF MOISTURE

Drying is probably one of the oldest methods of preservation, Biltong, Pemmican, and Jerked beef being modern variations of this practice, The latest application of this principle is the minced, dehydrated meat, which was developed with the war-time object of saving shipping space. Lean, fresh meat contains about three-quarters water and one-quarter solids, and on this basis, lean meat *completely* dried would contain over 85% of protein. With this lean dried meat any proportion of fat can be incorporated. Expressed as the equivalent of *fresh edible meat*, allowing for wrapping and containers, dried meat occupies 20 cubic feet (0·56 m³/kg) to the ton, whereas similarly expressed, frozen carcase meat requires over six times this volume. Meat powders have been recommended for many years by the medical profession on account of their digestibility and ease of administration. Meat extracts might also be considered under this heading, as they usually contain between 20% and 40% of water.

There is of course a great similarity between freezing and drying, as in the latter case the moisture is removed, whilst with freezing its state is changed so that it is unavailable to the organisms. Dry-salting depends upon this shrinkage or loss of water, whilst the curing ingredients also exert a certain chemical preservative effect. Even in the course of pickle-curing a similar principle holds good, as the osmotic interchanges between the organism and the medium is interfered with.

A modern method of dehydrating meat is the A.F.D (accelerated freeze-drying) process whereby the frozen meat is lightly heated under vacuum. The heat supplied provides the energy for sublimation of the ice to water vapour, without raising the temperature of the product to a level which would result in the thawing of the product.

The rapid sublimation of moisture produces a cooling effect sufficient to prevent thawing. Meat so treated is very porous in structure and is simple to rehydrate. The inclusion of salt and sodium pyrophosphate in the water used for rehydration is considered to improve the texture, whilst the use of enzymes in the solution to tenderize tough portions of meat has received attention.

One problem with such products is the development of rancidity in the fat, especially in the case of pork. This can be retarded by the use of suitable anti-oxidants.

Using a suitable nitrogen pack it has been found that A.F.D. raw beef has a shelf life of many months at relatively high temperatures.

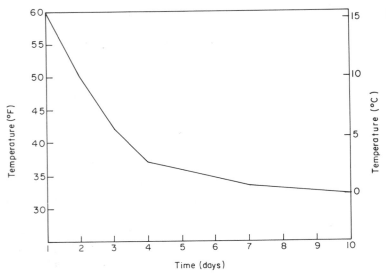

Fig. 31   Temperature against time for bacterial slime to develop on meat surfaces exposed under moist conditions. (After Haines and Smith)

CHEMICAL PRESERVATIVES

Apart from the curing ingredients already mentioned, and certain flavouring substances, the only chemical preservative permitted by law in this country is sulphur dioxide, and this is allowed only in the case of sausage meats. The 'Linley process' for the storage of beef consisted of sterilization by means of formaldehyde vapour followed by wrapping in sterilized cotton covers. This vapour was also introduced into the hold of the vessel and the temperature maintained at just below the freezing-point of water. This process was very successful in retarding the growth of moulds and bacteria. Formaldehyde was found to be present in the meat, and in one case 463 imported quarters were condemned. CO_2 slows down the growth of micro-organisms, and its use in the transport of chilled beef has resulted in bringing Australia and New Zealand within the chilling range.

Ultra-violet rays have been used for the surface sterilization of meat, but suitable filters must be incorporated in the lamps, to block the wave-band which will produce ozone and result in oxidation of fat. Ozone also acts as a deodorizer, but here again the fat is affected, and even with very low concentrations the flavour of fat so treated is markedly unpleasant.

Commercial application

COLD STORAGE ROOMS

The temperature at which the average butcher's cold store is held is usually between 32 and 38°F (0 and 3°C), though in the case of cooked meats and sausage a somewhat higher temperature is frequently required. The preservative effect is more marked at the lower temperature range, so that a decrease in temperature near the freezing-point will make a much greater increase in the storage life than a similar decrease higher up the scale. Bacteria on meat can broadly be considered under two divisions, those having an optimum growth temperature at about blood heat, and the remainder which prefer a temperature of about 70°F (21°C). The former will cease to grow at about 40°F (4°C), whilst the latter can still grow at about 27°F (-3°C). Moulds can grow at much lower temperatures, say down to about 20°F (-6.7°C).

With ordinary retail storage a certain amount of 'sweating' is unavoidable during the summer months, as the dew-point in England during June to September is over 45°F (7°C). A small degree of sweating will not seriously affect the appearance of fresh meat, but if continued it will result in the loss of bloom as the collagen fibres absorb the moisture and, swelling, give an opaque appearance. The degree of sweating can be reduced by gradually increasing the storage temperature before bringing the meat into the atmosphere.

To prevent spoilage the following recommendations should be followed.

(1) Meat should be handled as little as possible.

(2) As far as practicable, place the meat in the refrigerator, immediately following receipt.

(3) Destroy all trimmings which show obvious growths of moulds or bacterial slime. After touching such meat, wash hands and immediately sterilize, in boiling water, knives and tools used in trimming.

(4) Avoid cutting into portions meat which can be stored equally well in the form of carcases or quarters.

(5) Open the refrigerator door as infrequently as possible and for as short a time as possible.

(6) Do not overload the cold room beyond the capacity recommended by the makers.

(7) Cleanse the chamber periodically, and as soon as possible after finding spoiled meat which has been stored in it.

(8) Maintain the desired level of temperature, with a minimum of fluctuation.

CHILLING

In theory, chilling consists of the rapid reduction in temperature of the meat to a point just above its freezing-point. A temperature of about $29.4°F$ ($-1°C$) is considered ideal, but under practical conditions a slightly lower temperature is sometimes employed. In fact, there is no line of demarcation between chilling and light freezing. During this storage the meat undergoes a maturing process similar to that advocated in the case of English meat, though the lower temperature probably slows down the rate of these changes. Transport from the Argentine takes about three weeks and, allowing an additional period of about a week for slaughter and marketing, chilled beef was usually retailed in this country within about four or five weeks of slaughter. This fact gave the South American trade a big initial advantage over Australia and New Zealand. It has, however, been found that mould growth is inhibited by high concentrations of carbon dioxide. By using carbon dioxide it is possible to extend the commercial life of chilled beef to about 60 days, provided that the initial contamination of bacteria is relatively light. During chilling very little damage is done to the muscle fibres, and when thoroughly dried out its appearance is very similar to that of the fresh product. As a general rule the commercial life of chilled beef depends to a great extent on the resistance of the fat to chemical breakdown. The practical man will appreciate that, if trimming does become necessary, it is the fat that usually requires attention first.

FREEZING

As already mentioned, the grading seriously affects the initial quality of frozen beef, and experiments carried out on prime English beef by the Food Investigation Board demonstrated that freezing at various temperatures had very little effect on the tenderness, flavour, and palatability of the flesh.

With quarters of beef, freezing must of necessity be a somewhat slow process, and in well-fatted quarters the outer layer of fat is a poor conductor for the passage of animal heat to the cooling medium. With this low freezing a big proportion of the water passes through the fine membrane surrounding the muscles, to freeze between the muscle fibres. This has the effect of shrinking and distorting the muscle fibres, and on microscopic examination these tiny fibres will be seen surrounded by areas containing ice, and the membrane may be damaged. On defrosting, some of this water is not re-absorbed and consequently 'drip' occurs, particularly from a cut surface. This drip consists of water together with certain salts, proteins, some flavouring matter and the damaged blood-cells. There is a zone of maximum ice formation between about 25 and 31°F (-4 and -0.5°C). Therefore, if a long period is spent in passing through this temperature range, large crystals will form between the muscle fibres, and should the meat be stored within this range the crystals increase in size. The superiority of frozen lamb as compared with frozen beef is most probably associated with the rapid reduction of temperature.

At one time freezing chambers were held at about 10 to 14°F (-12 to -10°C), but most modern stores tend to maintain temperature levels of 0°F (-18°C). If mammalian muscle is frozen very rapidly and subsequently stored at a low temperature, the small ice crystals tend to remain within the muscle substance and the water does not separate to between the muscle fibres. Muscle so treated will not. on being thawed, drip to any extent. It is usually assumed that the quantity of drip is a direct indication of the damage brought about by the freezing process.

Air blast chambers or tunnels are normally designed for their specific duty. Basically they consist of an insulated structure containing banks of direct expansion coils and fans, capable of producing a brisk circulation of air over the product. Operating temperatures may usually run from -20 to -40°F (-29 to -40°C).

Rapid freezing by using liquid nitrogen is a relatively new development and it provides very low temperatures. With the gas/liquid refrigerant in direct contact with the product fast rates of heat transfer are possible. For certain foods this system gives better results than conventional mechanical refrigeration methods.

Experiments have also shown that immersion in a special form of Freon 12 at $-22°F$ ($-30°C$) gives results comparable with those obtained with nitrogen at $-238°F$ ($-150°C$). Although this special Freon 12 acceptable for use in direct contact with foods is expensive, it can be reliquified after use, by the normal mechanical refrigeration plant. Whilst it is a relatively easy matter to freeze small cuts in a short period, Moulton has suggested that to freeze a hindquarter of beef 10 in (25 cm) thick in 30 min would require a temperature of $-400°F$ ($-240°C$).

DEFROSTING

In spite of popular opinion to the contrary, the rate of thawing under normal atmospheric conditions (UK) has little effect on the quality of the final product. When frozen meat is removed from a cold store it will tend to increase in weight, owing to absorption of moisture from the air. The degree of increase will depend upon humidity and temperature, but in the case of hinds an increase in weight of 0.5% is not uncommon.

Various methods of thawing have been evolved, aiming at both temperature and humidity control as a means of reducing drip and improving appearance. A German method starts this process at a temperature of $32°F$ ($0°C$) with 70% humidity. The temperature is gradually increased to $50°F$ ($10°C$) and the humidity to about 90%. A hindquarter subjected to this process will require about 80 hours, and a forequarter about 65 hours for complete thawing. In the case of imported sheeps' livers, etc., these are frequently left in their cans, and their contact with the resulting exudate appears to improve their appearance.

A method of defrosting meat, which is used in Sweden, employs a defrosting chamber in which the desired temperature and humidity conditions are automatically controlled. Ultra-violet lamps of a suitable range of wavelength are fitted, and this results in a marked reduction in the bacterial count on the surface of the meat.

Warm air is circulated at a high velocity (4 to 5 metres/second) and an extremely high humidity is maintained. The appearance of the defrosted meat is very good whilst the weight loss is negligible, and in some cases a slight weight increase is obtained.

For normal retail purposes, it is suggested that frozen quarters of beef should be allowed to defrost *almost* completely, in their wrappers, at atmospheric temperatures, preferably in a good current of air. Following this the wrapper should be removed and the meat placed in the cold room at about 34°F (1°C) prior to cutting for retail sale. The practice of leaving wrappers on frozen meat will tend to collect atmospheric moisture which would otherwise settle on the surface of the meat and may absorb any exudate from the meat.

CURING

It is obviously beyond the scope of this book to discuss the various methods employed in the curing of meats, and there are many books dealing with this subject. Curing can be divided into two broad methods: (a) dry-curing, and (b) pickle-curing. The ingredients commonly used in all methods consist of (1) *common salt*, sodium chloride; (2) *saltpetre*, potassium nitrate (KNO_3), Chile saltpetre, sodium nitrate ($NaNO_3$), or in some cases nitrite may be employed.

Other substances such as various sugars, spices, vinegar, and even ale may be used for different types of cure, but in the quantities generally used it is doubtful whether the preservative effect exerted by them is very great, though it should be remembered that the essential oils in the spices do retard bacterial growth, and vinegar has a similar action. In the case of sugar, in addition to the improvement in flavour, it may be possible that its presence favours fermentation which adversely affects organisms which may cause spoilage. In the case of pickle-curing one must not overlook that important ingredient, the water. Though as a rule water is reasonably sterile, many practical men prefer to boil the water to destroy any stray organisms that may be present. It is of course well known that a freshly made brine does not function as well as a 'matured' one, and frequently a pig's head from an old brine may be introduced to give the new one an initial start, although the reason for so doing may be little understood. If salt alone were used, the cooked meat would have an unattractive dark colour. The characteristic pink colour of cooked cured meats is obtained by the presence of nitrite. Saltpetre is generally used and this is converted to nitrite by the action of bacteria.

The actual action appears to be: the bacteria change the nitrate in the brine into nitrite, and the nitrite and salt in solution penetrate the meat by diffusion. The nitrite coming into contact with the haemoglobin forms nitroso-haemoglobin, which is red in colour, and, on heating, yields a stable red compound. Thus the pig's head introduces the necessary bacteria to accelerate the change from nitrate to nitrite. As the concentration of salt is much greater than that of nitrite, the latter does not penetrate the meat as rapidly as the salt. In many countries the use of nitrite itself instead of nitrate is permitted, which provides a more accurate control. In this country added nitrite is now permitted in bacon, ham, or *cooked* pickled meat, and in the case of the latter the nitrite must not exceed 200 parts per million, calculated as sodium nitrite. With hams and ox tongues the arterial method of curing is frequently employed, the pickle being injected through the arteries; this system permits very accurate control of the curing ingredients introduced, and ensures an instantaneous distribution of the cure.

Work carried out at Cambridge by M. Ingram, J. R. Hawthorne, and D. P. Gatherum has added materially to our knowledge of the control of nitrite concentration in brines used for the curing of bacon. A number of factors were indicated as influencing the composition of the brine. Temperature, the amount of meat cured, the structure of the meat before curing, and the method of replenishing the brine all play an important part.

It was shown that as the pickling proceeds the salt concentration in the brine as a whole falls, and the nitrite concentration rises. At the bottom of the pickling tank the salt concentration is usually high and the concentration of nitrite low, whilst at the top the salt is low and the nitrite high.

These observations suggest that too little salt causes over production of nitrite, and too much causes nitrite to disappear. Thus it is necessary to maintain the balance very carefully.

In dry curing the meat juices are largely retained, but here temperature is very important as too low a temperature will slow up the cure, and thus give rise to trouble in the deep-seated portions, whereas too high a temperature may cause souring before the cure has had time to penetrate. Frequently a combination of the two methods is favoured, an injection of brine followed by dry curing. With the 'emulsion' method, used in sausage manufacture, the cure is chopped into the meat, and owing to the small size of the meat particles and the rapid distribution a very quick cure is obtained, whilst the meat juices are retained in the mix.

COOKING

This chapter would be incomplete unless we included cooking as a means of delaying putrefaction. It can be stated as a general rule that vegetable foods tend to become richer in water when cooked, and that animal foods become less watery. With meat, the majority of the shrinkage is due to loss of water and, to a less extent, the removal of fat. Beef when boiled will lose about 25% of its initial weight and when baked approximately 30%, and in this loss must be included a certain amount of extractives and salts. Here, then, we have sterilization by heat coupled with the extraction of some water. On an actual test with beef the percentage of water present before and after boiling was found to have decreased from 70·88% to 56·82%. It is possible that this shrinkage is influenced by the contraction of the connective tissues exerting a stress upon the other meat constituents.

OTHER METHODS OF PRESERVATION

There have been many attempts to produce substances which provide a surface protection for meat products, such as heavy gelatine glaze, usually incorporating glycerol and a chemical preservative, painting with various solutions that form a film at normal temperatures, and dipping in a metallic pectinate. Complete immersion in refined cotton-seed oil and coating with oat flour have been employed, particularly in the case of hams. A recent development is to place the meat in a plastic film container, to draw a vacuum and to heat-seal, so that the atmospheric pressure ensures a close contact between the meat and wrapper. Such a method reduces considerably the risk of contamination and prevents dehydration, thus obviating loss of weight.

The use of ionizing radiation for the preservation of foods in packages or even within cans is theoretically attractive and considerable scientific work has been carried out in this field. There are, however, a number of serious disadvantages and the use of high energy levels may induce radioactivity in certain elements of the meat. In addition, objectionable off flavours are produced if sterility is to be obtained. The most promising approach is probably that of light 'pasteurizing' doses of irradiation, combined with chilling, and such a technique might be applied to pre-packed portions of meat. Antibiotics have been employed to retard bacterial growth, either by surface application or intravenously. However, a consignment of chilled beef, surface treated and shipped to this country, had developed a profuse and extensive mould growth. Thus it would appear that the natural balance of bacterial:mould growth had been upset.

As Prof. Lawrie stated: 'Elimination of normal spoilage organisms, and thereby the unpleasant superficial symptoms of contamination, could conceivably permit the growth of dangerous bacteria whose toxic by-products would not be easily detectable before consumption of the meat.'

Post-mortem changes in meat

The following information was obtained from reports originally made by the Food Investigation Board of Department of Scientific and Industrial Research. This body carried out extensive and valuable work of great interest and practical use to the butcher.

The slaughterman-butcher would probably consider the changes taking place in a carcase in the following stages.

(a) The soft, flabby condition of the muscle and the oily condition of the fat immediately following slaughter.

(b) The 'setting' of the carcase, the muscle becoming stiff and hard, and the fat firm.

(c) 'Hanging', or conditioning, the meat again becoming soft, but not returning to its flabby condition. This latter fact probably being due to the setting of the fat.

(d) Rancidity in the fat and putrefaction in the lean meat.

RIGOR MORTIS

During the onset of rigor mortis there is an actual *rise* in temperature, the peak being reached in about 2 hours. As it rises and then falls to its normal body-heat, protection from bacterial contamination during this stage is extremely important.

Rigor mortis consists of (a) a hardening, stiffening, and shortening of the muscle, (b) loss of transparency, and (c) loss of elasticity. These three factors are easily observed; other changes such as the formation of lactic acid, loss of sensitivity, and the production of heat are also important but are not so obvious from superficial examination.

CHANGES FOLLOWING RIGOR MORTIS

The resolution of rigor is a relatively slow process and the important point is that the rate at which these changes take place is dependent on temperature. The higher the temperature the greater the rate, so that the butcher has considerable control over these changes by a choice of suitable storage conditions. Storage at below the freezing-point of meat almost entirely stops them.

The quantity and the type of fat laid down on and in a carcase will depend to a great extent on feed; therefore the resistance of fat to chemical breakdown is not entirely a question of storage conditions. Previous to death, fatty tissue consists of connective tissue containing fat cells, and these cells contain a drop of oil. After death, the reduction of temperature results in these cells solidifying, and the fat 'sets'. Rancidity can be caused by mould growth, bacteria, enzymes, and by oxidation with atmospheric oxygen, resulting in undesirable flavours and odour.

It would appear that in the case of chilled beef it is the fat rather than the lean meat which determines the commercial storage life.

COOLING

The rate of cooling (Fig. 32) will depend upon the temperature difference between the beef and the cold store, the depth of the flesh, and particularly the thickness of the fat on the surface, as fat is a very poor conductor of heat, and finally, the circulation of air and its humidity. Much of the cooling effect is obtained by evaporation from the surface of the meat; thus in a saturated atmosphere the cooling rate will be greatly reduced (roughly one-third of the total cooling effect, in reducing the temperature from 100 to 50°F (38 to 10°C), with a weight loss of 2%, is due to evaporation).

Extreme drying should, of course, be avoided, as it will result in excessive loss of weight and the appearance will suffer, particularly the cut surfaces. On the other hand, too humid an atmosphere will promote the growth of mould and bacteria. The weight loss during the first 24 hours from slaughter should not exceed 2% and can be reduced to 1·5%. The condition of the beef will affect this loss, a well-finished side losing less weight than a poor lean one. For normal storage a temperature of 32–36°F (0–2°C), with a relative humidity of 75–80%, is recommended for fresh beef.

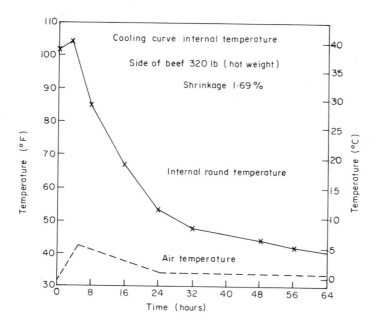

Fig. 32   Rate of cooling test for side of beef. The cooling curve is for the internal temperature. Side of beef weighs 320 lb (145 kg) (hot weight). Shrinkage is 1·69%

SWEATING

When beef is taken from a store the air surrounding it is cooled to the temperature of the beef, and should this temperature be below the dew-point, water will be condensed on the surface of the meat and 'sweating' will occur. With storage at about 40°F (4°C) sweating will occur during the summer months, as during this period the mean dew-point is usually higher than 45°F (7°C). A small degree of sweating may not affect the appearance of the beef very markedly; prolonged sweating will affect the typical bloom of a bright fresh carcase and its keeping qualities are reduced. This suggests that, where practicable, during the summer months the storage temperature should be raised above the dew-point prior to removing the meat from the store.

CONDITIONING MEAT

The modern consumer appears to be more concerned with the question of tenderness rather than flavour, yet in this country the technique of scientifically controlled conditioning has been somewhat neglected.

With the exception of some types of mutton, maturing is largely confined to beef. In a recent survey it was found that the period of maturing employed by retailers, varied from nil to a maximum of 3 weeks. In the USA matured (aged) beef from heavily fatted cattle may be held up to 6 weeks, although considerable trimming is necessary prior to retail sale (or deep-freezing). In some cases light rays may be used to assist in surface sterilization.

Increased tenderness can be obtained by hanging at a high temperature for a short time or at a lower temperature for a longer period. Thus the following will indicate the approximate temperatures and times in order to obtain a comparable degree of increase in tenderness.

32–36°F (0–2°C)	2–3 weeks
45°F (7°C)	5–6 days
55°F (13°C)	3–4 days
68°F (20°C)	2 days using ultra-violet light to prevent spoilage
110°F (43°C)	1 day using antibiotics

The 68 and 110°F (20 and 43°C) methods are not practised in the United Kingdom, but illustrate the progressive reduction of time, which temperature increase permits.

The specialist butcher dealing with physiologically mature cattle and catering for a high-class trade might favour the following method.

(1) Holding the dressed sides at 34–36°F (1–2°C) for 6 days, followed by

(2) Holding at 36–38°F (2–3°C) for 2 days, followed by

(3) Holding at 40–42°F (4–5°C) for 1 day prior to cutting and sale.

In some cases the coarse meats may be removed and sold and the steak meats and ribs, etc., matured. In this case the increased cut surfaces will result in greater percentage weight loss and some extra trimming may be involved.

With the increasing emphasis on younger cattle, shorter maturing periods may be found satisfactory. With sides from such cattle, rapid cooling following slaughter and holding at about 32°F (0°C) for about 6 days, followed by increasing the temperature slightly over the last 24 hours, will provide a good time margin for sales.

The cost of maturing, in terms of capital investment in stock, weight loss and possible trimming, needs careful consideration when pricing the final product. However, in certain types of retail trade and high-class restaurants where eating quality is a prime factor, cost may be considered as very much a secondary factor.

Many buyers are turning to beef which has been tenderized by pre-slaughter treatment (see p. 115) or by other methods, in order to obtain a tender product without the personal responsibility of maturing.

Ageing in Film

The restriction on the importation of bone-in beef from Argentina has resulted in the shipping of boneless chilled primal cuts in cryovac film. To ensure a satisfactory product which will stand up to fairly pro-longed marine transport and subsequent distribution in this country, the initial degree of contamination must be carefully controlled.

It is suggested that the sides of beef should be cooled to 50°F (10°C) within 24 hours of loading the chiller. Following thorough chilling, the period of cutting, packing in film and returning to the chiller, should not exceed 30 minutes.

A heat-shrinkable, gas-impermeable film is used and after the cut has been placed in the bag, it is evacuated, sealed and then heat-shrunk.

The meat and the bacteria in the bag release CO_2 which cannot escape and therefore accumulates. This restricts the growth of normal organisms which require oxygen for their growth and are retarded in the presence of CO_2. Other organisms which are resistant to CO_2 are capable of growing, but only develop very slowly. On meat which is stored too long, these resistant organisms give rise to 'souring' in place of the usual slime development of spoiled meat. The packed meat has an unattractive purple colour, whilst in the pack, but when the pack is opened, contact with atmospheric oxygen rapidly restores the charac-teristic red-pink meaty colour. The meat should be packed with any fatty surface uppermost in order to avoid blood staining of the fat.

It is important that an even temperature be maintained throughout, which in the case of Argentine beef is about 30°F (-1°C).

Owing to the prolonged maturing period such meat is tender and of course the amount of butchering involved in preparation for retail sale is reduced as compared with bone-in meat.

Meat spoilage

The practical man fully realizes that different species of food animals exhibit varying degrees of (to use an American term) durability.

Beef will generally have good keeping qualities, with mature bull beef high up the list, followed by mutton, veal, and pork in decreasing order. Bull beef can carry a relatively high bacterial count without deterioration as recognized organoleptically, whereas pork with a similar bacterial flora may show marked organoleptic changes.

At temperatures slightly above the freezing-point of meat, the meat will tend to retain its natural fresh appearance for a limited period, whilst freezing meat and holding it under suitable conditions of temperature and humidity will retard any serious deterioration taking place for periods of up to about 6 months for beef and lamb and somewhat less for pork.

After a period, depending on many factors, unfrozen meat first passes to a condition which has been described as 'souring'. This is characterized by a sour odour, dull appearance, and slightly sticky surface. Sourness may be considered as an early stage of putrefaction, but the condition does not of itself render the meat unfit for human consumption, and for practical purposes could be considered as being distinct from putrefaction proper.

The practice of 'ripening' salt legs of pork intended for hams is an example of using this characteristic to enhance a full 'hammy' flavour. However, the progress from souring to putrefaction is a continuous process so that determining the line of demarcation calls for considerable practical experience and both conditions may be present in different parts of the same carcase.

Putrefaction implies the bacterial decomposition of organic substances and putrefactive bacteria are widely spread and may be carried to the surface of the meat by infected tools, hands, dust, etc., during and subsequent to slaughter and dressing. Their growth is stimulated under moist conditions and relatively high temperatures.

Putrefaction is usually recognized by colour changes to a grey, yellow, or green, a softening of the tissues, an objectionable odour, chiefly due to the formation of ammonia and a resultant alkaline reaction.

Rancidity of the fat, particularly during prolonged storage, may be brought about by atmospheric oxidation and/or the action of micro-organisms which may give rise to hydrolysis. Resistance to such changes is influenced by the type of fat, which in turn can be affected by feed.

Off-odours or flavours in fat may be caused by the absorption of foreign odours during cold storage and occasionally by the type of feed consumed by the live animal.

Many efforts have been made to evolve chemical tests to demonstrate meat spoilage, but it is probable that at the present time none of these tests can completely replace the time-honoured method of judgment by the texture, taste, smell, and appearance of the meat.

pH MEASUREMENTS

pH is the unit employed for the numerical expression of acidity or alkalinity. The scale covers a range from 0 to 14, chemically pure water (neutral) being 7. Below this figure is acid and above it is alkaline.

In the meat trade generally, the pH value most frequently encountered will tend to lie between 5 and 6.

The value of pH measurements to the meat industry covers a wide field, including assessment of the condition of the carcase, potential keeping qualities and the water-holding capacity of the meat. In canned products, the pH has an influence on the time/temperature of processing. Thus it is a valuable tool in quality control.

The meat from freshly killed cattle will usually have a pH of 6·5 to 6·8 (slightly acid), but it falls to its lowest level, around 5·5, within about 48 hours of slaughter. It is an unfavourable indication if the pH does not fall below 6·1 within 24 hours of slaughter. In Germany, a colorimetric method is widely used, and 24 hours after slaughter, meat with a pH of 6 is considered to be of 'good durability', 6·4 is classified as of insufficient durability, whilst meat with a pH of 6·8 is unfit for food.

In Denmark pH readings of over 6·5 are regarded as evidence of poor keeping quality and such meat must not be sold through ordinary channels, but may be used in sterilized canned products under the control of the meat inspection service.

Many bacteria have an optimum pH for growth which is near neutrality (pH 7), with maximum and minimum values around 8·0 and 5·0 respectively. As supported by the inspection standards referred to, meat with a pH of 6 or above will spoil bacteriologically more rapidly than at a lower figure.

In bone-taint, a significant factor is the pH of the infected tissues. For example, the 'joint oil' of the stifle joint (patella) has a pH of about 7 which favours the growth of anaerobic bacteria, but their development can be checked by a rapid decrease in temperature.

Thus, the old custom of opening up the stifle joint and/or hip joint during the warmer weather had the double effect of draining off an ideal media for their growth and admitting the air.

Dark cutting beef is associated with the pre-slaughter treatment of the animal, depleted muscle glycogen and a high pH being a characteristic of such beef.

The pH immediately following slaughter and the final pH can provide a good indication of the condition of the live animal, prior to slaughter.

TEMPERATURE CONTROL

Chemically, lean meat tissue consists of roughly 70% water, 25% of protein and 5% salts, and provides an ideal medium for the growth of micro-organisms. The time taken for the evidence of bacteria to become apparent in the form of slime development and smell depends upon two factors: the initial number of bacteria present and the rate at which they multiply, the latter being mainly determined by temperature.

The initial number of bacteria present is greatly influenced by the standard of hygiene exercised during slaughter and dressing (see p. 261). This may vary from under 100 to over 100,000 per cm^2 of surface. If the number of organisms double every day, in the case of the 100, it may take 10 days for them to reach 100,000, a count which may be present initially with bad slaughter technique.

The number needed to form obvious slime is about 50 million per cm^2. Thus at about 32°F (0°C) (where the growth may be about the rate stated) with good slaughter technique, the storage life may be 19 days as compared with under half this period in badly handled meat (Fig. 33).

At higher temperatures, growth is of course much more rapid and consequently the storage life is reduced. It has been shown that a freshly exposed surface of lean beef at a temperature of 50°F (10°C), held for a period of 24 hours, and then placed in cold store, may not *show* visible slime, but the period at which visible slime will occur is about half of that compared with meat stored at 32°F (0°C) throughout. A decrease of a few degrees towards freezing-point will make much more difference to the storage life than would a similar drop in temperature higher up the scale. As a general rule it may be assumed that, based upon similar samples of fresh meat, spoilage will be twice as fast at 41°F (5°C) as at 32°F (0°C) and four times as fast at 50°F (10°C) as at 32°F (0°C). This has been appreciated by the retailer, particularly in the case of refrigerated show cases, and whereas at one time tem-

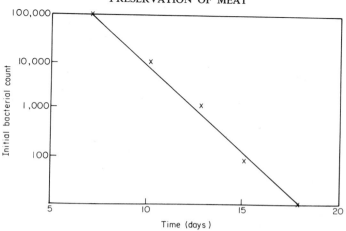

Fig. 33 Initial contamination and storage life. This shows the time for the bacteria to reach the critical number producing slime at 32°F (0°C). (After Haines)

peratures of around 40°F (4°C) were common, the present tendency is to operate at much lower temperatures.

Spoilage organisms are usually considered in three categories.

(1) Those that grow most readily between about 28 and 45°F (−2 and 7°C) (psychrophiles).

(2) Those that grow most readily between about 50 and 105°F (10 and 40°C) (mesophiles).

(3) Those that grow most readily between about 110 and 150°F (43 and 65°C (thermophiles).

This classification forms a general distinction and exceptions may occur. However, most bacteria are mesophilic and normal cooler refrigeration will prevent their growth.

Beef prepared from cattle in tropical areas will tend to carry a relatively small percentage of micro-organisms and will keep better at chill temperatures (about 29°F) (−1·5°C) than beef prepared from cattle in a temperate zone. This is due to the fact that the majority of organisms on beef surfaces arise from the soil, and they are adapted to grow at the high soil temperatures of the tropics. With sides of beef, it is usually found that the internal surface of the sticking (neck) will have the heaviest bacterial count and if the beef is to be held for maturing, such surfaces should be trimmed for utilization whilst they are still sound.

The incidence of bone-taint in English beef appears to have decreased, and this may be due to the tendency towards lighter-weight leaner beef, combined with more efficient refrigeration. Bone-taint is caused by anaerobic spore-forming bacteria. They usually grow best at temperatures near that of the body temperature of mammals, slowly at 68°F (20°C), and not at all below a temperature between 50–40°F (10–4°C). Therefore the more rapidly the centre of a carcase passes through this temperature range the less the probability of bone-taint. It has been stated that, to avoid bone-taint, the deep buttock temperature should not exceed 60°F (15°C) at 18 hours from slaughter, followed by 40°F (4°C) within 48 hours.

When meat is brought from a cold store into the atmospheric temperature, water condenses on the surface and it is said to 'sweat' because the carcase is colder than the air and brings its temperature down below the dew-point. During the summer months, sweating is unavoidable and, in the case of carcase meat, once it has dried out it may affect the 'bloom' but little, yet if prolonged or repeated will impair it. Obviously a moist surface will tend to promote and facilitate the distribution of micro-organisms. With the object of reducing the amount of sweating, some operators when maturing meat will, during the summer months, increase the storage temperature for about 24 hours, prior to removing the meat from the store (see p. 256).

17 Meat cutting

Effects of miscutting

It is generally recognized that half the success in a modern business can be attributed to a strict attention to detail. In no craft is this better exemplified than that of the butcher. In fact, I can think of no better maxim for the potential craftsman than 'more calculation and less cutting'. It must always be borne in mind that bones, fat trimmings, gristles, etc., only fetch a very small fraction of the *cost* price of the carcase, therefore these portions must be reduced to an absolute minimum.

The instant a butcher quarters off a side of beef, the two portions, e.g. hindquarter and forequarter, take on different values, the forequarter depreciating and the hindquarter appreciating in price. It is therefore obvious that unless the greatest precision is practised with each cut, small amounts of the more valuable portion may be left on parts of less value. Thus, wherever less desirable portions adjoin a more popular cut, thought and manual dexterity must be applied in severing these portions.

A good example of this is the flank and loin.

		Loin	Flank
Accurate cutting might give		75%	25%
Value ratio, say		3 :	1
This represents	$(75 \times 3) + (25 \times 1) =$	250	
Inaccurate cutting (5% error) would give			
	$(70 \times 3) + (30 \times 1) =$	240	
	A loss of	10	

$$\frac{10}{250} = 4\% \text{ or a loss of £4 per £100 sales}$$

This state of affairs is pretty general throughout meat cutting, although one must realize that other factors also play an important part in the methods employed.

Important factors in meat cutting

SKELETAL FORM

There are variations in the methods of cutting in various parts of the world, and even in Great Britain surprising differences are met with. As would be expected in a craft based on primitive custom, there appears to be a broad, general correlation between all these systems, based on the skeleton of the animal. No individual, not even an Ancient Briton, would go to the trouble of chopping through a bone if it were possible to find a convenient joint which could be severed with far less physical effort, and even today with more complete tools and mechanical saws, with the exception of the vertebrae, use is made of the anatomical make-up to facilitate jointing. There are, of course, exceptions, such as 'hough' of beef, dearly beloved by the Scot, consisting of the shank meat cut through in small sections *including* the bone, but as a general rule the relatively hard 'long bones' are left severely alone, to be removed in one piece from the gross portions.

In many cases some bones are removed, e.g. rolled ribs, loin, etc., to give the butcher more latitude, so that he can cut these portions to desired weights without the necessity of splitting a bone. From the consumer's aspect, this would appear to be a desirable practice and it eliminates the possibility of bone dust, or even of bone splinters. The division of stewing beef from other portions is again an anatomical matter, as the function of the muscle in the live animal will decide this classification.

LOCAL PREFERENCES

The average customer has learnt, probably from mother, that certain joints are preferable to others, and this custom is influenced by the spending power and the type of cooking normally indulged in. In some parts of the Midlands and Scotland 'pot roasts' are extremely popular, and this permits a greater latitude in the selection of roasting meat as compared with the housewife in other areas. This is, of course, reflected back to the method employed by the meat retailer.

The type of 'cut' meat normally sold on Smithfield Market (London) allows for a great smoothing out of these demands. The butcher requiring these cheaper cuts, for a trade where spending power is limited, can purchase those portions, whilst the high-class purveyor, catering for, say, an hotel or restaurant trade, can obtain grills and roasts, leaving for sale the cheaper portion. This type of trade is an interesting contrast with the self-contained small country butcher, who must dispose of all his beast and few 'smalls' to his own clients.

SEASONAL VARIATIONS

As well as the variations in demand occurring at certain periods—for example, pork with an R in the months; lamb at Easter; poultry, and legs of pork at Christmas—there is still the general tendency for baking joints for the Sunday dinner in the normal working-class household. The remainder of the Sunday joint will probably last, say, cold for Monday, with the remains stewed. Throughout the rest of the week, chops, steak, sausages, and meat pies will probably be the routine. Certain denominations will call for a fish day, and frequently the retailers' early closing day will mean a rather hurried purchase prior to one o'clock. Thus it will be seen that the demand for meat from the retailer is practically negligible on Monday, gradually increasing towards the week-end, until on Saturday he probably makes 40% of his week's sales.

Lamb and mutton are usually considered as 'light' meats and consequently the demand is greater during the summer months. The quantity of fat demanded, particularly in the case of beef, is greater in the heavy industrial (iron, etc.) and agricultural districts than in areas where manual work is less.

PURCHASING POWER

Industrial prosperity or depression are factors over which the butcher has little control. There is, however, a fairly close relationship between them, and depression, either purely local or national, will result in a rapid drop both in the demand and the quality of the meat required. The response is very sensitive, and on a return to prosperity the beef trade is one of the first to benefit.

It is frequently stated that modern demand is less discriminating than was previously the case. This, however, is not substantiated by the wide disparity in the price variation between best English meat and inferior grades. Meat is, of course, a relatively expensive method of purchasing protein, but the psychological value of good roast beef or a juicy fillet steak is probably beyond the power of science to assess. It is, however, true that in countries where meat is relatively cheap, e.g. South America and Australasia, the meat consumption assumes terrific proportions. The effect therefore of a reduction in income is to create a demand for smaller joints of a poorer quality.

SALES PROCEDURE

It is commonly recognized that as the area of the cut surfaces increases, the loss by evaporation and, in the case of frozen meat, drip also increases, so that, critically, the less cutting and the shorter the period elapsing between cutting and sale the smaller this loss will be. However, in practice the method of display will determine the quantity of small joints to be cut; it must be appreciated that this form of advertisement is not cheap, and individual circumstances must determine to what extent a display of small cut joints is justified.

GENERAL

Less important features which influence cutting are: demand for salt meats (particularly if the arterial method is employed), the requirements of meat for sausage, the sex and general conformation. From the foregoing it is obvious that cutting is a skilled craft requiring considerable experience of carcase types, anatomy, and diet, with no mean knowledge of human psychology. Intelligent study will greatly supplement experience, but the practical work of accurate cutting can only be acquired by continual application.

APPLICATION OF PERCENTAGE ANALYSIS

It is generally assumed that an 80 lb (36 kg) pork carcase will give a leg weighing 10 lb (4·5 kg), or, as it was expressed prior to the abolition of the 8 lb stone, 1 lb of leg meat per stone of carcase. This gives us $\frac{20}{80}$ or 25 % of the carcase as leg meat (2 legs). As animals are built, more or less, on a common plan, and the grading, particularly of imported meat, is very consistent, we can apply similar percentages to the various portions, and within fine limits they prove surprisingly accurate. This will enable us to calculate the quantities of the various cuts obtained from a portion and also check the cutting to ensure that it is consistent. For contract work, where a certain weight of roasting or stewing meat is called for, this system is invaluable, as it will indicate the quantity of quarters or carcases required to give the weight of the portion required. For example, a good grade of New Zealand lamb carcase cut fairly, according to London and Home Counties practice, would probably yield the following weights:

	lb	oz	
Legs	7	8	
Shoulders	6	0	
Loins	6	6	
Targets	7	2	(Forequarters less shoulders)
	27	0	

To calculate the percentage of the carcase represented by the joints, place the weight of the joint over the gross weight of the carcase and multiply by 100, e.g.

$$\frac{\text{weight of joint}}{\text{gross weight}} \times \frac{100}{1}$$

For this purpose it is a great advantage if we decimalize our ounces as part of a lb:

$$\left.\begin{array}{ll} 8 \text{ oz} & 0\cdot5 \\ 4 \text{ oz} & 0\cdot25 \\ 2 \text{ oz} & 0\cdot125 \\ 1 \text{ oz} & 0\cdot0625 \end{array}\right\} \text{ of 1 lb}$$

To return to our lamb, this will give us

Legs $\qquad \dfrac{7\cdot5}{27} \times \dfrac{100}{1} = $ approx. $27\cdot77\%$

Shoulders $\qquad \dfrac{6\cdot0}{27} \times \dfrac{100}{1} = $ approx. $22\cdot22\%$

Loins $\qquad \dfrac{6\cdot375}{27} \times \dfrac{100}{1} = $ approx. 23.61%

Targets $\qquad \dfrac{7\cdot125}{27} \times \dfrac{100}{1} = $ approx. $\underline{26\cdot39\%}$

$$\underline{99\cdot99\%}$$

Conversely, we can figure that a pair of legs of 7 lb 8 oz, if fairly cut, can be obtained from a carcase of

$$\frac{\text{weight of joint}}{\% \text{ of carcase}} \times \frac{100}{1} = \text{gross weight}$$

which in this case is

$$\frac{7\cdot5}{27\cdot77} \times \frac{100}{1} = \text{approx. 27 lb, carcase weight.}$$

The two examples given above will illustrate the application of this form of figuring, and the experienced butcher will probably be very surprised at the accuracy of his own cutting. It should be possible to cut a fair lamb carcase to give a total error on weighing the four portions of not more than 3%.

Every master butcher should attempt to compile his own set of percentages, based on the style of cutting in his particular business, with the type of commodity he usually purchases. A fair range of actual examples should be taken to offset individual variations, and by this method it should be possible to check *potential* as against actual sales, the ratio being an index of efficiency.

Meat pricing

Economic distribution depends upon the following considerations.

(A) *Cost price.* Within limits the butcher has little control over this factor, but under normal conditions, particularly in the case of English meat, the open competition in a free market will cause prices to find their own level.

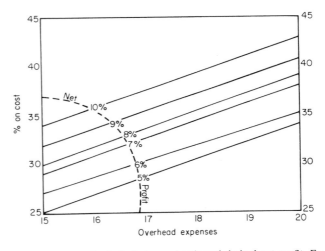

Fig. 34 Percentage on cost price to include overheads and desired net profit. Example: overhead expenses $17\frac{1}{2}$%, desired net profit 10%, approximate percentage on *cost* = approx. 38%

(B) *Overhead expenses.* Those costs involved in transport, preparation, storage, and selling. Overheads are not directly related to turnover. For example, an increase of 50% in turnover does not of necessity mean an increase of 50% in wages. In fact, one usually finds that the bigger the turnover the smaller is the wage ratio.

(C) *Net profit.* This must be adequate to recompense the butcher for his enterprise and possible risk of capital. A fair salary should, of course, be included under (B). This latter figure may be difficult to arrive at accurately, but it should represent his fair market value were he employed in a similar capacity by some other trader.

Gross profit is the difference between the cost price and actual sales. Net profit is the balance remaining after the cost price and all expenses have been met. Thus all *waste* and *loss must come out of the profit.*

In theory there are two main methods employed in determining the sale price of a product: (a) by obtaining the cost price and adding to it the desired margin of gross profit, or (b) to work from the sale price and deduct from this figure the desired gross profit, to establish a maximum wholesale price.

In practice there may be a certain amount of overlapping, as wholesale prices can show rapid fluctuations and consumer demand can be influenced by many factors.

It is, however, a great advantage to establish a general guide, which will indicate the minimum retail prices, in relation to the wholesale prices paid. Such a guide can be prepared in the following manner and can be expressed in terms of a constant, which might be termed a desirability factor, or for purposes of simplification, in the form of a pricing graph, covering the normal wholesale range of prices anticipated.

(1) Take the ruling retail prices for the various portions.

(2) Multiply the appropriate percentages for the various portions by these prices and total them.

(3) Deduct from this total the desired gross profit on sales.

(4) Divide this total by 100 which will give the maximum wholesale price to obtain the desired profit.

(5) Divide this wholesale price in pence per lb into each of the prices of the retail portions (in p per lb) to obtain the desirability factor (D.F.) for each joint.

Once this figure is obtained, it is obvious that, by multiplying the wholesale price (whatever fluctuations may occur) by the D.F., the basic range of retail prices, to include the required margin of gross profit, will result. The theoretical example below, based upon an English lamb, will illustrate the method of approach.

(1) Assuming that the ruling prices are: legs 120p; shoulders 90p; loins 100p; whole necks 60p; and fat and trim loss is 2%

Thus we have the following:

(2)

	% of carcase	p per lb	£.
Legs	25	120	30·00
Shoulders	22	90	19·80
Whole necks	27	60	16·20
Loins	24	100	24·00
Loss	2	—	—
	100		90·00

(3) Less gross profit, say $33\frac{1}{3}\%$ on sales

			30·00
			60·00

(4) Maximum wholesale price per 100 lb of carcase

$$\frac{60 \cdot 00}{100} = 60\text{p per lb}$$

(5)   Desirability factor
                                                         approx.

Legs $\dfrac{120}{60}$ $=$ 2·00

Shoulders $\dfrac{90}{60}$ $=$ 1·50

Whole necks $\dfrac{60}{60}$ $=$ 1·00

Loins $\dfrac{100}{60}$ $=$ 1·67

An alternative method of costing, which permits price adjustments between various joints, can be prepared as follows. For convenience the units may be taken as pence.

(1) Take the gross initial weight of the carcase (or quarter) as 100 lb
(2) Multiply this by its cost in p per lb.
(3) Add to this the required gross margin on sales e.g.

$$33\tfrac{1}{3}\% \text{ gross on sales} = 50\% \text{ on cost.}$$
$$25\% \text{ gross on sales} = 33\tfrac{1}{3}\% \text{ on cost.}$$
$$20\% \text{ gross on sales} = 25\% \text{ on cost.}$$

Thus a carcase costing 45p per lb, to show a gross margin of 25% on sales, would require:

$$
\begin{array}{ll}
 & \text{Units.} \\
100 \times 45 & = 4500 \\
\text{Plus 25\% profit} & = 1500 \\
\hline
 & 6000 \\
\hline
\end{array}
$$

It is obvious that the sum of the various joints (joints % × their price in p per lb) must be equal to the carcase units plus the profit. For example, it may be found that, in the case of a good quality New Zealand lamb, the following percentages and prices might apply:

Joints	% of carcase weight	@ p	Units
Legs ·	25·00	75	1875·00
Loins	23·75	75	1781·25
Shoulders	21·25	62	1317·50
Best end necks	10·00	62	620·00
Breasts, middle			
& scrag	18·75	22	412·50
Loss	1·25	–	–—
	100%		6006·25

This is fairly close to the required figure and, with this information, price adjustments between the various joints, as related to the overall total, can be made.

For the purpose of simplification, a graph can be prepared to indicate the total units necessary to include the desired profit, an example being given below (Fig 35).

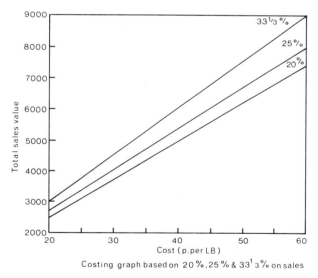

Costing graph based on 20%, 25% & 33$\frac{1}{3}$% on sales

Fig. 35 Costing graph, based on 20%, 25% and 33$\frac{1}{3}$% on sales

Quartering Sides of Beef

The methods of quartering sides will vary somewhat (see Figs. 40, 41). However, the current tendency is towards a ten-rib $F\frac{1}{4}$, leaving three rib bones on the $H\frac{1}{4}$. In beef of very good conformation, such quartering

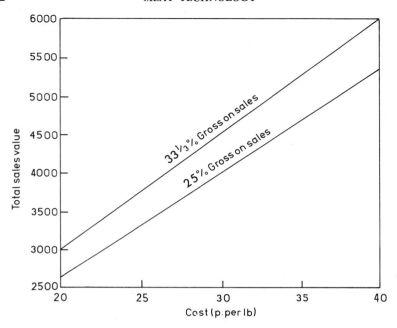

Fig. 36 Costing graph based on 25% and 33⅓% on sales

might result in the H¼ representing 54% of the side weight and the F¼ 46%. This ratio will be influenced by the amount of kidney and channel suet present in the H¼.

During the summer months the tendency will be towards an increase in the value of the H¼ per lb, and a proportionate decrease in that of the F¼. The opposite will apply during the colder weather. On average it may be found that the total value of the H¼ is about 60% of the side value and the F¼ about 40%. With good commercial beef a ratio of about 52%:48% (weight) is a good general basis. On this assumption, the diagram will enable the following approximate relative values to be established.

(1) The value of the side in pence per lb in relation to the known cost of the H¼ and F¼.

(2) The value of the H¼ in pence per lb, in relation to the known cost of the F¼ and side.

(3) The value of the F¼ in pence per lb in relation to the known cost of the H¼ and side.

In the example shown by the dashed line (Fig. 37), with the H¼ at 40p and the F¼ at 20p, the value of the side would be approximately 30·4p per lb.

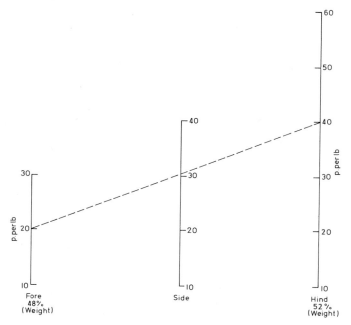

Fig. 37 Conversion value in pence per lb for hind, fore (10 kg) and side of beef with KKCF

With sides of beef ex KKCF the hind:fore ratio will be markedly affected, but in price calculations some allowance should be made for the value of the kidney and suet fat.

Based upon the average figure of 3·75% of the side as being KKCF, the position in relation to with KKCF would be:

Assuming that the original weight of the side is 300 lb and the hind 156 lb (52%) and the fore 144 lb (48%), the weight of the side will be reduced by 3·75%, i.e. 11¼ lb, thus giving a side weight of $300 - 11\frac{1}{4}$ = 288·75 lb. As the KKCF is removed from the hind, it will then weigh $156 - 11·25$ lb = 144·75 lb. Thus the percentage of hind to fore, i.e. 144·75 lb:144 lb respectively, = hind 50·13% and fore 49·87%.

Meat arithmetic

Considerable effort has been devoted to finding a 'sample' joint capable of providing an indication of the carcase composition as a whole. However, it is generally agreed that a high degree of accuracy can only be obtained by complete dissection of the carcase, usually in terms of muscle, bone, tendon, and fat. This is time-consuming and the resultant meat is severely depreciated in value. Although such work is of scientific value in determining breed differences, the effect of nutrition and growth, genetical influences and similar considerations, it will obviously have little direct appeal to the butcher, concerned primarily with the yield of prepared retail cuts.

In the past, dissection of a rib joint as an indication of carcase composition has been popular. It is easy to obtain and does not materially affect the value of the carcase. The use of such joints has not proved to be very satisfactory, probably owing to the difficulty in cutting an absolutely uniform joint in terms of bone proportion, angle of cutting and the amount of 'tops' attached to it.

The practical man has assumed that the fore-shin/shank will give a useful indication of muscle:bone ratio, not only in beef, but also in lamb and pork carcases. With beef, the normal method of jointing ensures a fairly accurate anatomical division, thus eliminating one of the variables incurred with most other joints. Callow's work on the dissection of 24 sides of beef from Hereford, Dairy Shorthorn and Friesian steers on 4 levels of nutrition, indicates that the shin (radius/ulna) appears to be the best bone for obtaining an estimate of total bone and it also proved to be the best joint for estimating the total weight of muscle. Even so in the case of the latter, the standard error was about 12 lb (5·4 kg), the average side weights being 377·6 lb (171·3 kg). In this work Callow states that approximately one-third of the live weight of the animal is muscular tissue and that on average this assumption will give a greater degree of accuracy than that obtained by dissecting a single joint.

The following is given as a rule-of-thumb method for estimating the composition of a carcase.

(A) The weight of muscular tissue in a carcase is approximately one-third of the live weight of the beast (farm weight).

(B) The weight of bone and tendon is one-quarter of the weight of the muscular tissue.

(C) The remainder of the weight of the carcase is the weight of the *total* fatty tissues.

It should be noted that the total fatty tissue includes kidney and kidney fat, subcutaneous and intermuscular fat and the cod fat, some of which would be sold on or in the meat.

On the sides dissected (average 377·6 lb cold weight) and the tissue weights, it was shown that the above method of estimation gave values within ± 10·1 lb for muscular tissue, ± 11·8 lb for fatty tissue, and ± 3·1 lb for bone and tendon. Based on this rule-of-thumb method, a 9 cwt beast, dressing out at 57%, should have the approximate composition as follows:

lb

(A) Muscle (fat free) $\dfrac{1}{3} \times \dfrac{1008}{1} = 336$

(B) Bone (with tendon) $\dfrac{1}{4} \times \dfrac{336}{1} = \underline{84}$

$\phantom{(B) Bone (with tendon) \dfrac{1}{4} \times \dfrac{336}{1} = } 420$

(C) Carcase cold, say 570 lb

Fatty tissue $\qquad 570 - 420 \quad = 150$

Total carcase $\quad = \underline{\underline{570}}$ lb

Prof. Briedenstein, University of Illinois, carried out tests involving the use of 398 sides of beef (105 steers and 94 heifers), with the object of analysing the various practical factors concerned in estimating 'retail' yield. The joints were trimmed to give an external fat thickness of 0·3 in (8 mm) and the internal fats were removed. All the joints were boneless with the exception of the short loin and rib and in these two portions the chine bone was removed. The weight range for heifer carcases was 500 to 650 lb (227–295 kg) and for steers 500 to 700 lb (227–317 kg). Using mathematical procedures, holding all other factors constant whilst observing the effect of one other criterion or total retail yield, the following effects were deduced from the carcases tested.

Fat thickness. An increase of 1 in (2·5 cm) in fat thickness resulted in a reduction in yield of total retailable product of 6·39% for steers and 6·50% for heifers.

Carcase weight. A 100 lb (45·4 kg) increase in steer carcase weight resulted in a reduction in percentage yield of 1·42%.

Kidney fat weight. An increase of 1 lb (0·45 kg) in kidney fat weight resulted in a reduction yield of 0·38% for steers and 0'44% for heifers.

Loin–eye area. An increase of 1 sq in (6·5 cm²) in loin–eye area resulted in an increase of 0·37% for steers and 0·42% for heifers.

*Conformation grade.** An increase of one-third of a grade in conformation resulted in an increase of 0·34% for heifers.

Sex. Total retail yield for steers was 1·73% higher than that for heifers after accounting for the effects of fat thickness, carcase weight, kidney fat weight, loin–eye area and conformation grade.

It is possible to predict the percentage of total retail yield of a carcase from the following equations.

---

*Conformation grade is a scoring system based on descriptions of conformation contained in the USDA grade specifications. The code used in the interpretation of it is as follows:

Prime +24	Choice +21	Good +18
Prime 23	Choice 20	Good 17
Prime −22	Choice −19	Good −16

STEERS

$$\% \text{ total retail yield} = 67 \cdot 99 - (0 \cdot 0142 \times \text{carcase weight (lb)})$$
$$- (6 \cdot 39 \times \text{fat thickness (in)})$$
$$- (0 \cdot 38 \times \text{kidney fat weight (lb)})$$
$$+ (0 \cdot 37 \times \text{loin–eye area (sq in)})$$
$$+ (0 \cdot 14 \times \text{conformation grade*})$$

HEIFERS

$$\% \text{ total retail yield} = 52 \cdot 56 + (0 \cdot 0011 \times \text{carcase weight (lb)})$$
$$- (6 \cdot 50 \times \text{fat thickness (in)})$$
$$- (0 \cdot 44 \times \text{kidney fat weight (lb)})$$
$$+ (0 \cdot 42 \times \text{loin–eye area (sq in)})$$
$$+ (0 \cdot 34 \times \text{conformation grade†})$$

AVERAGE FIGURES FOR CHARACTERISTICS OBSERVED

	Steers 210 sides	Heifers 188 sides
Side weight at cutting time (lb)‡	292·9	282·8
Fat thickness (in)	0·57	0·57
Kidney fat weight (lb)	7·87	9·27
Loin–eye area (in²)	11·10	11·32
Conformation grade	18·73	18·20
% total retail yield	63·87	61·61

TURNOVER RATE

The more rapidly the stock is turned over, the less overhead expense will be absorbed in a given period and the capital invested in stock is proportionately reduced. Assuming that we plan to sell a given quantity of meat in a certain time, we know within close limits the overhead expenses for the period and the desired profit commensurate with good trading, and the diagram on p. 277 (Fig. 38) will help us to visualize the importance of turnover rate. We cannot think in terms of trade without the element of time. For example, the moment we purchase our meat, expense begins and accumulates; salaries, rent, storage, etc., have to be borne by the goods in an increasing volume. Therefore if we sell our quota in the period planned—that is, from A to B—we shall incur reasonable expense in its sale, leaving a fair net profit.

*See footnote on p. 275.
†See footnote on p. 275.
‡Weight taken after approximately 14-day age and with approximately 5% shrink from 48-hour weight.

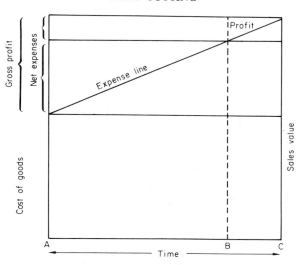

Fig. 38   Time and profit

Beyond that point our net profit will decrease, until we reach C, where no profit at all is possible. Should we take still longer in disposing of our quota a loss must result. This factor of time applies very strongly to the meat trade, as not only do the goods absorb an increasing expense, but after a short time they themselves depreciate rapidly in value until a point is reached where they become valueless. In frozen

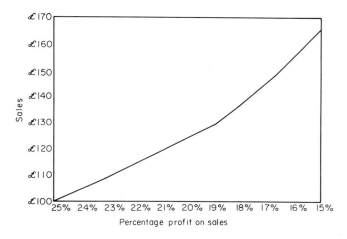

Fig. 39   Sales increase necessary to maintain profit with a reduction in the percentage on sales. Based on 25% at the £100 sales level

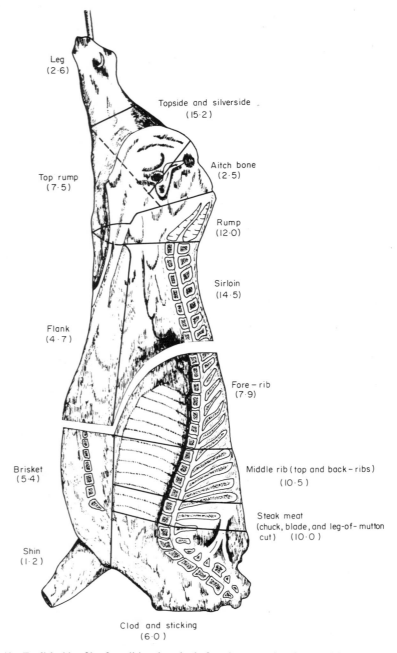

Fig. 40   English side of beef, traditional method of cutting as used at the Royal Smithfield Show. The figures in brackets represent the approximate percentage of value for the retail joints in relation to the total value of the side

meats, efficient refrigeration will of course offset this latter point, but even here a time will be reached where storage cost will accumulate to such a degree that net profit becomes impossible.

PRICE CUTTING

Happily the practice of price cutting to ridiculous levels has decreased considerably of recent years, and it is generally appreciated that the average purchaser will prefer a fairly standard price to violent fluctuations. Very few butchers appreciate the tremendous trade increase required to maintain a standard profit when the selling price is reduced. Reference to the graph above (Fig. 39) will show that should a shop doing £100 per week, showing £25 gross profit, cut its profit on sales by only 5%, it will be necessary to increase that trade to £125 to obtain *the same profit*. Therefore the wisdom of price cutting, though it may depend on individual circumstances, is a practice that should be approached with considerable caution.

Cutting technique
Beef cutting

It is desirable, in fact one might say essential, that the craftsman should possess his own set of tools and should maintain them in good condition. If a high standard of skill is to be reached, the constant use of a certain boning knife or well-balanced chopper can do much to achieve this object and also foster a pride of execution in the operative.

HINDQUARTER (Fig. 42)

The initial cutting may be dealt with either with the quarter hanging or placed on a cutting block, depending upon circumstances.

(A) *Suet.* It is probably better to remove the kidney knob and rump suet first, as this will obviate small portions of suet being wasted during the subsequent sawing and cutting. In some cases a small quantity of suet may be left attached to the loin, depending upon the specific trade requirements. This suet is a very valuable food substance, with a high calorific value of about 3800 calories per lb. Normally, it would be sold fresh, either as removed from the quarter, or shredded or chopped, though it may be necessary to break it down on a mincing machine, rendering it down to yield a high-grade dripping.

(1) *Thin flank.* The difference between the values of the thin flank and its adjoining loin might be in the ratio of 1:3 respectively, therefore when making this cut great care is necessary in deciding the line of

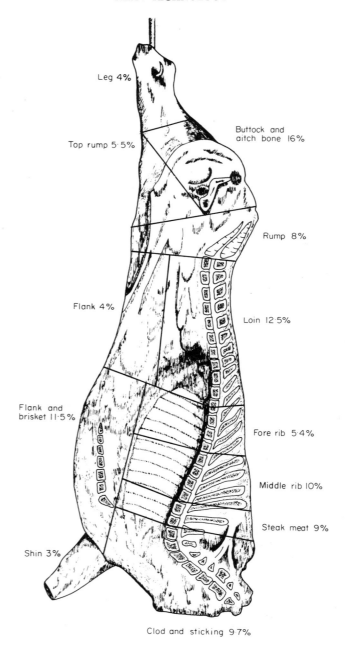

Leg 4%

Buttock and
aitch bone 16%

Top rump 5·5%

Rump 8%

Flank 4%

Loin 12·5%

Flank and
brisket 11·5%

Fore rib 5·4%

Middle rib 10%

Steak meat 9%

Shin 3%

Clod and sticking 9·7%

Fig. 41   Beef cutting, London and Home Counties method. Percentage of weight, cutting loss, etc. is 1·4%

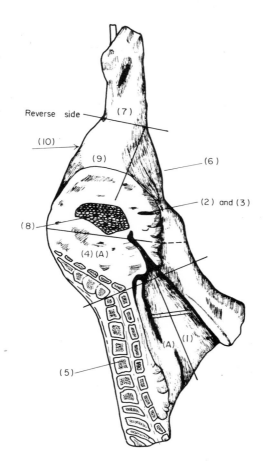

Fig. 42 Hindquarter of beef

Portions in order of removal	Use
(A) Rump and kidney suet	Puddings, etc.
(1) Thin flank	Braising, stewing, pickling and boiling, sausage, pies, etc.
(2) Cod fat	Tied on lean meat for basting, or minced and rendered for dripping
(3) Goose skirt	Stewing and pies
(4) Rump and fillet	Grilling, frying, braising, and roasting
(5) Loin	Roasting
(6) Thick flank or top rump	Roasting, braising, pickling, and boiling
(7) Leg	Beef tea, stewing
(8) Pubic bone (aitch bone)	Stock
(9) Topside	Roasting and braising
(10) Silverside	Pickling and boiling, braising and roasting
Kidney	Is used for flavouring

demarcation to ensure the maximum yield of loin, without affecting its marketability. In this respect the question of selling with or without the bone will influence the position of this cut. As a rough guide, some butchers estimate that a point twice the length of the eye muscle from the chine is satisfactory for the wing end, whilst the cut should be started just below the small red external muscle, usually found below the cod fat. This cut will mean using the knife down as far as the ribs, completing the division by sawing across the three rib bones. At times one may find the practice of removing the cod fat, goose skirt, and the thin flank in one operation, and from the aspect of simplification and reduction of cutting motion there appears to be much to recommend this method. It would of course be unsuitable if the topside is intended for steak with the cod fat attached. The thin flank is usually looked upon as a lower-grade joint, suitable for salting and boiling, pot roast, sausage manufacture, etc., but its reputation can be greatly enhanced if the inner skin (peritoneum) is stripped out, the portions of the three ribs removed, and the tough sheet of gristle lying between the muscles carefully skinned away prior to rolling.

(2) and (3) *Cod or udder fat and goose skirt*. The goose skirt is part of the inner muscle of the belly-wall. It is situated beneath the cod fat and it is desirable to make a light incision where it joins the rump, stripping it away from the underlying portion, prior to making a clean cut, removing the cod or udder fat with the goose skirt attached. Care should be taken to ensure that the underlying muscle is not cut into. As previously mentioned, if the buttock is intended for steak, the fat may be left on the topside. Flavour in meat is largely influenced by the fat, so the cod fat may be cut into strips and flattened out to be strung to roasting portions and it will exert a basting effect during the cooking. (In the case of cow beef, if the mammary gland is present, the milk tissue would have to be removed.)

Should the quantity of fat available be excessive it can be sold fresh as fat or broken down on a mincer and rendered for dripping. Here it must be remembered that this latter course will result in some loss of weight, and the cost of rendering must not be overlooked. The purchaser is more prepared to accept a thin layer of fat extending well over the surface of the meat than a similar quantity in a thick compact mass. The goose skirt provides an ideal stewing portion, though it is frequently used for a grill or for frying.

(4) and (5) *Rump and loin*. The hindquarter is then divided into the rump, loin and wing end, and the top-piece, and here again the differences in value as between the rump and the top-piece is an important point. The actual cutting-line will to some extent be influenced by the quarter, cow beef having a different conformation from that of the ox,

but as a general guide the division should be made approximately three finger widths below the round end of the aitch bone (a little over two inches) and the same height above the end of the rump bone. This should be carried out by cutting through the undercut, or fillet (psoas muscle), sawing across the bone, and completing the division by making a clean straight cut with the steak knife. This cut must be absolutely square as sloping towards the top-piece will mean cutting into a bone, whilst sloping towards the loin results in a loss of rump steak. Normally, if this cut is correctly made, two lymphatic glands (kernels) will be cut through, one on either end of the rump (ischiatic and iliac). When separating the rump and loin some slight variation occurs, but the normal practice is to find the cartilaginous pad between the sacral and lumbar vertebrae and, using this point as a guide, place the portion chine bone down; with the point of the knife locate the cartilage on the end of the rump bone (ilium), and make a cut downwards, just catching the cartilage and sloping the knife slightly towards the rump, to the point between the vertebrae, completing the separation by sawing through the bone. The fillet, or undercut, is carefully removed from the rump with the skirt attached. Incidentally the fillet is the most tender portion of the entire carcase. If it is intended to cut the rump in steaks from the bone, the flesh should be loosened from the sacral vertebrae with a boning knife to facilitate cutting. Some butchers prefer to remove the rump steak entirely from the bone, laying the boneless steak flat on a board, claiming that there is less loss with this method than when cutting on the bone.

(5) *Loin and wing end.* The loin can be prepared for retail sale in many ways. The three-bone wing end may be removed for sale as a wing rib, the remaining portion being rolled either bone in or boneless; the entire portion may be boned and rolled, and the fillet may or may not be left in. When rolling with the bone in, it is advisable to saw across the tips of the transverse spinal processes to facilitate rolling, but do not penetrate the muscle beneath. The flap of the loin is knocked over and held in position by steel skewers, prior to securing by inserting skewers at the centre of each vertebrae, picking up the gristle, and then running upwards into the loin. These skewers must be straight and follow the line of the bone, otherwise cutting single joints of sirloin will be difficult. If it is intended to hang the individual joints, it is necessary to string up, again at the centre of each vertebrae. If the loin is to be completely boned, the undercut must be carefully cut away and can be used for steaks, or it can be placed in the boneless loin with the thick end of the undercut in the wing end of the loin to produce a parallel joint. When boning, the portions of the three rib bones should be carefully boned out, avoiding deep incisions, and the vertebrae bones removed. It is

probably better to remove these bones individually (they can be loosened by pressing a chopper into the cartilage pads between them) rather than by 'chining' it with a saw. Having removed the bone, it is a good plan to trim out the sheet of gristle extending up the loin between the outer layer of fat and the muscle. This only weighs a few ounces and will greatly improve the joint. Beat out flat, roll tightly, insert skewers, and string up with a good twine.

(6) *Thick flank.* This joint is sometimes referred to as the top rump and it can be removed either before or following the leg of beef, provided that the latter is 'jointed'. To remove the thick flank, find the leg end of the stifle joint (patella) with the point of the knife and make a straight cut down on to the thigh bone (femur). Insert the point of the knife under the skin covering the bone (periosteum), and strip back the thick flank from the bone. Under this bone will be found the seam of the silverside; cut open this seam until the end of the silverside muscle is reached and make a small incision in the stifle joint, to enable the portion to be held, by inserting the fingers. Then cut through the skin in one clean cut, removing the thick flank. This can best be carried out with the joint projecting over the end of the cutting block, supporting it by the stifle joint as it drops free.

The thick flank can be used for second-grade steaks, for baking purposes or braising. It is sometimes pickled where a lean joint is required. If it is intended for baking or roasting (retail trade), the cramp bone is removed and the portion cut along the centre-line, one part, the cod fat side, being rolled and tied up, whilst the other is usually fatted up and tied.

(7) *Leg of beef* (shank, hind shin). This can be jointed by cutting between the tibia–fibula and the femur, or in cold weather when there is a good demand for leg of beef it may be removed by sawing and chopping through the femur, to obtain a full cut leg. The leg meat is usually removed from the bone, though in some parts the leg muscle, including the bone, is cut through so that the purchaser has the advantage of the bone marrow and the stock from the bone as well as the meat. When deboning the leg *all* the meat should be removed, also a fair proportion of tendon. Leg muscle is popular for beef-tea and mince, and the tendons can be rendered down for gelatine.

(8) *Aitch bone.* At one time the aitch bone was a very popular weekend joint, but in these days of small families the bone (pubic bone) is frequently removed to provide a full topside (No. 9) and a long cut silverside (10). Provided that the division of rump–top-piece is fairly made, the pubic bone, which is a late developing part, can give a good indication of the total bone content of the hindquarter. The weight of the bone (picked clean) multiplied by 10 will give the total weight of bone

in the quarter, within a very small margin of error. To remove the bone, the thin layer of muscle and fat on its surface, the aitch-bone skirt, should be laid back, starting from the cup-bone side, exposing the surface of the bone. Pass the point of the boning knife along the under side of the bone to loosen the muscle, follow the line of the hole with the tip of the point and then proceed to cut down the back of the pubic surface, cutting the tendon in the cup-bone and removing the bone cleanly from the buttock. The aitch-bone skirt can be left attached to the silverside and rolled in with the aitch-bone cut.

(9) and (10) *Topside and silverside*. These two portions should be divided by splitting through the 'seam' between them. This should be carefully carried out, particularly if the silverside is intended for salting by pumping through the arteries. This division can be made from the bone side of the buttock by cutting round the thigh bone until the seam is located, and following it until the external fat is reached and then cutting through the fat to remove the topside (9). Some butchers prefer to chop off a small portion of the leg end of the thigh bone, so that the buttock will lie flat, bone downwards, and then proceed to split from the external surface. If this method is employed, the shank end should be pointing away from the cutter, and the eye of the meat at the top of the buttock can be found, at the shank end, usually separated by a layer of fat. This layer of fat should be carefully followed though, leaving the eye muscle on the silverside. When the bone is reached, strip off the topside, leaving the bone clean and attached to the silverside.

(9) *Topside*. This joint, forming the inner side of the leg, is subjected to less stress in the live animal; consequently it is more tender and in good beef is more prone to marbling than the silverside. It can be used for steak, though it is better for roasting or baking, in which case the topside is cut longitudinally, fatted, and tied up.

(10) *Silverside*. Custom usually associates silverside with salting and boiling, and in this respect removing the bone and pumping arterially cuts down the pickling period and produces a consistent article. Boiling will tend to gelatinize the connective tissue, rendering it tender. Under some circumstances it may be necessary to sell it as a baking joint, and here it is essential that the sheet of gristle should be skinned out prior to rolling. The aitch-bone cut is removed by making a transverse cut, and rolled with the skirt attached, the remaining portion then being split, fatted, and tied up. It is desirable to trim away the popliteal gland. Where there is a demand for larger joints the whole silverside should, of course, be rolled. The shank end will contain a great deal of gristle and this portion is sometimes trimmed off for sale as leg or stewing beef.

FOREQUARTER (Fig. 43)

In this country it is usual to place the quarter on the cutting block and commence operations by removing the thin skirt (diaphragm).

(1) *Shin.* This is removed at the elbow joint (radius–ulna and humerus articulation) by using a boning knife, though in the case of frozen beef which is fairly 'firm' it is advisable to saw across the tip of the elbow to facilitate 'breaking' the joint. This is best achieved by pushing the shin forwards and downwards whilst loosening the joint with the knife. The muscle of this joint is very similar to that of the leg, except that in most cases it contains a little less fat. It is used principally for stewing, beef-tea, and for mincing.

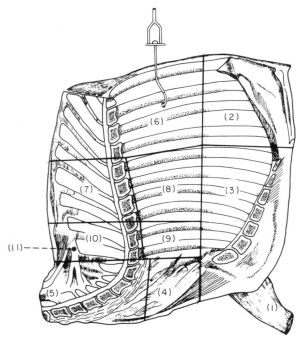

Fig. 43   Forequarter of beef

Portions in order of removal	Use
(1) Shin	Beef tea and stewing
(2) Flank	Braising, pickling, and boiling, sausage, pies, etc.
(3) Brisket	Pickling and boiling, braising and roasting
(4) Clod	Stewing
(5) Sticking	Stewing
(6) Fore-rib	Roasting
(7) Back-ribs	Roasting and braising
(8) Top-ribs	Roasting and braising
(9) Leg-of-mutton cut	Roasting and braising
(10) Chuck	Stewing
(11) Blade bone	Stewing

(2) and (3) *Flank* (2) *and brisket* (3) or, as they are together referred to, the 'coast' can then be removed. Some butchers cut off the clod (4) and sticking (5) first, though this is largely a matter of personal preference. The precise position of the cut will depend to some extent on the specific circumstances, but it must be borne in mind that there is a marked difference in price as between the coast and the adjoining portions. Usually a line about 2 in (5 cm) from the termination of the skirt, at the 10th rib, to the 1st bone of the sternum will provide a general guide. The rib bones can be sawn through, followed by cutting, or the muscle on the flesh side cut, followed by sawing the ribs. The latter method probably produces a better cut surface, as there is little risk of the flesh being sawn. In both cases care must be exercised, when removing the brisket end, to find the seam between it and the leg-of-mutton cut, to avoid cutting into the muscle. The flank and brisket is divided by cutting *between* the 6th and 7th rib bones, and in young animals the cartilage can be cut through fairly easily by applying pressure with the shoulder on the handle of the knife. Occasionally the flank is cut longer than the brisket, to avoid removing a small portion, the flat ribs, from the fore-rib.

The forequarter flank (2) is somewhat similar to that of the hindquarter, but slightly thicker, and it can be treated in the same fashion.

The brisket (3) is a very good portion for salting and boiling, but it must be boned out carefully to obtain a reasonable profit. This can be carried out as follows. With a narrow-pointed boning knife, trim away the skirt from underneath the sternum, so that no meat is left on it. Make a cut outside the sternum in the hard bosom fat, following the line of the bone. Stand the brisket up on end and take the breast bone in the left hand. With the knife, run down the joints between the breast bone and the small bones, which extend from the ribs, and so take out the breast bone. Remove the small bones from the ribs proper, and then remove the ribs. Some people prefer to leave the ribs in until after cooking and then to pull them away, but the periosteum should be removed from the brisket as it is rather tough. Finally, trim away the hard fat, as the public like lean presses. When pricing the finished product allowance must be made for trimming, etc., and the sale price can be arrived at as follows:

$$\frac{\text{'P' pence}}{1} \times \frac{\text{original weight}}{\text{weight as sold}} \times \text{factor} = \text{sale price in pence per lb}$$

where 'P' pence is the original cost value. If the desired gross profit is to be 25% on sales, the multiplying factor must be $\frac{4}{3}$; for 33$\frac{1}{3}$%, $\frac{3}{2}$; and for 50%, $\frac{2}{1}$.

(4) and (5) *Clod* (4) *and sticking* (5). These two portions are generally

removed together. Find the joint of the clod (humerus) and blade bone (scapula) (in imported quarters the incision made for inspecting the pre-scapula gland will provide a landmark) and cut about 1 in (2·5 cm) on the fore-rib side of the joint; to find the cup bone of the blade, cut down on to the sticking bones (cervical vertebrae), saw across, and remove the clod and sticking in one piece. Rather favour the steak meat when making this cut, as it is the more valuable part. The clod is separated from the sticking by cutting through a natural fissure between the muscles, leaving the fat on the clod. The clod is a heavily muscled portion which is used chiefly for stewing, therefore the excessive fat should be removed in one portion, and after removing the lymphatic gland it can be used for fatting up the back-ribs, etc., sold as fat, or rendered down for dripping. The clod bone is removed, and situated beneath it is a very heavy muscle somewhat like one of the shin muscles, and where a cheap roasting or salting joint is required this muscle is carefully removed and sold as leg of beef, the remaining joint being rolled. The sticking is the most difficult portion to debone properly, on account of the irregular form of the cervical vertebrae. In this respect a very thin boning knife will be found useful, the flesh being laid back from the vertebral column prior to removing the individual bones. The name of this joint obviously originated from the fact that this is the region in which the animal is 'stuck' during the process of slaughtering. Consequently there is always a certain amount of discoloration on the throat surface, and during warm weather this area will rapidly exhibit signs of slime caused by bacterial contamination. The small portion of yellow tissue originally known as 'pax-wax',* and even now frequently referred to as paddy-wax, consists almost entirely of elastin, so it is of no value from the butchers' aspect.

(6) *Fore-rib.* The fore-rib is one of the most valuable portions in the forequarter, and every effort should be made to keep it absolutely rectangular, so that the four individual ribs may be cut with the fair quota of meat or, in the case of rolled ribs, to produce a neat roll with square edges. When cutting this joint the steak knife should be kept protruding between the 6th and 7th rib and drawn towards the chine, rather than using a sawing motion, followed by sawing and chopping. If it is intended for rolling, the rib and vertebrae bones should be carefully removed, the cartilaginous tip of the blade bone trimmed out, and the whole tightly rolled. As already mentioned, a short cut fore-rib is sometimes prepared by a strip from the top of the ribs (flat tops). If this method is followed, less should be removed from the gristle rib-side, as its greater thickness will tend to offset the length; in other words, the flat tops should slope slightly, being wider at wing-rib end.

*The Experienced Butcher, 1816.

(7) and (8) *Middle rib*. From the remaining portion, the pony, a four-bone middle-rib is removed. This is carried out by inserting a steak knife between the 2nd and 3rd rib and drawing it towards the chine until the blade bone is reached, cutting the surface muscles over the top of the bone, and when the edge of the bone is reached, cutting down through the dorsal and crest muscles to the chine. It is then necessary to saw through the blade bone, which, incidentally, is one of the hardest bones in the carcase. The cut between the ribs is then completed to sever the muscles beneath the blade bone, the chine bone then being sawn and chopped through. The division into back-ribs (7) and top-ribs (8) is accomplished by cutting across the middle rib at a slight angle down on to the blade bone. Saw across this bone from the bone side towards the cartilage end, continuing the cut with a knife, down to the ribs at an angle which will produce a square joint, and finally saw through the four rib bones fairly closely to the chine.

(7) *Back-ribs*. The fin bones (spinal processes) should be *partly* sawn through and knocked over with the back of the chopper; to produce a more compact joint, strip out the yellow tissue. Remove the blade bone, making certain not to cut through the outer skin when going over the spine of the scapula; place in the pocket a suitable portion of fat, adjusting the quantity according to the fatness of the ribs. Skewer over the flap, picking up the ends of the four rib bones, and insert another row of skewers to retain the fat in position. String up, the strings being in line with the skewers and rib bone. The back-ribs or, as they are sometimes termed, short-ribs can be completely boned and rolled or, if there is a heavy demand for stewing steak, it may be more profitable to sell it as chuck steak.

(8) *Top-ribs*. Though these ribs are sometimes sold with the blade bone in, it is probably better to remove it as it is a very difficult little bone for the housewife to carve round. This small portion of scapula can be easily removed and replaced with a layer of fat. It is usual to take a strip off the top of the ribs, the thick tops; this cut should be sloped slightly, as the thick end of the ribs will stand more 'length'. The top ribs should be skewered up with two rows of skewers, keeping close to the rib bones, and finally strung up with one string to each rib, keeping close to the bone and its respective skewers, so that single ribs can be removed without cutting the string or exposing the skewers. Both the top-ribs and back-ribs are generally looked upon as a rather second-grade roast, but if carefully prepared their popularity can be increased.

(9), (10), and (11) *Steak meat*. This remaining portion of the quarter frequently gives rise to some confusion as it is cut into three parts. The steak meat is laid on its back and the two ribs sawn through, followed by a knife cut, just missing the blade bone. For some strange reason this part is called the leg-of-mutton cut top-ribs (9), frequently abbreviated to leg-of-mutton cut, or leg tops. The part remaining is divided into the chuck (10) and the blade bone (11) by splitting through the seam, leaving the majority of the fat on the chuck, only a small strip remaining on the blade bone.

(9) *Leg-of-mutton cut*. This joint is sold as a second-grade roast and in some cases the portions of the two rib bones may be left in, though if it is to be cut into smaller joints it is desirable to remove them. Beneath these bones is situated some rather heavy blood-vessels and it is a good plan to remove them by twisting them round a skewer and steadily pulling, prior to skewering and tying up.

(10) *Chuck*. The bones and the yellow tissue should be removed, the meat then providing a very good stewing steak. The toughest portion is the crest muscle of the neck, and frequently a transverse cut is made to remove this portion for sale as a cheaper-grade stewing steak.

(11) *Blade bone*. If the point of the boning knife is inserted under the periosteum the meat can be cleanly stripped away from the blade bone. This again provides a good-class stewing steak, and from the aspect of display many butchers prefer to remove the major portion of the 'flap', cutting the 'roll' of the blade bone into attractive fillet-like steaks.

Lamb and mutton cutting (Fig. 44)

From the purely profit angle the jointing of lamb and mutton carcases is probably less important than that of beef or pork as (A) the price ratio as between the various joints tends to show less variation, and (B) most of the joints are sold with the bone in. However, from the aspect of sales appeal, skilful cutting can make a great difference in the appearance of the joints.

In a very good carcase the legs, loins, shoulders, and best necks, which show little price differential, represent about 80%, and this leaves only the breast, middle, and scrag, about 20%, at a much lower price level. Therefore, this apparently large discrepancy in price per lb should be divided by 4 and added to the rest of the carcase to enable us to obtain a true picture of value in relation to cost. For example, assuming we purchase a mutton carcase at 40p per lb and the value of the scrag, middle, and breast retail is 20p per lb, the other portions must be increased to 45p per lb to bring the cost of the whole carcase to 40p per lb.

As in the case of beef, minor variations in cutting methods are met with, but the following will indicate the general procedure.

The sheep normally possess 13 pairs of ribs (14 are sometimes found),

TABLE 32

London and Home Counties beef cutting

No.	Joint	Bones	More important muscles
		Hindquarter	
(1)	Thin flank		Rectus and oblique and trans-
(2)–(3)	Fat and skirt	3 ribs (part of)	verse abdominal muscles, parts of back muscles
(4)	Rump	Ilium and 5 sacral vertebrae	Iliopsoas, gluteus, longissimus dorsi, multifidus spinae, etc.
(5)	Loin and wing end	6 lumbar vertebrae, 3½ dorsal vertebrae, 3 ribs (part of)	Longissimus costarum, longus dorsi, multifidus spinae, psoas
(6)	Thick flank	Patella	Quadriceps femoris
(7)	Leg of beef	Tibia–fibula, and some tarsal bones	Gastrocnemius, parts of semi-tendinosus, semi-membranosus and biceps; flexors and extensors of digits
(8)	Aitch bone	Pubic bone, part of femur	Gluteus, semi-tendinosus, semi-membranosus biceps, gracilis, etc.
(9)	Topside		Biceps femoris, gracilis, adductors of thigh, part of quadriceps
(10)	Silverside	Femur	Semi-tendinosus, semi-membranosus, part of quadriceps
		Forequarter	
(1)	Shin	Radius and ulna, some carpal bones	Brachialis anticus, biceps brachii, triceps, flexors and extensors of digits
(2)	Flank	4 ribs (part of) and cartilages	Oblique and transverse abdominal muscles
(3)	Brisket	6 ribs (part of), sternum (7 segments)	Deep pectoral, serratus ventralis, part of abdominal muscles
(4)	Clod	Humerus	The neck muscles, particularly portions of sterno-cephalis, brachio-cephalis, pectorals,
(5)	Sticking	7 cervical vertebrae	biceps brachii

TABLE 32 *continued*

No.	Joint	Bones	More important muscles
Forequarter *continued*			
(6)	Fore-rib	4 ribs (part of), 4 dorsal vertebrae, some cartilage of scapula	Longissimus dorsi, erector spinae, parts of abdominal muscles
(7)	Back-ribs	4 ribs (part of), 4 dorsal vertebrae, scapula (part of)	Parts of trapezius, long costal, rhomboideus serratus, lattissimus dorsi and deltoid
(8)	Top-ribs	4 ribs (part of), scapula (part of)	Parts of deltoid, pectorals, serratus, etc.
(9)	Leg-of-mutton cut	2 ribs (part of)	
(10)	Chuck	2 dorsal vertebrae, 2 ribs (small part of)	Triceps, supraspinatus, infraspinatus, deltoid muscle, trapezius (parts of)
(11)	Blade bone	Scapula (part of)	

The vertebrae referred to above consist of half the bone, as in splitting the carcase the spinal column is divided

and it is usually *quartered off* by finding the cartilaginous pad between the 12th and 13th vertebrae with the point of the knife, and then cutting between the ribs. The amount of breast left attached will be determined by circumstances, but, if the loin is to be sold whole, it is obviously desirable to leave a fair amount of 'flap' attached to it; not so if it is for chops, as excessive trimming will be necessary.

The hindquarters are split by inserting the knife in the vent and using the tail as a lever, drawing the knife forward to divide the aitch bone by cutting through the cartilage (symphysis pubes). In the carcase of a young animal where ossification is incomplete this will require very little pressure. The vertebrae of the tail should then be cut with the knife and the portion divided by chopping down the backbone. Lay the hind on the block, cut a small portion of the flap on to the leg, and at a slight angle saw across the bone. The actual line of demarcation will depend on the demand for chump chops and their value as compared with the leg, but care must be taken not to cut too tightly on the bone. Following the saw cut, complete the division with *one* clean cut of the knife.

(1) *Leg.* As a rule this joint is sold whole for roasting or baking. A thick stocky leg is preferred, and though it might contain the same quantity of bone as a shanky one, it will provide better slices across the main muscles and the meat does not tend to 'draw up' from the shank

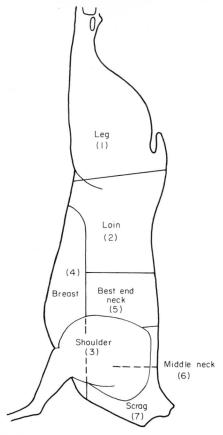

Fig. 44 Mutton cutting, London and Home Counties method

Portions in order of removal   Use

(1) Legs   Roasting, braising, boiling; leg cutlets grilling or frying
(2) Loins   Roasting, braising, or as chops for grilling or frying
(3) Shoulder   Roasting, braising
(4) Breast   Stewing, or stuffed and roasted
(5) Best neck   Roasting, braising, or as chops for grilling or frying
(6)
and
(7) Middle and scrag   Stewing

on cooking. If cutlets are taken from the centre of the leg the value of the remaining portions will be greatly depreciated, therefore the cost of the cutlets must be proportionately increased.

For some classes of trade a 'Frenched leg' is required, and this is prepared by cutting around the shank muscle about 2 in from the break joint and trimming the meat away from the bone. In institutions or establishments where the meat, after cooking, is cut on a slicing machine, it may be necessary to completely debone the leg. This can be carried out by cutting down as far as the stifle joint and removing the leg bone, followed by the patella (cramp bone). The aitch bone is next taken out and finally the thigh bone (femur). This should be tunnelled out without cutting through the outside of the leg. The shank meat is then tucked into the pocket in the centre of the leg and held in position by securing it with two stitches, using a trussing needle.

(2) *Loin*. The kidney suet may be removed or sold with the loin. If the loin is to be sold whole, it greatly assists the housewife if the loin is 'chined', i.e. the transverse processes of the vertebrae sawn across, and the chump bone sawn through two or three times. The loin chops can, of course, be divided by chopping through between the cartilage pads, but too frequently the muscle is cut into and often the joints are missed altogether. For display purposes it was frequently the custom to exhibit a saddle or chine with the tail split through, and bent round, placing a kidney in the spaces so formed, the back then being decorated by raising the fat into an artistic pattern, followed by dusting with flour. Occasionally the loin is rolled after removing the vertebrae to supply double cutlets. The chump end lends itself particularly well to this form of cutlet.

(3) *Shoulder*. The cartilaginous tip of the blade bone (scapula) can usually be located with the point of the knife at about the 6th rib and this will provide a good guide as to the correct cut. The actual shape may vary from a round to almost a square cut shoulder, but in all cases the underlying neck muscle should not be cut into. As much weight as possible should be obtained on the shoulder without spoiling the sale of the 'target'. If carried out properly, the butcher aims at showing the 'five fingers', five distinct marks caused by cutting through the thoracic muscles. If it is necessary to cut the shoulder into two, it is advisable to avoid cutting on the thick part of the clod bone (humerus) and to hold the knife vertically when cutting as far as the bone, then saw through, completing the cut with the knife. This will prevent the bone dust and marrow from being spread across the entire cut surface. The shoulder also can be boned and rolled, and this should be attempted as follows.

Loosen the meat on each side of the blade bone, find the joint, and pull the blade bone away from the meat. Tunnel round the clod bone, taking care not to cut through the outside of the shoulder, and break the joint over the edge of the block so that the bone can be easily removed. Remove the meat from the shank bone and, after the bone is taken out, insert the meat in the pocket of the shoulder, secure as in the case of the leg, and roll. For display purposes 'mock duck' is prepared in a similar fashion, except that the shank bone is left in to form the neck.

(4) *Breast*. This is removed from the target, and a slight slope when making the cut will increase the area of the cut surface and improve the appearance. If it is to be displayed cut across, cut almost completely through the breast at the last bone of the sternum and this will give a lean surface. In some parts of America it is the practice to cut a wide breast straight down, including the knuckle end of the shoulder, the whole being then boned and rolled, the lean meat providing a good centre to what might otherwise be a somewhat fatty roll. Normally the breast is looked upon as an inferior stewing portion, though it can provide a very sweet roast, particularly if stuffed.

(5) *Best end neck*. As with the loin, this portion, usually containing 6 rib bones, is better chined. When prepared as cutlets it is sometimes worth while to remove a small portion of the top of the rib bones, folding the meat over, somewhat like the loin chop. With French lamb chops the chine bone is removed and about two inches of the meat is cut away from the ends of the ribs previous to cutting it into chops. A rather fancy product is prepared by treating the pair of necks in this fashion and moulding them in shape, with the ribs projecting in a circle at the top to form a 'crown roast'. The end rib bones can be held in position with a stitch.

(6) *Middle neck*. As a rule this contains six rib bones and is essentially a stewing portion. Here again when chopping through the joints every care must be taken to avoid bone splinters. The middle neck and the scrag are frequently sold together. Under extreme conditions it is possible to obtain one or two poor grade cutlets from the best end of the middle neck. During the summer weather it is probably more economical to cut a full shoulder, trimming the remaining meat from the middle neck and utilizing it for manufacturing purposes.

(7) *Scrag*. This is the cheapest portion of the carcase, and efforts have been made to change it from a stewing joint pure and simple into cutlets suitable for braising. In this case the scrag is left whole and it is cut across to form double cutlets leaving the throat side of the scrag to form an attachment for the two portions. These cutlets can be slightly improved by removing the yellow tissue which runs along the back of the scrag.

Removing bark. It is usual to remove the bark or fell from the best end neck and loin, as it is an extremely tough membrane. Also, the appearance of the meat is improved by its removal. In the case of the leg its removal is not desirable, as during roasting it tends to retain the meat juices and preserves the shape of the leg.

Splitting fores. This operation has not been mentioned in the normal sequence of cutting, as the following variations may be found.

Shoulders and/or breasts may be removed prior to splitting, the best necks may be cut off as a pair and then chopped down, and less frequently the entire carcase may be chopped down into sides. Some butchers, particularly in the case of imported carcases, prefer to remove the breasts before the carcase is quartered.

Pork cutting (London and Home Counties) (Fig. 45)

There is no rigid sequence of cutting, as much will depend upon the individual circumstances, and as with the case of beef and mutton, a general indication of the various operations will be given. Great care is necessary in jointing, particularly as the differences in value as between, say, the head and fore end and to a lesser extent the belly and loin, are very great.

The carcase is usually suspended by the tendons of its right leg. In the carcase of a young pig it is possible to split the first few vertebrae from the tail by pulling down steadily with a knife. The line of the spinal processes is then found by finger pressure, and a light cut through the skin is made from the original cut down to the nape of the neck. The left ear of the pig is then held and a clean incision made across the back of the neck in line with the first bone of the vertebrae. The cut is continued round the left side of the jowl, following close to the line of the jaw bone. If the head is to be used for manufacturing purposes, little harm is done in actually exposing the bone; on the other hand, should they be intended for retail sale it is desirable to leave a small margin of muscle over it.

In a small pig it is possible to support the weight of the left side with the left forearm whilst chopping down, but with a heavy carcase it is necessary to hook up the leg.

The bones of a pig are relatively soft and, for chopping down, a sharp, fairly light chopper is preferable. A steady swing should be acquired, keeping the chopper at a slight angle so that the vertebrae followed by the spinal processes are split through. The side is then removed by loosening any attachment to the head.

After laying the side on the block, the trotter is usually broken over by cutting across the back and applying a sharp press forwards. If the leg is intended for arterial pumping, this knuckling should not be carried out until after pumping. A square or round cut leg may be cut, some butchers leaving the tail on the leg whilst others prefer it on the loin. The pork saw should be sloped at a slight angle when cutting through the rump bone, following through with one clean sweep of the knife.

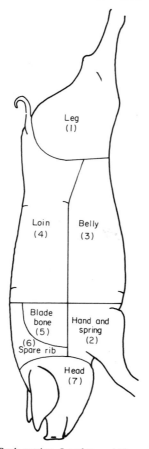

Fig. 45 Pork cutting, London and Home Counties method

Portions in order of removal	Use
(1) Legs	Roasting, salting, and boiling
(2) Hand and spring	Roasting, salting, and boiling
(3) { Belly	Salting and boiling, roasting
{ Flare	Lard
(4) Loin	Roasting, chops frying or grilling
(5) Blade bone	Roasting
(6) Spare-rib	Roasting, chops frying or grilling
(7) Head	Salting and boiling, boar's head roast

(1) *Leg.* A fairly cut leg from a good carcase will represent about 25% of the side. For many classes of trade it is necessary to cut the leg in two, and at one time it was the practice to sell a portion of the trotter with the best or fillet end. They may be roasted or salted and boiled, and in some parts steaks are cut from the larger legs. If it is necessary

to take out the bone, this can be carried out as described in the case of mutton, but a proper ham gouge is a great help.

To separate the hand and belly from the long loin, find the joint between the blade bone and humerus, and from this point mark down over the ribs (usually 14), and at the last rib cut through the belly-wall down to the chump end. Remember the difference in price between the two portions. Then saw through the ribs, using a pork saw, do *not* saw into the meat. If the left hand is placed under the 'jacket', the ribs can be pushed upwards whilst sawing and thus protect the underlying muscle. Complete the separation by loosening the clod bone from the blade and making one clean cut. When making this cut, slope the knife *very* slightly away from the belly.

(2) and (3) *Hand and spring, and belly.* When cutting the hand and spring (2) from the belly (3) the knuckle of the hand should be pulled forward to avoid cutting the end of the shank bone and it is usually cut with the portion of one rib bone. It is a relatively cheap portion and is used as a second-grade roast, or it may be salted and boiled. As it is lean, it provides a good centre for pressed bellies, particularly if the latter are fairly fat. The belly is seldom sold with the flare, or as it may be termed 'flick' or 'flead', attached. It is removed by cutting lightly along its attachment to the skirt and stripping away. Where arterial pumping is employed this cut *must not* penetrate the muscle, or the artery will probably be severed. Though the belly is generally looked upon as a boiling cut it can be boned and rolled for roasting. A condition referred to as 'seedy cut' is sometimes found in the milk ducts of female pigs descended from black pigs, and though this pigment is harmless, it produces an objectionable appearance which necessitates trimming.

(4) *Loin.* The loin is separated from the long loin by severing from it the 'neck end'. The actual line of demarcation varies somewhat, but between the 4th and 5th rib, so that a small portion of the cartilage of the blade bone is left in the short loin, appears to be generally favoured. This cut can be made by cutting through the cartilage on to the chine, followed by chopping or by sawing through the chine, and by completing the division with the knife. The short loin is again divided by cutting through at the kidney, so that both the hind and fore loin each possess half of the kidney, which enhances their appearance. As already mentioned in the case of mutton, chining is probably preferable to chopping. In an excessively fat pig it may be necessary to strip off the rind and a quantity of the back fat, in which case the loin is referred to as a hog meat. Incidentally you will notice that there are two distinct layers of fat laid down.

(5) and (6) *Blade bone and spare rib.* The blade bone (joint) is sepa-

rated from the spare rib (6). If the latter is intended for chops it should be favoured slightly, but under no circumstances should the blade bone itself be exposed. If the rind is on the neck end, it is wise to cut round the line of the blade bone and, placing the left hand on the top, press lightly so that the bone is tilted slightly away from the spare rib. Then, if a clean cut is made, there is little risk of cutting on to the bone. Both these portions may be used for roasting, but as the blade bone is a difficult joint to carve it is probably better to remove the bone.

(7) *The head.* In the case of the right side the head will of course be the first joint removed. To split the head, chop through the point of the lower jaw bone *without* damaging the tongue, chop lightly through the bone at the back of the head where it joins the spine, and split down the frontal bone with the chopper *without* damaging the brain. In this way the brain and the tongue can be removed intact if desired. By inserting a knife behind the eye, the ligaments can be loosened and the eyeball levered out of its socket prior to cutting its attachments. At times the halves of the head are subdivided into eyepieces, jowls, and ears.

Veal cutting (Fig. 46)

The cutting of small calves, i.e. the bobby type, follows closely the method employed for mutton carcases. In 'veal' calves the traditional manner is to cut the leg above the aitch bone, leaving a loin and chump, the leg portion ex the knuckle then being referred to as a fillet. The shoulder minus the fore knuckle is termed the oyster, and the remaining portions possess a similar nomenclature to that of mutton. The calf is chopped down into sides, and the sides quartered, usually by cutting between the 12th and 13th ribs—that is, one rib on the hind. The fillet together with the knuckle is cut off just above the aitch bone (symphysis pubes).

(1) *Fillet.* The fillet is separated from the knuckle by jointing through just above the cramp (patella). This is the most valuable part of the carcase and the thigh bone (femur) is frequently removed prior to sale.

(2) *Knuckle.* This portion is in great demand for stewing for children or invalids, though it may show a better return if the meat is removed for pie veal and the bone sold separately.

(3) and (4) *Loin and chump.* The loin is cut through between the lumbar and sacral vertebrae and can either be used for roasting or cut into cutlets. There is usually demand for these cutlets in the hotel and restaurant trade. The chump contains an awkward-shaped bone and is somewhat difficult to carve when roasted. It is probably better to remove the rump end, cutting it into chump chops and using the remaining portion boned out as pie meat.

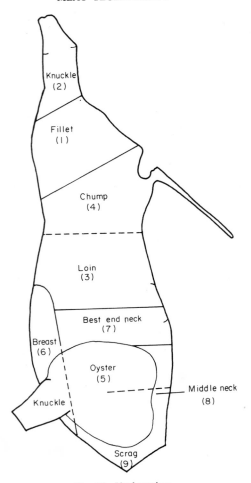

Fig. 46   Veal cutting

(5) *Oyster and fore-knuckle.* The shoulder is treated in a similar fashion to that of mutton as are also the remaining portions.

(6) *Breast.* This is marked down with a knife and the cut is followed through by sawing across the ribs. It is a cheap portion and, though it can be stuffed and baked, is frequently used for stewing.

(7) *Best end neck.* In good-sized calves veal cutlets should be cut from this portion by cutting one cutlet with the rib bone and one without to ensure that they are not too thick. If intended for roasting, it should be chopped through or chined and the tops of the ribs cracked over to reduce the apparent length. It is a good plan to trim out the cartilage of the blade bone from the 'gristle-rib' end.

(8) and (9) *Middle neck and scrag*. These joints are used for stewing and may be divided or sold together. The vertebrae is chopped across between the pads, though in some cases it may be better to remove the bones and use the meat for pie veal or manufacturing purposes.

ROLLED FOREQUARTERS

Bobby calves—that is, calves up to about 3 weeks of age—are frequently looked upon as a rather troublesome, though necessary, by-product of the dairy industry, and as such can frequently be obtained at a reasonable figure. With this type of carcase the fores, on account of their size, always present something of a problem. They can supply a valuable product to the sausage-maker, but the average retailer may have to look to some other method of dealing with them. If handled carefully, they can be turned into a very attractive boneless, rolled roast. The following is probably the best method of preparation. Cut off the knuckle, for sale whole or boned. Trim away any discoloured portions of the throat, and remove the sticking bones as far as the first rib. Loosen out and remove the brisket bone (sternum), and with the point of the knife cut into the gristle between the top of the ribs and the brisket. *This must not be cut right through* or the ribs will not strip out. Cut the pleura over the ribs and, standing the fore on its chine, beat the meat from the ribs with the back of the chopper. Provided that the thin membrane between the rib and the flesh side is intact, the ribs will skin out and can be removed by boning the chine. Next, tunnel out the clod bone (humerus), turn the fore over and remove the blade bone from the inside, taking care not to cut through the outer skin. Square up the boneless fore by trimming and beating it out flat. Place a piece of flare fat in the centre and roll tightly, with a thin layer of fat on the outside.

Bacon cutting (Fig. 47)

The cutting of bacon is somewhat similar to that of pork, provided that we remember that the chine, aitch bone, blade bone, and usually the sternum bone have been previously removed. For normal purposes the rib bones should first be removed, starting them with a knife and completing their extraction with a string.

(1) *Gammon*. The demand for gammon as against rashers will determine to some extent where the cut is made. Usually it is cut across about half an inch from the exposed end of the thigh bone (femur). This cut should be absolutely square.

(2) *Fore-end*. This is divided from the jacket or, as it is sometimes termed, spencer, by cutting between the 3rd and 4th, or the 4th and 5th

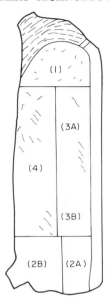

Fig. 47   Bacon cutting

Portions in order of removal	Use
(1) Gammon	Boiling and rashers
(2A) Collar	Boiling and rashers
(2B) Hock	Boiling
(3A) Best back	Rashers
(3B) Long loin	Rashers
(4) Streaky (thick and thin)	Rashers

ribs, from the neck end. As far as possible this cut should be parallel with the gammon end. The fore end consists of two portions, the collar (2A) and the fore-hock (2B). The division between these parts can be made by first finding the knob of the humerus, in the blade bone pocket, and cutting squarely just to miss this bone.

(3) *Loin* (3B) *and best back* (3A). This is removed from the middle by cutting across approximately on the centre line and it may then be sub-divided into the long loin and best back. Where the rib bones are left in, it is of course necessary to saw across prior to cutting.

(4) *Streaky*. The remaining portion is referred to as streaky but is frequently subdivided into thick streaky, thin streaky, and flank.

Tests on beef

TABLE 33

Test on wholesale cuts, imported beef

Hinds (average quality)		Fores (average quality)	
Joint	%	Joint	%
Top-piece and flank	60·7	Clod, sticking, and shin	29·7
Rump and loin	39·3	Coast	24·0
	100·0	Crop	46·3
	First Quality %		100·0
Top-piece and flank	60·4	Clod and sticking	24·0
Rump and loin	39·6	Shin	5·7
		Fore-rib	9·3
	100·0	Pony	37·0
		Coast	24·0
	Average quality %		100·0
Flank	8·3	Shin	5·7
Thick	11·5	Clod and sticking	24·0
Leg	10·1	Flank	12·0
Aitch bone	6·3	Brisket	12·0
Topside	13·0	Fore-rib	9·3
Silverside	10·7	Middle-rib	19·0
Loin	20·1	Steak meat	18·0
Rump	15·5		100·0
Kidney knob	4·5		
	100·0		

TABLE 34

Test on imported loins, clods, and briskets of beef (boned and rolled)

	A (%)	B (%)	C (%)
Rolled loin	67·5	63·0	55·0
Suet	10·4	15·8	23·5
Kidney	3·8	3·6	2·2
Fillet	6·5	5·3	7·0
Bones	11·5	10·8	10·6
Trimmings and loss	0·3	1·5	1·7
	100·0	100·0	100·0

Imported clods and stickings	(%)	Imported briskets	(%)
Meat, untrimmed	73·5	Trimmed	65·0
Fat	7·4	Fat trimmings	6·8
Clod bones	10·9	Bones	19·1
Sticking bones	8·0	Skirts	8·7
Loss	0·2	Loss	0·4
	100·0		100·0

TABLE 35

Tests on bone content

(a) Australian GAQ hindquarters*

Weight, ex wrapper lb	Weight bone lb oz	Weight net lb oz	% bone in ¼ (approx.)
194	30 13	163 3	15·9
210	31 10	178 6	15·1
194	27 8	166 8	14·2
193	26 5	166 11	13·6
194	30 0	164 0	15·5
194	31 5	162 11	16·1
Total 1179	177 9	1001 7	Average 15·1

*Including kidney knob.

TABLE 35 *continued*

(b) Australian GAQ top-pieces

Weight lb	Weight bone lb oz		Weight net lb oz		% bone in top-piece (approx.)
120	17	0	103	0	14·1
117	15	10	101	6	13·5
89	11	13	77	3	13·2
127	18	0	109	0	14·2
Total 453	62	7	390	9	Average 13·8

(c) Australian GAQ rumps

Weight lb oz		Weight bone lb oz		Weight net lb oz		% bone in rump (approx.)
28	10	4	7	24	3	15·5
34	8	4	13	29	11	13·9
30	10	4	8	26	2	14·7
27	4	4	10	22	10	17·0
27	14	4	8	23	6	16·1
36	11	5	5	31	6	14·5
28	0	4	2	23	14	14·7
Total 213	9	32	5	181	4	Average 15·2

Wholesale cuts (Smithfield)

BEEF

Hindquarter ex KKCF. A hindquarter, less kidney knob and channel fat.

Hindquarter × (H¼ ×). A hindquarter, less the thin flank.

Hindquarter × × (H¼ × ×). A hindquarter, less the thin flank and kidney knob.

Top-piece (Tpce.). Topside, silverside, thick flank, aitch bone, and leg.

Top-piece and flank (Tpce. and Flk.). A top-piece, with the thin flank attached.

Rump and loin (Rp. and Ln.). Rump, loin, and kidney knob.

Rump and loin × (Rp. and Ln. ×). Rump and loin, less the kidney knob.

Forequarter × (F¼ ×). A forequarter, less the flank.

Forequarter × × (F¼ × ×). A forequarter, less flank and brisket.

Forequarter × × × (F$\frac{1}{4}$× × ×). A forequarter treble ×. A forequarter minus flank, shank, and brisket, or Australian crop.

Crop. A middle-rib, steak meat, and fore-rib.

Short crop. Fore-rib and middle rib.

Pony. Steak meat and middle rib.

Bottom-piece (Btm.-pce.). Clod and sticking, steak meat, and shin.

Coast. Flank and brisket.

Clod, sticking, and shin (C.S. and S.).

Side. H$\frac{1}{4}$ and F$\frac{1}{4}$, together.

Scotch short side (S.S. Side). Side, less bottom-piece.

Roasting top-piece. Loin and fore-rib.

Gun bit. Rump, loin, fore-rib, and top-piece.

Buttock (But.). Topside and silverside, with bone.

Short. F$\frac{1}{4}$, less fore-rib and flank.

MUTTON

Haunches. A pair of legs with the chump ends of the loins attached.

Chine or saddle. A pair of loins.

Chines and ends. A chine and pair of best end necks.

Hinds. Pair of legs and loins.

Hinds and ends (H$\frac{1}{4}$ and ends). Pair of legs, loins, and best end necks.

Fores. Pair of F$\frac{1}{4}$s.

Short F$\frac{1}{4}$s. F$\frac{1}{4}$s, less best end necks.

Jacket. Carcase, less legs and shoulders.

Trunk. Carcase, less legs.

Necks. Pairs of F$\frac{1}{4}$s, less shoulders.

Sets. Pairs of scrags, middle necks, and breasts.

PORK

Loin. Loin, including neck end.

Short loin. Loin, less neck end.

Hog meat. Loin, less rind and some back fat.

Hand and belly. Hand and spring and belly.

Fore end. Neck and hand and spring.

Hands. Hand and spring.

Jacket. Side, less leg, ex-head.

Pig ×. Carcase, less head.

Neck end. Blade bone and spare-rib (sometimes in pairs).

Back fat. Rind and fat removed from loin.

Middles. Short loins and bellies.

Cutting tests (imported beef)

The following analyses were obtained from the averages of a test carried out on 50 hinds and 50 fores, weighed de-frosted and without wrappers. Reasonable care was taken in de-boning, and the small quantity of meat left on the bones was probably comparable with normal commercial practice. The joints were cut in the London and Home Counties fashion, the pubic bone being removed, leaving a long cut silverside. None of the portions were trimmed and for the sake of convenience the average gross weights of the quarters were adjusted to the nearest lb.

TABLE 36

Cutting tests on imported beef

50 hinds (average 156 lb)			50 fores (average 167 lb)		
Joint	Weight lb oz	Approx. % of H¼	Joint	Weight lb oz	Approx. % of F¼
Thin flank	11 4	7·2	Shin	9 9	5·7
Cod fat	3 10	2·3	Clod	19 4	11·5
Goose skirt	1 0	0·6	Sticking	13 3	7·9
Loin	28 8	18·3	Flank	16 12	10·0
Kidney suet	6 5	4·0	Brisket	21 2	12·7
Kidney	1 1	0·7	Fore-rib	18 7	11·0
Rump	23 8	15·0	Top-ribs	15 8	9·3
Rump suet	1 13	1·1	Back-ribs	17 11	10·6
Thick flank	16 8	10·6	Leg-of-mutton		
Leg	12 8	8·0	cut	12 9	7·5
Topside	18 5	11·9	Chuck	14 0	8·4
Long silverside	28 8	18·3	Blade bone	8 0	4·8
Pubic bone			Loss	15	0·6
(part of)	2 4	1·4			
Loss	14	0·6			
Total	156 0	100·0	Total	167 0	100·0
Total bone 21 lb 3 oz, approx. 13·6%			Total bone 28 lb 8 oz, approx. 17·0%		

TABLE 36 *continued*

Good quality Argentine hindquarter (195 lb)			Very poor quality Imported hindquarter (118 lb)		
Joint	Weight lb oz	Bone lb oz	Joint	Weight lb oz	Bone lb oz
Thin flank	14 5	7	Thin flank	7 8	7
Goose skirt	1 7		Goose skirt	1 2	
Cod fat	4 10		Cod fat	2 4	
Kidney knob	12 9		Kidney knob	3 3	
Loin	41 9	4 12	Loin	22 8	4 4
Thick flank	23 6	6	Thick flank	14 4	5
Leg of beef	13 4	5 9	Leg of beef	9 11	4 9
Topside	20 9		Topside	13 7	
Long silverside	32 0	6 0	Long silverside	23 0	4 14
Pubic bone	2 5	2 5	Pubic bone	2 1	2 1
Rump	25 6	4 2	Rump and suet	18 2	3 9
Rump suet	1 14				
Aitch bone trimmings	1 12		Aitch bone trimmings	14	
	195 0	23 9		118 0	20 1
Approximately 12% bone			Approximately 17% bone		
Good quality Argentine forequarter (191 lb)			Very poor quality Imported forequarter (114 lb)		
Joint	Weight lb oz	Bone lb oz	Joint	Weight lb oz	Bone lb oz
Shin	10 11	4 1	Shin	7 1	3 10
Clod	22 0	4 4	Clod	13 5	3 8
Sticking	15 6	2 4	Sticking	12 5	2 7
Brisket	26 0	4 11	Brisket	10 11	3 6
Flank	18 8	1 12	Flank	9 2	1 7
Fore-rib	17 15	2 3	Fore-rib and thin tops	14 12	2 12
Thin tops	4 11	11			
Leg-of-mutton cut	13 7	8	Leg-of-mutton cut	10 2	10
Blade bone	8 13	1 3	Blade bone	5 8	13
Chuck	15 11	2 2	Chuck	8 5	2 2
Back-ribs	21 0	2 3	Back-ribs	11 7	2 6
Top-ribs	16 4	1 5	Top-ribs	10 12	1 11
Trimmings	10		Trimmings	10	
	191 0	27 3		114 0	24 12
Approximately 14·2% bone			Approximately 21·7% bone		

TABLE 37

Test on bone content (imported forequarters)

Joint	Good quality (190 lb)		Average quality (162 lb)		Very poor quality (113 lb)	
	Joint as a percentage of quarter	Bone as a percentage of joint	Joint as a percentage of quarter	Bone as a percentage of joint	Joint as a percentage of quarter	Bone as a percentage of joint
Shin	5·5	38	6·0	41·5	6·2	46
Clod	11·6	19·4	11·7	24·5	11·8	26
Sticking	8·1	14·7	9·9	15·4	10·9	16
Brisket	13·6	18·2	13·0	18·8	9·5	31·5
Flank	9·7	9·5	10·0	12·2	8·1	15·8
Fore-rib	11·9	12·7	10·9	18·3	12·9	26·5
Leg-of-mutton cut	7·1	3·7	6·0	5·3	9·0	5·6
Blade bone	4·6	15·0	4·6	13·5	4·5	15·8
Chuck	8·2	11·2	7·3	12·5	7·4	25·5
Back-ribs	11·0	10·3	10·7	15·4	10·1	20·5
Top-ribs	8·7	7·9	9·9	12·5	9·5	15·8
Percentage of bone in quarter	14·3%		17·2%		22·6%	

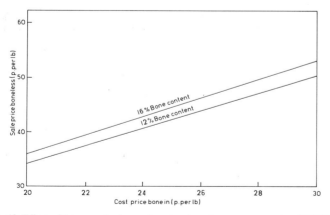

Fig. 48 Effect of bone content on sale price, based on gross margin of 33⅓%

Manufacturing beef

The following tests are averages obtained from a large number of manufacturing quarters. The trimming throughout was severe, skin, gristles, tendons being removed and the fat thoroughly trimmed. In the case of bone-in quarters, the standard of boning was typical of normal commercial practice.

AVERAGE YIELD TESTS

English manufacturing grade cow beef. All cuts trimmed free of skin, gristles, tendons, and excessive fat.

Hinds (bone-in)

	% of quarter
Lean trimmed meat	52·9
Fat	15·1
Kidney	0·8
Bones	19·4
Skin, gristles, tendons, etc.	10·3
Loss and waste	1·5
	100·0

Hinds (boneless), ex kidney knob

	% of quarter
Lean trimmed meat	68·0
Fat	14·9
Skin, gristles, tendons, etc.	15·4
Loss and waste	1·7
	100·0

Hinds—yield from boneless primal cuts

	% trimmed meat	% fat	% skin gristle, etc.	% loss and waste
Sirloin	70·3	15·8	12·7	1·2
Topside	78·5	4·6	16·0	0·9
Thick	66·8	9·0	23·1	1·1
Silverside	74·8	10·7	13·9	0·6
Flank	59·0	23·2	17·0	0·8
Hip (full cut rump)	77·6	11·3	10·4	0·7
Leg	71·5	—	27·9	0·6

Hind—flanks (good quality) bone-in

	%
Trimmed meat	61·3
Fat	17·0
Skin, gristle, etc.	11·8
Bones	9·2
Loss and waste	0·7
	100·0

Fores—bone-in

	%
Lean trimmed meat	53·8
Fat	11·6
Skin, gristle, etc.	9·1
Bones	24·0
Loss and waste	1·5
	100·0

Fores—boneless

	%
Lean trimmed meat	71·0
Fat	12·9
Skin, gristle, etc.	14·2
Loss and waste	1·9
	100·0

Fores—yield from boneless primal cuts

	% trimmed meat	% fat	% skin, gristle etc.	% loss and waste
Shin	81·2	—	18·3	0·5
Clod and sticking	78·2	14·9	6·1	0·8
Coast	61·0	30·5	8·1	0·4
Chuck	73·9	15·0	10·6	0·5
Chine	71·1	25·1	3·4	0·4
Shoulder (round cut)	61·2	30·8	7·5	0·5

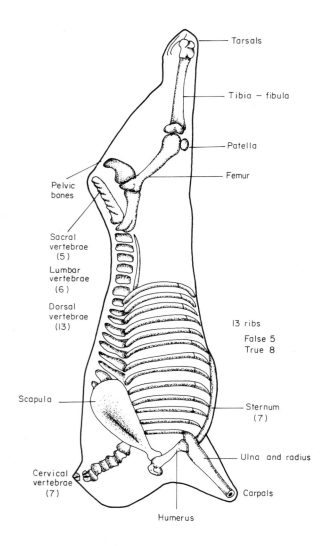

Fig. 49   Skeleton of beef carcase

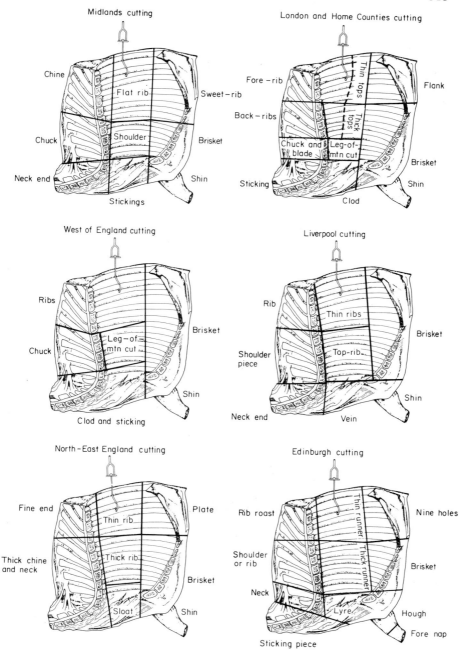

Fig. 50 Methods of cutting beef fores

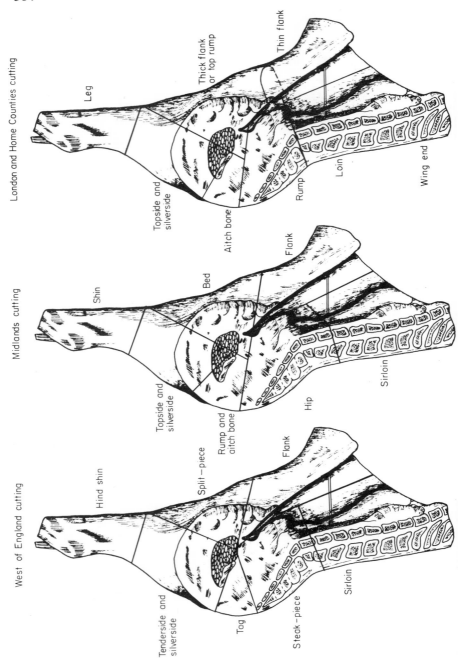

Fig. 51 Methods of cutting beef hinds

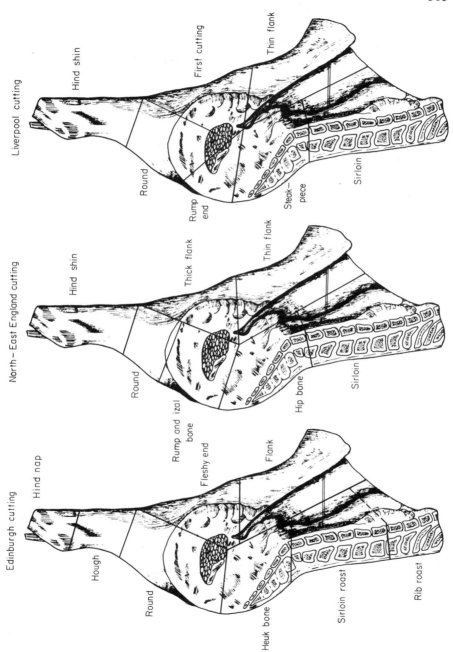

Fig. 51 (*cont.*)   Methods of cutting beef hinds

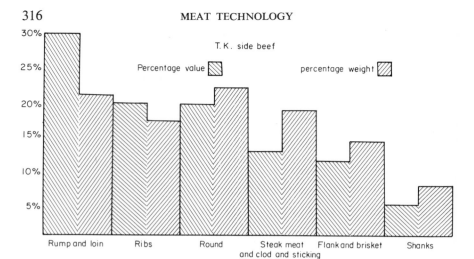

Fig. 52   Value to weight ratio (primal joints)

Regional variations

Methods of cutting vary considerably in different parts of the world and even within the United Kingdom; surprising differences may be found in relatively limited geographical areas.

A comparison of cuts becomes more complicated by the use of different nomenclature applied in various regions. For example, rump, steak-piece, head-piece, pope's eye, and hip bone are similar primal cuts of beef, although they may vary in the finer methods of cutting.

The list below includes some of the more uncommon terms used in different parts of this country.

The method of 'muscle' cutting common on the Continent has the advantage of separating muscles or groups of muscles of similar type, to ensure that the prepared joints possess almost identical eating characteristics. With such methods, considerable trim is involved and with the French method (see p. 321) about 5% of the initial side weight will represent 'muscle sheath' (connective tissue, gristles, etc.).

Tenderizing techniques can result in a higher proportion of the carcase being utilized for dry heat cooking. A suggested method of cutting such beef is indicated in Fig. 55.

Some regional terms for primal cuts of beef

Name	Region	Description (based on London cutting)
Shin, leg, shank	Many parts of UK	Shin and leg
Plate	Many parts of UK	Forequarter and flank
Rand	S. England	Forequarter and flank

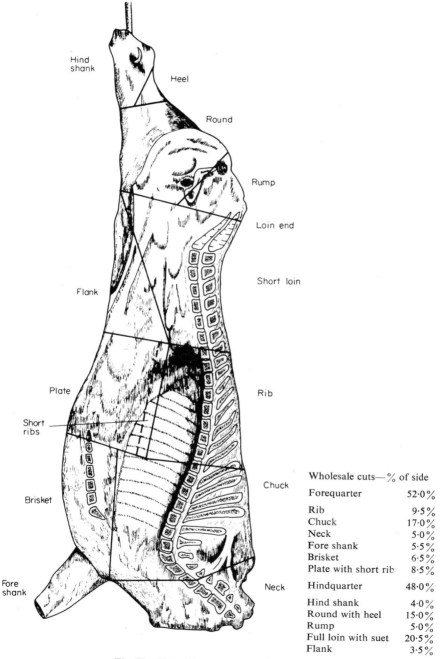

Hind shank

Heel

Round

Rump

Loin end

Short loin

Flank

Plate

Short ribs

Brisket

Rib

Chuck

Fore shank

Neck

Wholesale cuts—% of side	
Forequarter	52·0%
Rib	9·5%
Chuck	17·0%
Neck	5·0%
Fore shank	5·5%
Brisket	6·5%
Plate with short rib	8·5%
Hindquarter	48·0%
Hind shank	4·0%
Round with heel	15·0%
Rump	5·0%
Full loin with suet	20·5%
Flank	3·5%

Fig. 53   United States cutting, wholesale cuts

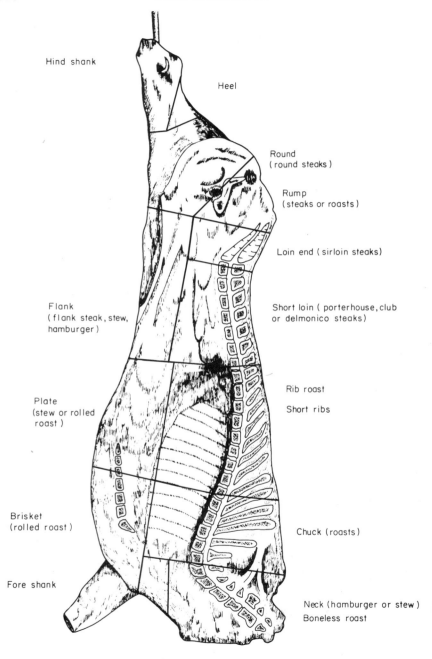

Hind shank

Heel

Round
(round steaks)

Rump
(steaks or roasts)

Loin end (sirloin steaks)

Flank
(flank steak, stew,
hamburger)

Short loin (porterhouse, club
or delmonico steaks)

Rib roast

Short ribs

Plate
(stew or rolled
roast)

Brisket
(rolled roast)

Chuck (roasts)

Fore shank

Neck (hamburger or stew)
Boneless roast

Fig. 54   An American method of cutting and use of joints

Name	Region	Description (based on London cutting)
Split-piece	W. England	Thick flank
Tenderside	W. England	Topside
Steak-piece and locking suet	W. England	Rump
Hip bone	Midlands	Rump
Neck end	Midlands	Sticking
Rump and Aitch bone	Midlands	As described
Shoulder	Midlands	Ribs (5) and part of chuck
Sweet-ribs	Midlands	Forequarter flank
Flat-ribs	Midlands and Home Counties	Top of fore-rib
First cutting	Liverpool and others	Thick flank
Head-piece	Liverpool	Short cut rump
Rump end	Liverpool	Aitch bone
Standing ribs	Liverpool and others	Fore-rib
Hind shin	Liverpool and others	Leg
Vein	Liverpool and others	Clod
Rump and izal bone	N.E. England	Rump and aitch bone and part of buttock
Fine end	N.E. England	Fore-rib
Chine and neck	N.E. England	Chuck and neck
Sloat	N.E. England	Clod
Thick ribs	N.E. England	Top-ribs and leg-of-mutton cut
Chine or thick chine and neck	N.E. England	Back-ribs, chuck, and neck
Rump cut	N.E. England	Aitch bone
Rump	N.E. England	As described
Hind shin or hough	N.E. England	Leg
Napp bone	Edinburgh and other parts of Scotland	End of leg or shin
Lyre	Edinburgh and other parts of Scotland	Clod and fat end of brisket
Hough	Edinburgh and other parts of Scotland	Leg or shin
Nine holes	Edinburgh and other parts of Scotland	Forequarter flank
Rib roast	Edinburgh and other parts of Scotland	Fore-rib
Shoulder or rib	Edinburgh and other parts of Scotland	Back-ribs
Thin runner	Edinburgh and other parts of Scotland	Fore-rib tops
Thick runner	Edinburgh and other parts of Scotland	Thick top-ribs and leg-of-mutton cut
Neck	Edinburgh and other parts of Scotland	Best end of sticking
Sticking piece	Edinburgh and other parts of Scotland	Head end of sticking
Side rump	Glasgow and district	Thick flank
Soft rump	Glasgow and district	Thick flank
Thick flank	Glasgow and district	Thick flank
Rump	Glasgow and district	Round
Pope's eye	Glasgow and district	Rump
Roast or sirloin roast	Glasgow and district	Sirloin
Foreseye	Glasgow and district	Fore-rib
Shoulder	Glasgow and district	Approx. chuck and part of back-rib
Neck	Glasgow and district	Sticking cut full
Gullet and runner	Glasgow and district	Middle cut of ribs with clod

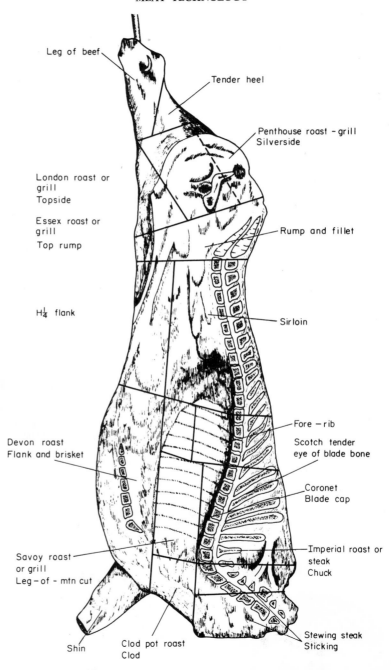

Leg of beef

Tender heel

Penthouse roast – grill
Silverside

London roast or
grill
Topside

Essex roast or
grill
Top rump

Rump and fillet

H¼ flank

Sirloin

Fore – rib

Scotch tender
eye of blade bone

Devon roast
Flank and brisket

Coronet
Blade cap

Imperial roast or
steak
Chuck

Savoy roast
or grill
Leg – of - mtn cut

Shin

Clod pot roast
Clod

Stewing steak
Sticking

Fig. 55   Proten cuts and equivalent regular cuts

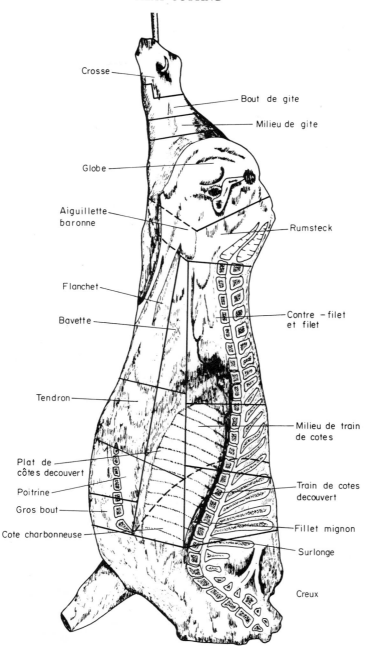

Fig. 56 French method of cutting—Paris, Creux. The shoulder including the shin is cut into ten joints

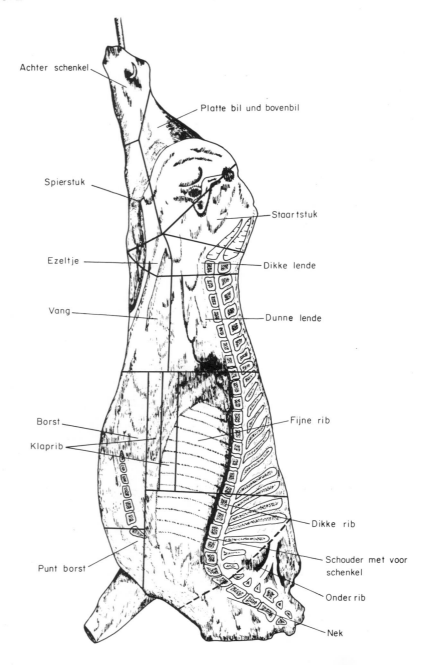

Fig. 57   Dutch method of cutting—Amsterdam

TABLE 38

Cutting tests

Comparison of A (very good side) with B (excessive fat). (All cuts boneless) *Hereford X Friesian carcase Ex. KKCF*

Joint	SIDE A 528 lb %	SIDE B 327 lb %
Topside	6·27	5·47
Silverside	5·66	5·00
Top rump	3·66	3·67
Rump	4·47	3·44
Fillet	1·97	1·61
Sirloin	6·78	6·57
Fore-rib	3·93	3·00
Flank	1·95	— *
Leg and shin meat	5·31	4·07
Coast	6·34	4·22
Middle-rib	7·17	6·36
Steak meat	8·07	5·43
Clod and sticking	6·03	4·72
Skirts	1·62	2·40
Lean Trimmings	3·20	3·75
Kidney	0·31	0·36
	72·74	60·07
Suet and fat trim	11·75	23·97
Bone and gristle	14·39	12·54
Loss	1·07	3·40
Total	99·95%	99·98%

Comparative values per lb A = 100: B = 83

*Flank unsaleable as such, consequently lean trimmed out and included under Trimmings.

Joints	Weight lb oz	% Cold carcase weight
Rumps, boneless	22 14	3·70
Fillets, long	10 14	1·76
Rump skirts	3 4	0·53
Goose skirts	3 10	0·59
Legs of beef and shins	25 0	4·05
Rolled sirloins	38 12	6·27
Silversides, best cuts	19 6	3·14
Silversides, 2nd cuts	14 12	2·39
Aitch bone cuts	8 2	1·31
Topside, best cuts	19 0	3·07
Topside, 2nd cuts	18 14	3·05
Top rumps, best cuts	17 0	2·75
Top rumps, 2nd cuts	15 12	2·55
Fore-ribs, Bone In	21 6	3·46
Flanks and briskets, rolled	48 0	7·77
Chops stickings	41 0	6·63
Top-ribs, bone in	14 14	2·41
Flat-ribs, bone in	12 12	2·06
Back-ribs, bone in	22 14	3·70
Leg-of-Mutton cut, boneless	21 8	3·48
Blade, boneless	12 4	1·98
Chuck, boneless	21 4	3·44
Lean trim—Flanks etc.	34 0	5·50
	467 2	75·59
Fat trim etc.	54 6	8·80
Bone and waste	88 8	14·32
Loss	8 0	1·29
Total	618 0	100·00

English side of beef ex. KKCF. Good quality ox (cold carcase weight 275lb, London and Home Counties cutting method).

Joint	Weight lb oz	% cold carcase weight (approx)	Suggested D.F. to give 30% gross on sales
Topside	17 0	6·18	2·28
Silverside	15 6	5·59	2·17
Top Rump	10 0	3·64	2·17
Rump steak	12 2	4·41	3·56
Fillet, long	5 0	1·82	4·35
Sirloin	18 6	6·68	2·39
Fore-rib	10 10	3·86	2·09
Coast, (rolled)	17 12	6·45	1·78
Clod and Sticking	170 0	6·18	1·48
Steakmeat	22 10	8·23	1·61
Top and back-ribs	20 3	7·34	1·61
Leg and shin	10 4	3·73	1·52
Skirts	4 8	1·64	1·74
Flank meat and lean trim	17 3	6·25	0·98
	198 0	72·0	
Fat trim etc.	28 0	10·18	
Bone and gristle	48 0	17·45	
Loss, evaporation etc.	1 0	0·36	
Total	275 0	99·99%	

TABLE 39

Pork cutting tests

Gross weight: 59 lb.
Country of origin: England.
Remarks: Middle White, porker.

Joint	Weight Gross lb oz	As sold lb oz	Per-centage
2 Legs	— —	13 4	22·5
2 Loins	— —	15 0	25·5
2 Bellies	— —	8 4	14·0
2 Neck ends	— —	9 0	15·2
2 Hands and springs	— —	7 14	13·2
1 Head	— —	5 10	9·6
Total	— —	59 0	100·00

Gross weight: 60 lb.
Country of origin: New Zealand.
Remarks: Pork carcase, ex head, probably Berkshire × Tamworth.

Joint	Weight Gross lb oz	As sold lb oz	Per-centage
2 Legs, ex trotters	— —	14 5	24·0
2 Loins	— —	16 8	27·5
2 Spare-ribs	— —	7 4	12·0
2 Blade bones	— —	5 12	9·5
2 Bellies	— —	8 10	14·4
2 Hands, ex trotters	— —	6 4	10·4
4 Trotters	— —	1 5	2·2
Total	— —	60 0	100·00

Gross weight: 75 lb.
Country of origin: England.
Remarks: Large White ×, long lean carcase.

Joint	Weight Gross lb oz	As sold lb oz	Per-centage
2 Legs	— —	16 6	21·9
2 Loins	— —	17 12	23·6
2 Bellies	— —	11 4	15·0
2 Neck ends	— —	13 2	17·5
2 Hands and springs	— —	8 14	11·8
1 Head	— —	7 10	10·2
Total	— —	75 0	100·00

Gross Weight: 120 lb.
Country of origin: England.
Remarks: Large White, very good quality.

Joint	Weight Gross lb oz	As sold lb oz	Per-centage
2 Legs	— —	28 8	23·7
2 Loins	— —	30 0	25·0
2 Bellies	— —	20 2	16·8
2 Neck ends	— —	17 8	14·6
2 Hands and springs	— —	12 14	10·7
1 Head	— —	11 0	9·2
Total	— —	120 0	100·00

TABLE 40

Scotch mutton cutting tests

Gross weight: 23 lb.
Country of origin: Scotland.
Remarks: Small Scotch Hill lamb, rather leggy.

Joint	Weight Gross lb oz	Weight As sold lb oz	Per-centage
2 Legs	— —	7 0	30·5
2 Loins	— —	5 2	22·2
2 Shoulders	— —	5 6	23·3
2 Best end necks	— —	2 0	8·8
2 Breasts	— —	1 4	5·4
2 Scrags	— —	1 0	4·4
2 Middles	— —	1 4	5·4
Total	— —	23 0	100·00

Gross weight: 40 lb (side 20 lb).
Country of origin: Scotland.
Remarks: Good average quality teg.

Joint	Weight Gross lb oz	Weight As sold lb oz	Per-centage
Leg	— —	5 3	25·94
Loin chops (and kidney)	— —	3 5	16·56
Loin chump	— —	— 6	1·87
Shoulder	— —	5 2	25·62
Best end neck	— —	1 13	9·06
Middle	— —	1 11	8·46
Scrag	— —	— 15	4·69
Breast	— —	1 7	7·18
Loss	— —	— 2	0·62
Total	— —	20 0	100·00

Gross weight: 40 lb (side 20 lb).
Country of origin: Scotland.
Remarks: Good average quality teg.

Joint	Weight Gross lb oz	Weight As sold lb oz	Per-centage
½ Leg, fillet	— —	2 15	14·69
½ Leg, knuckle	— —	2 11	13·44
½ Shoulder, blade	— —	2 13	14·06
½ Shoulder, blade	— —	1 13	9·06
Loin	— —	4 1	20·31
Best end neck	— —	1 10	8·13
Scrag and middle	— —	2 7	12·19
Breast	— —	1 9	7·81
Loss	— —	— 1	0·31
Total	— —	20 0	100·00

Gross weight: 56 lb.
Country of origin: Scotland.
Remarks: Excellent quality teg, more stocky than usual Scotch type.

Joint	Weight Gross lb oz	Weight As sold lb oz	Per-centage
2 Legs	— —	14 0	25·0
2 Loins (and kidneys)	— —	14 8	26·0
2 Shoulders	— —	12 6	22·0
2 Best end necks	— —	5 4	9·4
2 Breasts	— —	4 6	7·8
2 Scrags	— —	2 8	4·4
2 Middles	— —	3 0	5·4
Total	— —	56 0	100·00

TABLE 41

Imported lamb cutting tests

Origin: New Zealand   Origin: New Zealand
Grade: P.M.   Grade: Y.L.

Joint	Weight lb oz	% (approx)
2 Legs	7 15	24·8
2 Loins	7 5	22·9
2 Shoulders	6 14	21·5
2 Best end necks	3 6	10·5
2 Scrags and middles	2 14	9·0
2 Breasts	2 13	8·8
Wrapper and loss	13	2·5
Total	32 0	100·00

Joint	Weight lb oz	% (approx)
2 Legs	6 5	24·7
2 Loins	5 9	21·8
2 Shoulders	5 10	22·1
2 Best end necks	2 8	9·8
2 Scrags and middles	2 10	10·3
2 Breasts	2 3	8·6
Wrapper and loss	11	2·7
Total	25 8	100·00

Analysis N.Z. lamb

Grade: Y.M.—Gross weight: 31 lb.

Joint	Weight lb oz	% gross weight (approx)	Bone weight lb oz	% gross weight (approx)
2 Legs	7 11	24·8	1 11	5·44
2 Loins	5 15	19·1	1 5	4·23
2 Shoulders	7 5	23·6	1 2	3·63
2 Best end necks	3 3	10·3	11½	2·31
2 Scrags and middles	3 2	10·1	1 6	4·43
2 Breasts	3 1	9·9	12	2·42
Wrapper and loss	11	2·2	– –	– –
	31 0	100·00	6 15½	22·46

With imported lamb carcases, in considering the percentages based upon initial Gross Weight as compared with that of the joints as cut, an allowance of $2\frac{1}{2}\%$ is a realistic figure (wrapper, cutting loss etc).

To convert percentages on initial Gross Weight to those as cut, multiply by $\frac{100}{97.5}$. Conversely to change as cut to that based on initial weight, multiply by $\frac{97 \cdot 5}{100}$.

Comparison N.Z. lamb

Joint	A With kidney knob		B Ex kidney knob	
	Weight lb oz	%	Weight lb oz	%
Loin and chump chops	4 7	15·17	4 7	15·50
Chump ends	14	2·99	14	3·05
Best end neck	2 15	10·04	2 15	10·26
Legs	7 8	25·64	7 8	26·20
Shoulders	6 15	23·71	6 15	24·73
Scrags and middles	2 12	9·40	2 12	9·60
Breasts	2 11	9·18	2 11	9·38
Kidneys	3½	0·74	—	
Wrapper and trim	14½	3·09	8	1·75
	29 4	99·96	28 10	99·97

TABLE 42

Imported beef cutting tests

Gross weight: 164 lb.

Country of origin: Argentine.

Remarks: Fore¼, good average quality, joints sold with bone.

Joint	Weight		Per-centage
	Gross lb oz	As sold lb oz	
Shin (boneless)	9 14	5 13	6·0
Clod and sticking	35 2	27 13	21·5
Flank	16 5	16 5	9·9
Brisket	21 0	21 0	12·8
Fore-rib (long cut)	17 12	17 12	10·8
Back-ribs	17 6	17 6	10·5
Top-ribs	16 1	16 1	9·8
Leg-of-mutton cut	9 11	9 11	5·9
Blade (boneless)	7 9	6 8	4·6
Chuck (boneless)	11 14	10 7	7·3
Trimmings	1 0	1 0	0·6
Bones (8·5%)	— —	13 14	—
Loss	— 6	— 6	0·3
Total	164 0	164 0	100.00

Gross weight: 164 lb.

Country of origin: Argentine.

Remarks: Fore¼, good average quality, joints sold boneless.

Joint	Weight		Per-centage
	Gross lb oz	As sold lb oz	
Shin	9 14	5 13	6·0
Clod and sticking	35 2	27 13	21·5
Flank	16 5	14 5	9·9
Brisket	21 0	17 1	12·8
Fore-rib (long cut)	17 12	14 9	10·8
Back-ribs	17 6	14 11	10·5
Top-ribs	16 1	14 1	9·8
Leg-of-mutton cut	9 11	9 3	5·9
Blade	7 9	6 8	4·6
Chuck	11 14	10 7	7·3
Trimmings	1 0	1 0	0·6
Bone (17·2%)	— —	28 3	—
Loss	— 6	— 6	0·3
Total	164 0	164 0	100.00

TABLE 42 (*cont.*)

Gross weight: 165 lb.

Country of origin: Argentine.

Remarks: Hind¼, good average quality, joints sold boneless.

Joint	Weight		Per-centage
	Gross lb oz	As sold lb oz	
Thin flank (boneless)	— —	10 13	6·5
Round and fat (boneless)	— —	45 14	27·8
Thick (boneless)	— —	19 6	11·7
Leg (boneless)	— —	7 9	4·6
Rump and fillet (boneless)	— —	19 9	11·8
Loin and wing end (boneless)	— —	27 2	16·5
Suet	— —	9 2	5·6
Kidney	— —	1 3	0·7
Skirt and trimmings	— —	2 14	1·7
Bones	— —	21 1	12·8
Loss	— —	— 7	0·3
Total	— —	165 0	100·00

Gross weight: 165 lb.

Country of origin: Argentine.

Remarks: Hind¼, good average quality, joints sold with bone.

Joint	Weight		Per-centage
	Gross lb oz	As sold lb oz	
Thin flank	11 3	11 3	6·7
Round, cod and bone	51 6	51 6	31·2
Thick	19 13	19 13	12·0
Leg (bone in)	12 13	12 13	7·7
Rump and fillet (bone in)	23 7	23 7	14·2
Loin and wing end	30 14	30 14	18·8
Suet	9 2	9 2	5·6
Kidney	1 3	1 3	0·7
Skirt and trimmings	2 14	2 14	1·7
Pubic bone	2 3	2 3	1·3
Loss	— 2	— 2	0·1
Total	165 0	165 0	100·00

Gross weight: 114 lb.

Country of origin: Argentine.

Remarks: Fore¼, boneless, badly deboned, and discoloured.

Joint	Weight		Per-centage
	Gross lb oz	As sold lb oz	
Fore-rib	— —	6 12	5·9
Top-ribs	— —	13 4	11·6
Back-ribs	— —	8 12	7·7
Brisket	— —	10 8	9·2
Flank	— —	5 8	4·8
Shin	— —	5 8	4·8
Steak meat	— —	20 0	17·6
Clod and sticking	— —	23 8	20·6
Stewing pieces	— —	10 0	8·8
Fat trimmings	— —	8 0	7·0
Loss trim, etc.	— —	2 4	2·0
Total	— —	114 0	100·00

Gross weight: 114 lb.

Country of origin: Argentine.

Remarks: Hind¼, boneless, badly deboned and somewhat fat, ex fillet and suet.

Joint	Weight		Per-centage
	Gross lb oz	As sold lb oz	
Silverside (long)	— —	20 9	18·1
Topside	— —	17 9	15·4
Thick	— —	12 15	11·4
Sirloin	— —	15 5	13·5
Flank	— —	12 9	11·0
Rump	— —	7 2	6·2
Leg	— —	7 6	6·4
Stewing pieces	— —	4 9	4·0
Stewing pieces	— —	8 8	7·4
Fat	— —	4 12	4·2
Meat scraps	— —	1 4	1·1
Loss	— —	1 8	1·3
Total	— —	114 0	100·00

TABLE 43

H.K. veal cutting tests

Gross weight: 64 lb.
Country of origin: England.
Remarks: Veal calf, fair average quality.

Joint	Weight		Per-centage
	Gross lb oz	As sold lb oz	
2 Legs, ex knuckle	— —	15 4	23·9
2 Loins	— —	10 0	15·6
2 Shoulders, ex knuckle	— —	14 6	22·4
2 Best end necks	— —	4 2	6·5
2 Breasts	— —	5 14	9·2
2 Middles	— —	2 12	4·3
2 Scrags	— —	3 4	5·1
4 Knuckle bones	— —	4 6	6·8
Knuckle pie meat	— —	4 0	6·2
Total	— —	64 0	100·00

Gross weight: 64 lb.
Country of origin: England.
Remarks: Veal calf, fair average quality.

Joint	Weight		Per-centage
	Gross lb oz	As sold lb oz	
2 Legs	— —	20 0	31·25
2 Shoulders, ex knuckle	— —	14 0	21·88
2 Knuckles	— —	4 0	6·25
2 Loins	— —	10 0	15·61
2 Best end necks	— —	4 0	6·25
2 Breasts	— —	6 0	9·38
2 Middles and scrags	— —	6 0	9·38
Total	— —	64 0	100·00

18 Pre-packed meats

In general, pre-packed meats are subjected to considerable handling in the course of preparation, and, unless high hygienic standards are rigidly maintained, the degree of initial contamination may be greater than that arising in the traditional cutting of joints. In addition, with a film designed to restrict the loss of water vapour, the retention of a moist surface on the meat tends to promote bacterial growth.

The efficient pre-packing of meat and meat products implies some knowledge of the chemical and physical characteristics of the film used as well as a basic knowledge of the commodity to be wrapped.

It must be emphasized that packaging at its best can only help to maintain, in some degree, the quality of the product as packed. Recent American work indicates that the storage temperature, display period, and the amount and type of light in the display case affected the shelf life and saleability of packaged beef steaks more than the type of film employed.

When a freshly cut surface of beef is exposed to the atmosphere the purplish-red reduced myoglobin takes up atmospheric oxygen producing the bright red oxymyoglobin, a colour which is desired by the customer. Consequently, the case of consumer packs, exposure to the atmosphere for a short period following cutting and prior to packaging will ensure a maximum brightening effect. The degree of brightening will depend on the type and quantity of the pigment present and on the physical condition of other constituents of the meat. Myoglobin is a muscle pigment and normally constitutes about 80% of the total pigments, whilst the blood pigment, haemoglobin, contributes about 20%. The reaction of these pigments in colour change are identical, but the former is more important on account of its relative quantity.

No increased benefit is obtained from a greater oxygen pressure than that which is normally present in the atmosphere. Thus, for the packaging of fresh meat, a film which permits the passage of oxygen is necessary. The oxygen take-up of fresh meat occurs by its absorption by the surface fluid, and its subsequent diffusion into the surface layer. The solubility of oxygen in water increases as the temperature decreases; therefore a relatively low temperature, but one above the freezing point of water, is desirable.

It has also been found that colour tends to be brighter at a lower pH. Many of the micro-organisms which grow steadily at about 40°F (4°C) are inhibited at 32°F (0°C), whilst those that will grow at 32°F (0°C) will grow four times as quickly at 50°F (10°C). Thus the shorter the period spent at the 50°F (10°C) level, during the course of preparation, and the more rapidly the packed meat can reach the show case at 32°F (0°C), the more satisfactory the product.

In the case of frozen meats, one of the chief problems is that of freezer burn and for this type of pack a moisture-proof heat-shrinkable film, which will be durable at the low temperatures involved, is required.

Cured and salted meats are a different proposition, as the colour is not dependent upon oxygen, but originates from the cure (nitric oxide myoglobin). The continued retention of the typical cured meat colour depends upon the *exclusion* of oxygen. Therefore, in this case a film which is non-permeable to gases, or preferably a vacuum pack would be favoured.

Moisture is also important and surplus surface water may arise from fluctuations in temperature, i.e. meat removed from a fairly low-temperature cooler and held too long in the preparation room, causing condensation on the surface. In many cases the moisture transmission through a film may be more important than the actual moisture content of the product.

The darkening of meat due to drying will be influenced by the temperature and humidity. On drying, a somewhat gel-like superficial layer is formed, which differs from the underlying tissues by its increased rigidity and transparency. This change of transparency increases the penetration of light before reflection and this, combined with the increased concentration of pigment, leads to an increase in the depth of colour.

The overall colour impression as seen by the customer is influenced by the extent of drying, the oxymyoglobin on the surface and the reduced myoglobin present on the surface or at greater depths in the tissues.

Contamination

The cut surface of meat will always have some degree of bacterial contamination, but good hygiene standards in handling and care of tools and equipment should obviate any gross contamination. Although the film employed should not add to bacterial contamination, it can influence the subsequent rate of multiplication on account of moisture and/or the presence of air within the pack. Here again, suitable temperature control provides a valuable weapon against spoilage. It has been found that with pre-packed steaks with a surface temperature of 30°F (-1°C), bacterial counts actually decreased between the first and third day of display, presumably owing to temperature shock, as the bacteria began to multipy after the third day. The use of red meat cellophane film for wrapping generally gave a lower bacteria count than other films. It would, however, be desirable to test the consumer reaction to meat packed in such film.

Types of packaging film

The main criteria in the assessment of packaging films include the following: thickness, clarity, cost per square inch, strength, degree of stretch, permeability to water vapour and gases, heat characteristics, for sealing, shrinking, and the lower limits for cold storage. In addition, with meat products its resistance to grease is of importance.

Types of wrapping film available may be conveniently considered in the following groups.

(1) Non-moisture proof, which is chiefly used for greasy products. It readily absorbs moisture and is impermeable to gases when dry.

(2) Partially moisture-proof, for those products requiring a controlled rate of moisture control.

(3) Moisture-proof, non-heat sealing. This is used extensively for lining frozen food cartons and similar containers.

(4) Moisture-proof heat sealing, coated on one side, with a coating which is moisture-proof, but has a high rate of oxygen permeability. The uncoated side is placed next to the meat and becomes moist, thus increasing the permeability of the film to oxygen.

In this country, manufacturers use code letters for the various types of film. For example the different characteristics of cellophane are indicated as follows.

A   Bonded coating for water resistance
B   Coloured
C   Less moisture-proof
M   Moisture-proof
P   Plain
R   Rancidity retarding
S   Heat sealing
T   Transparent uncoloured

Thus a combination of the above letters will provide a good indication of the particular features of a film.

PLASTIC FILMS

These are prepared from synthetic resins, and can be sealed by heat and pressure. Following are representative examples of some of the films falling within this group.

Rubber–hydrochloride (*Pliofilm*). A rubber base, therefore a natural rather than a synthetic material. Extremely tough and can stretch up to about 500% of original value, available in many types including (1) excellent barrier properties for gas and water vapour, (2) very tough and flexible, with a somewhat lower protection against gas and water vapour, and (3) heavy-duty films for special purposes.

Vinylidene chloride (*Cryovac Saran*). Low water vapour permeability and gas permeability, therefore a good film for vacuum or gas packing. It can be produced as tough, highly flexible, opaque or transparent and can be heat sealed. As temperatures up to 300°F (149°C) can be tolerated for short periods, many meat products can be cooked in such a pack. Film can be heat-shrunk. Cryovac is now being extensively used for the packing of primal cuts. By packing beef immediately after cutting, before the colour change has taken place, full advantage of the colour change can be taken when the wrap is broken, exposing the meat to the atmosphere. The usual procedure is to place the meat in a bag, followed by drawing a partial vacuum and sealing with a clip. Finally the film is shrunk by immersion in hot water for a few seconds to obtain a tight shrink fit on the joint. The system is also used for maturing beef cuts.

An alternative system, of which the *Swissvac* is typical, obviates the need for heat shrinking the container. The joint is placed in an envelope-type film and passes into a vacuum chamber where the air is extracted, followed by contact heat sealing the open end of the container.

Polyethylene. Good packaging material, low levels of odour. Low water vapour transmission, but high transmission rate to gases. Flexible at low temperatures, therefore suitable for frozen foods. Tough and durable but the heat sealing temperature is critical; too high a temperature will result in melting.

Cellulose acetate. Possesses good dimensional stability, clarity, and general durability. The thinner gauges are frequently combined with paper or foil.

Cellulose acetate butyrate possesses the general characteristics of cellulose acetate, but has a greater stability in the presence of ultra-violet light.

Pre-packing

BEEF

In selecting beef for pre-packing it may become difficult to assess the yield value from differing types of carcase. For example, a mature overweight side of beef probably somewhat fat, might be purchased at a relatively low price whilst that from a younger smaller carcase lightly finished will probably have a much higher wholesale price per lb. It is only by a carefully conducted 'block' test that their true values per lb can be established.

Bone and muscle are fairly early developing tissues, followed by the deposition of fat. The rate at which their development takes place will be influenced by the type, i.e. early maturing breeds as against those developing slowly, the plane of nutrition, the weights of which the optimum standards are obtained. In general, heifers will reach their optimum yield at lighter weights than comparable steers. Thus the light-weight carcase will tend to carry a high proportion of bone and a low percentage of trimmable fat, whilst in the heavy carcase the proportion of bone may be low, but this advantage may be offset by the amount of suet and fat. The quantity of kidney and channel fats is the most important single factor influencing the yield of prepared cuts. The amount of kidney knob may be influenced in some degree by the breed. In general, Herefords tend to have relatively small kidney knobs, while many dairy breeds and to some extent their crosses, usually carry more suet.

Apart from weight considerations, while the heavier beef may be older and provide a more mature beef flavour, it may require considerable 'hanging' to obtain the degree of tenderness associated with the younger animal. The following figures are examples of the proportion of fat, bone and waste obtained from (A) a mature heavy-weight carcase, (B) a fairly stout side, (C) a good carcase within the 18–22 months age range, and (D) intensively fed barley beef of about 12 months.

	A	B	C	D
Cold carcase weight (lb)	709	646	608	485
Potential consumer meat	61%	66%	71%	68%
Total suet, fat, trim, bone, etc.	39%	34%	29%	32%
(Kidney and channel fat)	(4%)	(2·6%)	(2·4%)	(2·5%)
Relative value of side per lb based upon potential consumer meat	86%	93%	100%	96%

In favour of the relatively heavy-weight carcase are the following considerations. There are little, if any extra labour costs involved in the slaughter and preparation, so that the cost of a 700 lb (318 kg) carcase of beef would tend to be somewhat similar to that of a 500 lb (227 kg) carcase. This would represent a material reduction in the labour cost per lb. In addition, an increase in the killing out percentage of 1 % on an 8 cwt (405 kg) beast is approximately 9 lb (4 kg), whereas with an 11 cwt (560 kg) beast it becomes approximately 12·3 lb (5·6 kg). However, it may be found that the demand for heavy cuts such as striploins and ribs, may have a limited market as compared with such cuts from a lighter carcase. As a further complication, the various primal cuts have different values, and the changes which take place in the proportions of these cuts, which take place with growth, are of considerable commercial importance. Broadly speaking, as percentages of the side, the shanks and neck will decline with growth; while the percentages of loin, rib, brisket and flank tend to increase with maturity.

The amount of suet and fat trim is the most important single factor influencing the yield of primal cuts. In the case of carcases purchased ex-KKCF, one of the greatest variables is eliminated.

During the growth process, bone is an early developing tissue, followed by muscle and finally fat. A rough 'rule of thumb' method of calculating 'butchers' bone content can be found by: $100 - (\text{Killing out} \% + 27\cdot8)$. For example, assuming a killing out figure of 55 %, then $100 - (55 + 27\cdot8) = 17\cdot2\%$ butchers bone.

It must be emphasized that this figure applies to average commercial conditions, with removal of major gristles. With laboratory dissection, the true bone figure will be much lower, due to the fact that each bone is cleaned free of all adhering tissues.

The figures in the table below were obtained from a large number of beef carcases in New Zealand and provide a good comparison of gross yields from two types of carcases.

Average carcase weight	A 541·8 lb %	B 659·9 lb %
Prepared edible	66·8	67·0
Bone, etc.	19·8	19·1
Suet and fat trim	12·0	12·9
Loss	1·4	1·0
	100%	100%

A rather more obscure factor influencing yield is the degree and period of chilling prior to deboning. Beef deboned after holding for 24 hours in a chiller, may be relatively soft and pliable, which contributes to more efficient deboning. As the meat becomes progressively firmer, there is a tendency for the yield of boneless meat to drop. It may be found that with carcases of a similar type, holding for 3 days as against 1 day, may decrease the yield by about 1%.

From steer sides of good commercial quality of about 300 lb (136 kg), the type of yield of primal cuts which may be reasonably anticipated is indicated below.

Primal cuts

	% of initial cold weight	
Topside, silverside and thick	15·0	
Striploin	4·4	
Rump	4·0	
Long fillet (trimmed)	1·3	
Rib roll	2·8	
Pony	15·0	
Brisket roll	2·2	
	——	44·7
Clod, sticking and shank meat	25·0	
Kidney	0·3	
	——	25·3
Suet and fat trim	12·0	
Bone gristle and loss	18·0	
	——	30·0
Total		100%

With vacuum-packed primal cuts, the temperature has an important effect on the amount of drip whilst those cuts at the bottom of a double layer will have a higher drip loss than comparable cuts on top of them.

Effect of temperature on percentage drip loss, vacuum packaged beef, aged for two weeks

(Courtesy D. E. Hood, Eire Agricultural Institute)

	0°C	7°C	Difference
Fillet	1·52	2·81	1·29
Inside round	0·46	0·99	0·53
Outside round	0·88	0·91	0·03
Knuckle	0·58	1·57	0·99
Short sirloin	0·75	1·38	0·63

**Effect of stacking on percentage drip loss; vacuum
packaged beef, aged two weeks at 0°C. Two layers high**

	Top	Bottom	Difference
Fillet	1·57	2·43	0·86
Inside round	0·69	1·58	0·89
Outside round	0·68	1·12	0·44
Knuckle	1·13	1·27	0·14
Short sirloin	0·56	1·08	0·52

Joint Yield

Approximate % of quarters

Hind with KKCF	%	Fore	%
Rump, steaks	5·9	Fore-rib, rolled	8·4
Loin, steaks	6·7	Coast, rolled	14·4
Topside, steaks	8·2	Leg-of-mutton cut, roast	4·7
Silverside, roast and		Blade steak	3·9
braising steaks	7·5	Chuck steak	5·3
Top rump, roast	3·6	Top-ribs, ex bone	7·8
Top rump, steaks	3·2	Back-ribs, ex bone	6·8
Fillet, whole	3·0	Shin	3·6
Kidney	0·4	Clod and sticking, pie	
Leg of beef	4·8	meat	10·0
Goose skirt	1·2	Lean trim	1·8
Thin flank, ex bone	9·0		
Lean trim	11·1		
	64·6		66·7

The actual weight as packed will be influenced by the degree of trim and the overall standard of presentation required.

The preceding table is a summary of the yield obtained with fairly drastic trimming, the trimmings being utilized mainly for hamburgers and a smaller proportion for mince. The side of steer beef (Hereford × Friesian) weighed 274 lb (124 kg), as received and when cut and quartered 4 days later, gave a hind weight of 140 lb (64 kg) and a fore weight of 132 lb (60 kg).

The following test was on a good quality side of English beef, intended for pre-packing, with the emphasis on steak yield.

Primal cuts	lb	oz	Fat lb	oz	Bone, etc. lb	oz
Thin flank	15	1	8	3		14
Rump	27	0	4	6	4	0
Kidney knob	11	0	9	12	–	–
Loin	33	0		13	6	4
Top rump	15	13	2	9		12
Leg	16	1	–	–	8	4
Cod fat	2	3	2	3	–	–
Goose skirt	1	2	–	–	–	–
Pubic bone	2	8	–	–	2	8
Topside	18	11		9	–	–
Silverside, long cut	25	10	2	13	4	9
Shin	9	2	–	–	4	2
Clod and sticking	28	6	4	2	7	12
F¼ flank	17	14	9	12	2	8
Brisket	21	0	2	1	3	3
Fore-rib	16	10	–	–	3	9
Back-ribs	15	8		13	3	12
Top-ribs	16	0	2	4	2	0
Leg-of-mutton cut	11	10		9		10
Chuck	12	3	1	0	2	5
Blade	6	13		11	1	0
	323	3	52	8	58	0

Labour time

Cutting into primal cuts	27 min
Boning and gross preparation	89 min
Cutting and trimming steaks, dicing meat by hand, mincing, packing and weighing	150 min
	266 min

Weight prepared for packing

	lb	oz		
Entrecote steaks	11	8		
Rump steaks	8	3		
Fillet steaks	4	13		
Braising steaks	37	5		
Cubed steaks	37	12		
Rolled fore-rib, ex bone	13	1		
Rolled brisket, ex bone	15	12		
Lean, mince, etc.	62	2		
Ox kidney	1	4		
	191	12	=approx.	59·4%
Suet, fat, etc.	52	8	=approx.	16·3%
Fat and trim from cuts	14	0	=approx.	4·3%
Bone and gristles	60	0	=approx.	18·5%
Loss, evaporation, etc.	4	15	=approx.	1·5%
	323	3	=approx.	100·0%

Costing

There are many methods of approaching the question of costing pre-packed meats. Unless adequate allowance is made for 'rewraps' and similar contingencies, the practical result will not agree with the theoretical estimate. It is obvious that the closer these figures are, the more efficient is the operation of the pre-packing unit.

However, the basic principles involved in costing will probably include the following steps.

(1) Time/cost rate to cut, pack, wrap and price = (X packs)

(2) $\dfrac{\text{Direct labour} + \% \text{ of indirect labour} + \text{overheads}}{\text{Total direct hours}}$

= cost per hour and therefore labour and overhead cost per pack

(3) Cost of wrap, trays and labels, etc.

= *Total cost pence per pack*

(4) If the average pack is, say, 12 oz, then the packaging cost per lb is

$\dfrac{1 \text{ lb} \times \text{total cost pre pack}}{0·75}$

To this must be added the cost of the meat as packed, in order to ascertain the total cost price. The latter can be calculated as follows:

$$\frac{\text{cost price (pence per lb)} \times \text{original weight (lb)}}{\text{weight as packed (lb)}}$$

$$= \text{cost of prepared meat (pence per lb)}.$$

19 Meat as a food

Food consists of all those substances which taken into the living organism produce energy, build tissue, or regulate the life process without any harm accruing to the organism. The animal body requires food in order to obtain the necessary energy to repair wastage of tissue and to promote growth. This latter factor is of paramount importance in the case of childhood and the immature animal.

Foodstuffs may be conveniently classified as follows.

$$\left.\begin{array}{l}\text{Protein}\\\text{Fat}\\\text{Carbohydrates}\\\text{(Vitamins)}\end{array}\right\}\text{Organic}\leftarrow\text{Foods}\rightarrow\text{Inorganic}\left\{\begin{array}{l}\text{Water}\\[2ex]\text{Mineral salts}\end{array}\right.$$

It is sometimes found that one substance contains all five of these ingredients in varying proportions. The value of a foodstuff may therefore be said to depend on the following.

(A) The relative proportions in which the proteins, fat, carbohydrates, etc., are present.

(B) The quantity of heat it is able to supply.

(C) The amount of tissue it can build or replace.

(D) The ease with which the substance is absorbed by the system.

The question of palatability is a more elusive factor, yet how true is the quotation: 'One man's meat is another's poison.' Consumption of, say, strawberries can produce nettle rash in some subjects, and we are all familiar with the well-known case of protein intolerance. So, in considering foods generally, personal idiosyncrasy must not be overlooked.

For the supply of energy we rely mainly on carbohydrates and fats. Heat and energy can be obtained from protein, but this is an expensive method which, if carried too far, can place additional strain on the system, as proper elimination of nitrogenous waste from the protein is essential.

341

Bodily fuel needs

The fuel needs of the body have been carefully estimated and are measured in K/cals, this unit being the amount of heat necessary to raise the temperature of 1000 grams of water through one degree Centigrade. The calorific values of the food substances are obtained by completely burning one gram of the substance in a bomb calorimeter and measuring the heat produced. This does not give the true calorific value, as the amount of heat evolved is greater than could be obtained in the actual process of metabolism. For purposes of calculating the calorific values of foodstuffs, the following factors are usually employed: protein 4; carbohydrates 4; and fats 9. It is evident that the heavy manual worker will require more energy than the sedentary worker, and that a child would require more calories per kilogramme of weight than the average adult. Thus, at under one year 100 K/cals are required, dropping to about 50 K/cals at 12 years per kilogramme of weight. The amounts of protein, carbohydrates, and fat necessary to supply these calories in the best way are apportioned in slightly different ratios by the experts, but as a good average basis the relative proportions of protein, fat, and carbohydrates can be calculated as 1:1:4 to 5 respectively, assuming that the protein amounts to 100 grams.

Two methods are given below (Table 44), the first being more suitable for the sedentary worker and the second for the manual worker.

TABLE 44

Bodily fuel needs for sedentary and manual workers per day

	Sedentary (g)	Manual (g)
Protein	100	100
Fat	100	100
Carbohydrates	400	500
Approximate calorific value	2900	3300

A man doing severe muscular work requires a greater amount of food than the above, enough to produce, say, 4000 or even 4500 K/cals per day. Calorimeter tests suggest that, when resting, 2500 K/cals per day should be ample, but size and weight must not be over-looked.

No one foodstuff can supply all the necessary ingredients in the correct proportions. This fact will be appreciated from Table 45, the amounts being given as a percentage.

The calorific value for meat is variable as the quantity of fat it contains materially affects the figures. For example, the fat in the brisket from a well-finished three-year-old beast may be as high as 40%, and this would give the brisket a calorific figure of over 400, per 100 g.

TABLE 45

Composition of some common foods

Food	Edible portion				
	Water	Protein	Fat	Carbo-hydrate	K/cals per 100 g
Bobby calf	74	18	6	—	126
Lean beast	65	16	18	—	226
Beast (average)	56	15	28	—	312
Beast (fat)	48	13	38	—	394
Lamb	55	13	31	—	331
Pig (whole)	47	12	40	—	408
Bacon (side)	40	11	45	—	449
Fish, cod, etc.	81	16	0·5	—	69
Plaice, etc.	79	16	2·0	—	82
Milk, fresh	88	3·3	3·6	4·4	63
Lard, dripping	1	—	99	—	891
Butter	15	0·5	82·5	—	745
Egg, fresh	74	12·5	11·5	0·9	157
Potatoes	78	2·0	—	16·2	73
Cabbage	92	1·5	—	5·0	26
Apples, fresh	86	0·3	—	8·6	36
Bread	33	8·3	1·0	57·5	259

Protein

Protein may be obtained from both animal and vegetable sources, but the quantity of available protein absorbed by the system is much higher in those of animal origin than in those obtained from vegetables. Whereas the system will absorb about 97% of animal protein, only about 84% of those from vegetable matter are utilized. Thus a diet consisting exclusively or mainly of vegetables must of necessity be more bulky. (One might assume that had Mother Nature intended us for a herbivorous diet she would have provided us with bovine dentition and the ruminant stomach.)

Liver and kidney, in particular, have a very high biological protein value—that is, they are very valuable in replacing and maintaining body protein. Meat and milk also rank high in this respect, as they contain the correct constituents (amino-acids) which are necessary in building up the body-cells.

Fats

Fats give heat and staying power and are, in the main, absorbed into the system from 5 to 6 hours after ingestion. If fats are omitted from the diet, one is liable to feel the need for additional food before the next meal. Animal fats are more absorbable than the vegetable variety, the ratio being 95% to 90%. Meats generally contain a larger proportion of fat than is commonly supposed, and 'marbling', e.g. the infiltration of fat into the muscle, materially increases this quantity and incidentally improves the flavour. Even the heart muscle in fat beast may contain over 15% of fat. In theory it should be possible for man to live without including fat in his diet, as these substances could be elaborated from the starches and sugars of a carbohydrate diet. This method would not appear to be economical, as the fats have twice the energy concentration of carbohydrates, and therefore double the quantity would be necessary. As the human digestive system is relatively small this question of bulk is important. Professor Starling states: 'The human alimentary canal has been developed so as to cope with a diet in which 20–25% of the energy is presented in the form of fat.'

Carbohydrates

Carbohydrates are obtained mainly from cereals and potatoes in the form of starch; they are usually absorbed into the system about 3 hours after ingestion. Muscular energy should be obtained mainly from this source. Carbohydrates in food metabolism are mainly simple sugars, such as may be found in the grape and other fruits, and complex sugars, such as lactose and saccharose. The simple sugars are absorbed and stored as glycogen in the liver, while the complex ones must be broken down by the process of digestion before they can be absorbed. Many carbohydrates from vegetables although valuable, are boiled out in the cooking water. Although herbivorous animals feed principally on carbohydrates, only a negligible proportion of the live animal consists of such substances. They are either used immediately following digestion or formed into fat to provide an energy reserve.

Vital constituents

At one time it was considered that an adequate quantity of protein, fat, carbohydrate, water and certain mineral elements would provide a complete diet and maintain health. In 1910, the Polish scientist Funk, established the fact that a certain constituent of diet, to which he gave the name *vitamin*, was vitally essential and that only infinitesimal amounts were necessary. Their presence in the diet is essential, as the body is unable to synthesize them from other nutrients and various 'deficiency' diseases are associated with a shortage or absence of specific vitamins. The Hungarian biochemist, who first isolated vitamin C, defined the vitamin as 'a substance which makes you ill, if you don't eat it!'

Vitamins are complex organic substances, and as they were discovered they were distinguished by letters (A, B, C, D, etc.). For scientific purposes, these letters have been replaced by names, as their chemical nature became defined.

Although only minute quantities are necessary, vitamins are widely distributed in many different types of food and consequently, to ensure an adequate supply of all the vitamins, a mixed diet is desirable.

The vitamins which are most commonly referred to are designated A, B, C, D, less important are E and K, for which there are no recommended intake standards. Research has added to their number and resulted in subdivisions, which need not concern us here.

VITAMIN A

This is a fat-soluble vitamin. It promotes growth and resistance to infection and promotes a healthy skin. Its absence from diet leads to a disease of the eyes, xerophthalmia, and even a mild deficiency will cause night blindness. Any excess of this vitamin is stored in the liver, consequently animal liver, particularly that of the sheep, is particularly valuable in this respect. Other foods containing this vitamin are milk, eggs, and green and yellow vegetables, whilst kidney also possesses a considerable quantity.

VITAMIN B COMPLEX

This consists of several vitamins, seven of which are known to be essential in the human diet. Meat is an excellent source, and ranks high as a major dietary supplier of most of them. They are all soluble in water and any excess over immediate needs is excreted in the urine. Present knowledge indicates that a diet sufficient in foods of high quality protein, will also supply adequate amounts of all the B vitamins.

The more important are:

1. Thiamine. Which is essential to carbohydrate metabolism and is associated with a healthy nervous system. Pork is the best source; other meats and beans contain important amounts. Since the body cannot store thiamine in any quantity, it should be provided daily in the diet.

2. Riboflavin. Is widely distributed in animal and vegetable tissues. It is only slightly soluble in water and losses due to solution during cooking are small. In roasting, meat may lose about 25% of its riboflavin. It helps to maintain healthy skin and eyes and, in children, a deficiency will retard growth. Liver is the best source and other meats and milk are good sources.

3. Nicotinic acid (Niacin). Was first prepared from nicotine, long before its vitamin value was appreciated. The name niacin is now widely used in order to avoid an undesirable impression. Niacin functions in the body by helping to maintain a healthy skin and tongue and with thiamine assists in promoting a healthy nervous system. Large amounts are supplied by meat and fish, liver and kidney rank as two of the best sources.

Other vitamins in the B complex, essential in the diet but considered of less importance than those mentioned above, are pyridoxine (B6), pantothenic acid, biotin, folic acid and cyanocobalamin (B_{12}).

Vitamin C (Ascorbic Acid)

Prevents scurvy. It is present to a certain extent in all fresh raw foodstuffs. It is very sensitive to heat, and cabbage cooked at 80–90°C loses 90% of its vitamin C. These three vitamins must enter into any proper diet, and the Table 46 shows their presence in some of the foodstuffs previously mentioned.

Vitamin D (Anti-rachitic)

Regulates the mineral metabolism of the bones and teeth. This vitamin can be built up in the body by exposing the skin to ultra-violet rays. It can be produced artificially and introduced into foods deficient in this factor.

Vitamin E (Anti-sterility)

This sex vitamin is abundant in oil obtained from wheat, etc., and persists in lard, although other factors are lost in the rendering process.

TABLE 46

Vitamin content of some meats

Vitamin (Units/100g)	Liver	Pork	Beef	Mutton
A. Int. Nat. Units	20,000	Trace	Trace	Trace
B Thiamine (mg)	0·30	1·0	0·07	0·01
Riboflavin (mg)	3·0	0·20	0·20	0·25
Nicotinic Acid (mg)	13	5	5	5
Pantothenic Acid (mg)	8	0·6	0·4	0·5
Biotin (micrograms)	100	4	3	3
Folic Acid (micrograms)	300	3	10	3
B_6 Pyrodoxine (mg)	0·7	0·5	0·3	0·4
B_{12} Cyanocobalamin (micrograms)	50	2	2	2
C. Ascorbic Acid (mg)	30	0	0	0
D. (Int. Nat. Units)	45	Trace	Trace	Trace

(After McCance & Widdowson, H.M.S.O.)

Inorganic foods

WATER

Is necessary to life as it maintains the essential dilution by which food is absorbed by the tissues and for carrying off waste products. Approximately 75% of lean meat and 90% of vegetable tissue consists of water.

MINERAL MATTER

The mineral salts may be considered as regulating foods and they are of great importance in tissue building. The two most important are common salt and phosphate of lime. The greater portion of mineral matter is utilized in bone formation. Very minute quantities of other substances such as iron, potassium, phosphorus, iodine, etc., are necessary in a complete diet.

Summary

We must therefore arrive at the following conclusion. Diet must be essentially a mixed one in order to obtain the maximum benefit from it, and animal matter is richer in protein and fat than most other types of food, although it is correspondingly deficient in carbohydrates. Animal protein is the best builder of body-cells and animal fats give greater staying power.

Meat and income

It is sometimes suggested that man could manage on less animal protein than is customary. This is no reason why he *should* do so. The virile Australian race is a typical example of heavy meat-eaters, with a consumption far in excess of ours. Generally speaking, a vegetarian is incapable of continued manual work. The United States Bureau of Labor Statistics found that the protein consumption of representative workmen's families varied from 87 to 117 grams (3–4¼ oz) per day. In this country the protein consumption per head per day approximates to the lower figure, but over the last twenty years the percentage of animal protein has increased whilst vegetable protein has decreased. It is safe to assume that a protein figure of 100 grams per day per head should be aimed at (say 3½ oz).

The effect of a diet deficient in protein may not be obvious over a short period, but the final result, especially in young children is disastrous, if such a diet is continued for any length of time.

As the protein requirements of the growing child is greater per unit of body weight than that of the adult, it is extremely difficult to provide sufficient first-class protein, without a generous supply of meat.

In the middle and higher income groups, as income increases, the consumption of meats tends to increase.

Of recent years there has been a marked increase in the consumption of pork, whilst that of mutton and lamb has slightly decreased.

DEMAND

It is probable that there is a wider demand for beef than any other foodstuff, with the exception of bread and milk. It is, however, a relatively expensive food, and consequently the demand for it is closely associated with industrial prosperity and depression. In fact, the demand for beef is very sensitive to such conditions, and with a restriction of income the beef trade suffers not only as regards quantity but quality. A return to prosperity will show an almost immediate increase in demand. In the case of English beef this tendency is reflected back to the cattle market and farmer. It is frequently contended that the modern consumer does not exercise the same discrimination in selecting meat as his forebears, but the very wide variation in price as between, say, first quality baby beef and cow beef hardly gives support to this contention.

Beef is usually considered to be a heavy meat and the demand for it is greater in the cold weather. Thus, during summer weather the tendency is not only to eat less meat, but also to favour mutton and lamb rather than beef. Another minor influence is the redistribution of population at holiday times, usually with a modification of diet. Breeds with a local predominance are usually favoured in that particular area, but in the long run it is probable that weight and the degree of finish are more important factors. Usually, smaller animals are required for town than country, and where heavy trades predominate a more heavily finished beast is preferred, whilst, for example, textile workers dislike even a reasonable quantity of fat.

TABLE 47

Analysis of English side of baby beef (good average quality, 274 lb)

Joint	Weight boneless		Price per lb boneless	K/Cals per lb (approx.)	Approx. cost per 1000 K/cals
	lb	oz	p		p
Shin	4	3	60	400	150
Flanks	20	4	60	1150	52
Brisket	18	6	60	1650	36
Clod and sticking	18	8	60	1050	57
Fore-rib	12	15	75	1300	58
Middle-rib	22	2	60	1040	58
Steak meat	20	5	63	960	66
Rump	16	4	120	1600	75
Loin	24	4	100	1400	71
Thick	13	12	90	1480	61
Leg	6	8	60	450	133
Round	34	12	90	1050	86
Suet and fat	16	10	8	3800	2
Cod fat and skirt	6	0	—	—	—
Bone and fat trimmings	38	4	—	—	—
Loss		15	—	—	—
	274	0	—	—	—

Great Britain is *the* mutton-eating country of Europe, the consumption being five times as great as any other European country. This fact will stress the value of our imported requirements to New Zealand and Australia. As mutton and lamb are considered as 'light' meat, the heaviest demand for it is during the warmer months. Weight is a very important factor, owing to the demand for small joints. In the case of imported lamb, a small third-grade carcase fetches as much as a first-grade heavy carcase. The demand is very sensitive to price, and during the spring, when the English article is relatively expensive, the consumer tends to be driven to the imported article, gradually changing when the English lamb reaches its peak supply between June and September. Apart from this general trend, there is a special demand for lamb at Easter, and to a lesser extent at Whitsun. After September the quantity of lamb available decreases, its place being taken by mutton, and, by December, mutton has almost entirely replaced home-killed lamb. The relative demand for the home-killed as against the imported article depends largely on the differences in price, though the arrival of lamb from the southern hemisphere during the winter exercises some influence.

At one time the fallacy of the 'R' in the month had a marked effect on the consumption of pork during the summer months. This demand has now been smoothed out to some extent and, although the demand may drop during a really warm spell, there is a somewhat steady market throughout the year. During the last few years there has been a very marked increase in the consumption of pig meat. In the case of the London trade a carcase of 80 to 100 lb (36 to 45 kg) will invariably fetch the highest price on Smithfield. For manufacturing purposes there is always a steady demand for heavy carcases, lean sows being preferred. In certain areas 'cutters' of 140 or even 160 lb (64 or 72 kg) are not objected to, whilst in other regions, South Wales for example, a much lighter carcase is required.

TABLE 48

Meat supplies lb per head per annum, moving into
consumption in the United Kingdom
(Source: M.A.F.F.)

Description	1971	1972	1973	1974	1975
Beef—bone in	40·9	36·9	33·7	43·3	47·0
Beef—bone out*	5·1	7·4	7·7	6·0	5·0
Mutton and lamb	22·1	20·4	18·2	17·0	18·2
Pork	26·0	27·2	26·8	26·5	22·7
Offal	7·8	8·1	7·6	7·5	8·7
Canned meat (imported)	7·6	7·8	7·7	6·9	7·0
Bacon and ham	26·2	24·7	22·3	20·9	19·1
Poultry	23·6	26·8	25·8	25·7	25·0
Game and rabbits	0·6	0·6	0·6	0·5	0·4
	159·9	159·9	150·4	154·3	153·1
Total converted to edible weight	134·2	134·5	126·5	125·6	125·4

*Imported boneless beef converted to equivalent bone in weight (M.A.F.F.).

TABLE 49

*Composition of meat products**

Description	Protein (%)	Fat (%)	Carbo-hydrate (%)	K/Cals per 100 grams
Beef (fresh)				
Brisket, medium fat, edible portion	15·8	28·5		319
Chuck rib, edible portion, all analyses	19·0	13·4		197
Flank, edible portion, all analyses	19·6	21·1		268
Loin, edible portion, all analyses	19·0	19·1		247
Ribs, edible portion, all analyses	17·8	24·6		293
Shoulder and clod, edible portion, all analyses	20·0	10·3		173
Miscellaneous cuts, free from all visible fat	22·4	2·9		116
Brain, edible portion	8·8	9·3		119
Heart, edible portion	16·0	20·4		248
Kidney, as purchased	13·7	1·9	trace	72
Liver, as purchased	20·2	3·1	2·5†	119
Lungs, as purchased	16·4	3·2		94
Marrow, as purchased	2·2	92·8		844
Sweetbreads, as purchased	16·8	12·1		176
Suet, as purchased	4·7	81·8		755
Tongue, edible portions	18·9	9·2		158
Beef (cooked)				
Roast	22·3	28·6		347
Steak, round	27·6	7·7		180
Steak sirloin	23·9	10·2		187
Steak tenderloin	23·5	20·4		278
Beef (canned)				
Corned‡	26·6	11·4		209
Kidneys, stewed	18·4	5·1	2·1	128
Luncheon beef	27·6	15·9		254
Roast	25·9	14·8		237
Tongue, ground	21·4	25·1		312
Tongue, whole	19·5	23·2		287
Tripe	11·7	1·2	trace	58
Veal (fresh)				
Breast, edible portion, all analyses	20·3	11·0		180
Leg, edible portion, all analyses	20·7	6·7		143
Loin, edible portion, all analyses	19·0	10·0		170

*Based on *Structure and Composition of Foods*, Vol. III, A. L. Winton and K. B. Winton, U.S.A.,
Vol. III, 1937; and *Food Industries Manual*, 13th edition, London, 1944.
†Largely, or in part, glycogen.
‡Average 3·4% salt.

TABLE 49 (*cont.*)

Description	Protein (%)	Fat (%)	Carbo-hydrate (%)	K/cals per 100 grams
Lamb (fresh)				
Breast, edible portion	19·1	23·6		289
Leg, medium fat, edible portion	19·2	16·5		225
Loin, without kidney and suet,				
edible portion	18·7	28·3		330
Shoulder, edible portion	18·1	29·7		340
Lamb (cooked)				
Chops, broiled, edible portion	21·7	29·9		356
Leg, roast	19·7	12·7		293
Lamb (canned)				
Tongue, spiced and cooked, edible				
portion	13·9	17·8		216
Mutton (fresh)				
Leg, medium fat, edible portion	18·5	18·0		236
Loin, without kidney and suet, edible				
portion	16·0	33·1		362
Shoulder, medium fat, edible portion	17·7	19·9		250
Heart, as purchased	16·9	12·6		181
Kidney, as purchased	16·5	3·2		95
Liver, as purchased	23·1	9·0	5·0*	193
Mutton (cooked)				
Leg, roast, edible portion	25·0	22·6		303
Mutton (canned)				
Corned	28·8	22·8		320
Tongue	24·4	24·0		314
Pork (fresh)				
Loin chops, lean, edible portion	20·3	19·0		252
Loin chops, medium fat, edible portion	16·6	20·1		337
Shoulder, edible portion	13·3	34·2		361
Side, lard and other fat included,				
edible portion	9·4	61·7		593
Brains, as purchased	11·7	10·3		140
Heart, as purchased	17·1	6·3		125
Kidney, as purchased	15·5	4·8	0·7	108
Liver, as purchased	21·3	4·5	1·4*	131

*Largely, or in part, glycogen.

TABLE 49 (*cont.*)

Description	Protein (%)	Fat (%)	Carbo-hydrate (%)	K/cals per 100 grams
Pork (pickled, salted, or smoked)				
Ham, lean, smoked, edible portion	19·8	20·8		266
Ham, medium fat, smoked, edible portion	16·5	38·8		414
Salt pork, clear fat	1·9	86·2		783
Bacon, smoked, all analyses, edible portion	10·5	64·8		625
Sausage				
Bologna, edible portion	18·7	17·6	0·6‡	236
Pork, as purchased	13·0	44·2	1·4‡	454
Poultry (fresh)				
Chicken, broilers, edible portion	21·5	2·5		109
Fowls, edible portion	19·3	16·3		224
Goose, edible portion	16·3	36·2		391
Turkey, edible portion	21·1	22·9		291
Gelatine	84·2†	0·1		338

†Nitrogen factor 5·55.
‡Carbohydrate very variable.

20　World distribution of food animals

When considering the distribution of food animals throughout the world, one has to take into account the geographical conditions, but must not at the same time lose sight of the social factor nor of the advantages due to science. Speaking generally, animals are mainly dependent for their foodstuffs on nature herself, and natural products are in their turn the outcome of the climatic conditions experienced in any particular area. Climate itself is the sum total of several factors of which heat and rainfall may be considered the most important, so that the incidence of animal life may be presented in this way.

$$\text{Climate} \begin{cases} \text{Temperature and rainfall} \\ \text{Natural foodstuff} \\ \text{Animal life} \\ \text{Settlement of man} \end{cases}$$

The addition of the last factor—settlement of man—completes the table, for mankind is dependent on animal life for his sustenance.

Effect of rainfall

Where there is long grass one expects cattle, while the areas of scanty rainfall will ably support whole flocks of sheep. Generally, therefore, on the rainy side of mountains are to be found the cattle ranches, while the drier interior is more suitable for sheep farming. This is well brought out in New Zealand when the Canterbury Plains are considered. These are sheltered from excessive rain by the mountains of the west and provide magnificent finishing grounds for the sheep from the other parts. On the Banks peninsula, where the ground rises, the rainfall increases and cattle are reared in preference to sheep. Even on the rainy side of the mountain, however, the rainfall will decrease as one gets higher, and sheep may well be reared on the higher ground, although the rainfall on the lowlands be rather too heavy for them.

Human and social factors

It is often supposed that, as the human population of an area increases, the animal population must of necessity decrease since there is not sufficient room for them, but this supposition is not borne out in actual practice. There must, of course, come a time when the food animal has to give way to the increasing population, but it is driven only to the limit of the populated area, and as the call for food increases, so the rearing of animals becomes of greater importance and more intensive. The tendency on the fringe of thickly populated areas is for intensive mixed farming rather than extensive stock-raising alone, for the stubble after reaping can be utilized for animal food, and animals themselves, when turned out to graze, help to fertilize the ground. Where space is practically unlimited, as, for example, in South America, the need for extensive farming does not arise and the rule is rather for extensive stock-raising.

One finds also that the increased demand for food animals in the densely populated districts is met by an increased production of meat rather than an increase in the size of the herds. In general, one might say that the productivity and the number of food animals tend to increase as the human population increases, and as the countries concerned become more and more highly developed economically.

In this country the production of intensively fed beef has increased considerably over the last few years, as many as five hundred cattle being fed in one unit. In some cases the cattle are housed on slats, the dung dropping down to a lower level. The labour saving is considerable, as 'dunging' may only be necessary once a year. When this system is combined with automatic feed delivery, it has been found possible for one man to look after some 400 to 500 head.

Social conditions, which can be associated with religious observances, also play their part in this distribution of food-producing animals. The abhorrence of the Jew for pork is well known and respected; the Hindu regards the cow as sacred; and the Mohammedan world looks upon the pig as unclean. Some Japanese also have a prejudice against pork, and other Eastern races, particularly the Chinese, look with disfavour on beef, on religious grounds. Prejudices such as these are not confined to the Oriental; in the British Isles there was a disinclination to eat pork unless there be an 'R' in the month, and horse flesh, although used extensively by the peoples on the Continent, is not considered a delicacy by the English-speaking races. The availability of feeds and the distance from the chief markets also have their influence, but to a lesser extent than formerly; firstly because of more scientific methods of feeding, and secondly because of the coming of practical refrigeration.

Three important considerations

When studying figures on the world dispersion of food animals, one must proceed with caution, for bare statements are hardly sufficient to give a true picture of the case. For example, the yield of meat from a prime British steer might easily be double that from a Brazilian one, ignoring all considerations of quality. Thus the following factors require consideration.

(1) The ability to produce flesh economically.

(2) The live weight and its relation to carcase yield.

(3) The age of slaughter (to determine the percentage of the herd slaughtered annually).

Since prehistoric times there have been no new species domesticated, but improvements have been brought about in the existing stocks by selection and (during the last hundred years or so) by inbreeding so that new *types* have been evolved. A cross-bred animal possesses certain characteristics which are not all apparent and superficial, and these hidden features have a tendency to come out in future generations. By inbreeding the desired characteristics can be rapidly fixed and the undesirable eliminated.

Beef production

The current world cattle population was approximately 1,346 million (1976), and the figures for the more important cattle producing countries are given in Table 50. These cattle are produced under a wide variety of farming conditions from the intensive land-use systems of most West European countries, to the extensive ranching methods of America and Australia.

There has been a continuous increase in world cattle numbers in recent years. However, there are indications that a considerable proportion of the expansion is now among beef cattle, while downward trends are occurring in dairy cattle. In line with the increase in cattle numbers, production of beef and veal has expanded, particularly in North America and in Oceania.

The most important countries in terms of their contribution to world trade in beef and veal are not necessarily the largest producers. Although the USA has the largest cattle population, it is also now the world's largest importer of beef and veal. The European Economic Community is a major importing area and so also are other West European countries especially the United Kingdom. The principal exporting countries are Australia, Argentina, New Zealand and the Irish Republic. Both Australia and New Zealand send the major part of their exports to the

USA, with shipments to the United Kingdom of continually declining importance, and trade with Far Eastern countries, for example Japan, being encouraged. The majority of Argentina's exports are sent to Western Europe, with the United Kingdom the largest individual importer, and other countries, particularly Spain and Italy, also taking large quantities. There is a considerable volume of trade between the member states of the EEC and in recent years Yugoslavia has become an increasingly important exporter. The majority of this beef and veal is sent to Italy.

Mutton and wool

The sheep population of the world was roughly calculated to be about 1011 million (1976), and of these about one-quarter are within the Commonwealth. Approximate figures for sheep numbers in the major sheep producing countries of the world are shown in Table 51. World sheep numbers have shown only small increases in recent years. This is thought to be largely because of relatively low wool prices and the increased use of synthetics. In some countries droughts can seriously reduce sheep numbers. In Australia, for example, there was a particularly serious drought in 1966 which caused a sharp reduction in the sheep population.

Although sheep farming is widespread, mutton and lamb production is important in only a limited number of countries. The major producers are Australia, New Zealand, and the USSR, followed by the United States, the United Kingdom and Argentina. During the 1960s total world production of mutton and lamb remained relatively static, with increased flocks in Australia, New Zealand, and Argentine compensating for reductions in the United States, United Kingdom and USSR.

Live sheep are of some importance in the trade of many countries, but total world trade in mutton and lamb is small in relation to that in beef and pig meat. Most of the exports are from Australia and New Zealand and the major importing nations are the United Kingdom, Japan, and the North American countries. Argentina and the Irish Republic are the only other major exporters, and Greece and France have increased their imports in recent years.

Pig production

The 1976 estimate puts the world pig population at approximately 662 million. Table 52 shows pig numbers in some of the major pig-producing countries.

TABLE 50

Approximate figures of cattle in the principal cattle-producing countries (Thousand head), (USDA)

	1960/69 (a)	1970	1971	1972	1973	1974	1975	1976
WORLD	1,150,938	1,226,849 (b)	1,243,522	1,268,614	1,288,986	1,320,112	1,351,196	1,346,930(d)
NORTH AMERICA								
Canada	153,979	168,041	172,213	176,739	181,648	189,675	196,365	192,660(d)
Mexico	11,375	11,626	11,985	12,267	12,607	13,210	14,008	13,696
United States	20,602	24,876	26,053	26,371	26,830	27,512	28,700	28,772
	105,281	112,369	114,578	117,862	121,534	127,670	131,826	127,976
SOUTH AMERICA								
Argentina	177,623	180,478	185,143	193,047	198,656	207,015	218,918	214,700(d)
Brazil	46,082	48,440	49,786	52,312	54,771	58,000	59,800	60,500
Columbia	82,997	78,448(c)	81,131	85,134	86,135	88,136	96,160	98,160
Uruguay	17,000	20,200	20,508	20,960	22,100	23,032	23,888	24,724
	8,354	8,500	8,700	9,273	9,860	10,961	11,362	11,500
WESTERN EUROPE	84,671	88,468	87,053	87,216	90,754	95,339	95,124	94,800(d)
EEC	69,078	72,898	71,902	71,735	74,773	79,022	79,179	77,937
Belgium	2,590	2,713	2,715	2,643	2,750	2,896	2,889	2,812
Denmark	3,254	2,897	2,766	2,678	2,810	3,100	3,048	3,075
France	20,446	21,719	21,737	21,699	22,556	23,949	24,300	24,100
Western Germany	13,376	14,286	14,026	13,638	13,892	14,364	14,430	14,466
Irish Republic	4,608	5,229	5,405	5,516	5,946	6,408	6,500	5,966
Italy	9,449	9,612	8,776	8,669	8,738	8,487	8,243	8,888
Luxembourg	168	193	192	192	204	208	214	206
Netherlands	3,489	3,953	3,850	3,783	4,117	4,772	4,719	4,550
United Kingdom	11,778	12,296	12,435	12,917	13,760	14,838	14,836	13,874
Austria	2,410	2,418	2,468	2,499	2,514	2,624	2,582	3,683
Spain	3,780	4,293	4,235	4,249	4,475	4,413	4,417	4,425
Sweden	2,277	1,926	1,833	1,828	1,886	1,909	1,864	1,820

EASTERN EUROPE	32,789	33,487	33,827	34,731	36,162	37,898	38,982	38,870(d)
Czechoslovakia	4,416	4,223	4,288	4,349	4,466	4,556	4,566	4,560
Eastern Germany	4,724	5,171	5,190	5,293	5,379	5,482	5,585	5,532
Hungary	1,966	1,926	1,911	1,882	1,893	1,930	2,017	1,900
Poland	9,301	10,285	10,220	10,562	11,265	12,309	12,815	12,762
Romania	4,825	5,035	5,216	5,528	5,767	5,897	5,983	6,126
Yugoslavia	5,535	5,075	5,203	5,214	5,425	5,743	5,938	5,798
USSR	87,557	95,162	99,225	102,434	104,006	106,266	109,122	111,000
AFRICA	138,074	155,758	155,794	156,217	152,934	155,133	157,728	158,500(d)
Botswana	1,245	1,832	2,050	2,175	2,300	2,360	2,400	n.a.
Ethiopia	25,244	26,232	26,310	26,757	24,025	24,663	25,315	n.a.
South Africa	12,290	10,134	10,043	11,609	11,741	12,325	12,798	13,000
ASIA	450,380	474,063	476,589	481,576	486,109	487,987	491,835	492,500(d)
China (Mainland)	87,820	92,400	92,550	92,700	92,850	93,000	93,150	n.a.
India	228,309	230,650	232,000	236,800	238,850	239,300	240,550	n.a.
Iran	5,199	6,080	5,980	6,530	6,615	7,265	7,450	7,700
Japan	3,223	3,593	3,615	3,568	3,569	3,650	3,644	3,690(d)
OCEANIA	25,905	31,392	33,678	36,654	38,717	40,799	43,122	43,900(d)
Australia	18,432	22,162	24,373	27,373	29,101	30,839	32,806	33,700
New Zealand	7,104	8,777	8,819	8,774	9,088	9,415	9,755	9,650

(a) Annual average.
(b) Figures relate to numbers or estimated numbers at the beginning of the year in question. Selected countries' figures of major interest are shown underneath the relevant regional totals.
(c) Official census—data may not be comparable to previous years.
(d) MLC estimate
n.a. Not available.

TABLE 51

Approximate figures of sheep in the principal sheep-producing countries (thousand head), (USDA)

	1960/69 (a)	1970	1971	1972	1973	1974	1975	1976
WORLD	999,346	1,040,239(b)	1,036,908	1,017,375	999,927	1,009,753	1,017,334	1,011,530(d)
NORTH AMERICA	35,357	27,695	26,717	25,742	25,014	23,563	21,565	20,343(d)
Canada	817	528	546	597	579	562	541	505
Mexico	6,178	5,499	5,320	5,255	5,480	5,380	5,300	5,300
United States	27,054	20,423	19,686	18,710	17,724	16,394	14,512	13,346
SOUTH AMERICA	122,824	123,009	116,515	110,925	114,111	113,935	109,871	109,963(d)
Argentina	47,691	42,500	39,000	40,000	41,000	41,000	37,000	36,500
Brazil	21,114	25,700(c)	25,000	25,500	26,000	26,500	25,000	25,100
Uruguay	21,560	19,800	18,500	16,300	17,000	15,120	14,938	15,000
WESTERN EUROPE	78,677	74,048	72,711	71,500	72,013	72,635	72,910	72,793(d)
EEC	42,521	41,694	41,072	41,136	42,047	43,074	43,439	42,779
Belgium	66	85	66	66	69	74	81	88
Denmark	80	70	65	52	56	59	59	60
France	9,087	10,037	10,239	10,115	10,191	10,324	10,569	10,707
Western Germany	910	841	843	850	908	1,016	1,040	1,040
Irish Republic	3,217	2,788	2,836	2,862	2,835	2,845	2,711	2,503
Italy	8,083	8,138	7,948	7,846	7,770	7,809	7,995	8,050
Luxembourg	3	3	4	4	4	5	5	5
Netherlands	496	575	572	592	657	749	760	800
United Kingdom	20,580	19,157	18,499	18,749	19,557	20,193	20,219	19,526
Greece	8,827	7,546	7,391	7,534	7,874	8,350	8,403	8,900
Portugal	4,970*	3,500	3,300	2,420	2,300	2,250	2,000	1,950
Spain	19,500	18,729	18,443	17,863	17,191	16,306	16,430	16,519

EASTERN EUROPE	42,249	41,198	41,355	41,360	40,838	40,546	40,794	40,896(d)
Bulgaria	9,899	9,223	9,678	10,127	9,921	9,765	9,791	9,990
Romania	12,820	13,836	13,818	14,071	14,455	14,302	13,929	13,867
Yugoslavia	10,288	8,974	8,703	8,326	7,774	7,852	8,175	7,915
USSR	134,971	130,655	138,059	139,916	139,086	142,634	145,305	141,025
AFRICA	128,252	138,108	136,754	136,796	138,830	137,663	137,425	138,000(d)
Ethiopia	11,770	12,679	12,842	12,950	12,950	13,000	13,100	n.a.
Morocco	9,423	11,724	11,120	11,907	13,241	14,000	14,500	n.a.
South Africa	40,413	34,092	31,645	30,228	33,303	33,622	34,391	34,950
ASIA	240,932	265,157	268,079	267,328	273,306	277,702	281,794	283,000(d)
China (Mainland)	66,000	70,600	71,000	71,300	72,000	72,500	73,000	n.a.
Iran	25,843	32,000	32,000	32,000	34,000	35,000	36,500	38,000
Turkey	33,844	36,351	36,471	36,760	38,806	40,093	40,539	40,600
OCEANIA	216,084	240,369	236,718	223,808	196,729	201,075	207,670	205,600(d)
Australia	162,311	180,080	177,792	162,910	140,029	145,175	151,653	148,800
New Zealand	53,760	60,276	58,912	60,883	56,684	55,883	56,000	56,700

(a) Annual average.
(b) Figures relate to numbers or estimated numbers at the beginning of the year in question. Selected countries' figures of major interest are shown underneath the relevant regional totals.
(c) Official census—data may not be comparable to previous years.
(d) MLC estimate
n.a. Not available.

TABLE 52

Approximate figures of pigs in the principal pig-producing countries (thousand head), (USDA)

	1960/69 (a)	1970	1971	1972	1973	1974	1975	1976
WORLD	570,227	594,308(b)	633,819	644,505	646,064	666,344	676,617	662,030(d)
NORTH AMERICA	78,687	81,000	92,332	88,195	82,593	87,068	80,463	75,000(d)
Canada	5,499	6,559	7,720	7,388	6,944	6,991	5,895	5,467
Mexico	8,118	10,297	9,970	10,983	9,400	11,663	12,100	12,500
United States	58,461	57,046	67,433	62,507	59,180	61,106	55,062	49,602
SOUTH AMERICA	70,345	46,965	48,347	48,604	49,727	50,812	61,280	63,780(d)
Brazil	56,540	31,500(c)	32,100	33,000	34,000	35,000	45,000	47,000
WESTERN EUROPE	68,319	82,864	88,654	87,257	89,575	91,075	89,755	88,770(d)
EEC	53,094	65,218	70,126	68,362	68,945	70,357	69,712	68,735
Belgium	1,909	3,094	3,835	3,925	4,298	4,720	4,666	4,648
Denmark	7,469	8,350	8,733	8,726	8,699	8,242	8,054	7,585
France	9,264	10,462	11,572	11,279	11,374	11,425	12,040	12,030
Western Germany	17,270	19,323	20,969	19,985	20,028	20,452	20,234	19,865
Irish Republic	1,022	1,065	1,155	1,144	1,007	1,035	796	880
Italy	5,205	9,224	8,984	8,196	8,201	8,201	8,814	8,888
Luxembourg	104	103	106	96	90	101	95	86
Netherlands	3,601	5,471	6,226	6,129	6,409	6,914	7,143	7,100
United Kingdom	7,251	8,126	8,546	8,882	8,839	9,267	7,870	7,653
Austria	2,919	3,196	3,445	3,091	3,256	3,290	3,517	3,683
Spain	5,525	6,915	6,917	7,178	8,472	8,308	7,865	8,000

EASTERN EUROPE	47,874	48,362	51,834	57,391	60,221	65,559	68,076	67,900(d)
Czechoslovakia	5,701	5,037	5,530	5,935	6,093	6,266	6,719	6,683
Eastern Germany	8,852	9,237	9,684	9,995	10,361	10,849	11,519	11,500
Hungary	6,399	5,700	7,312	7,594	6,859	8,011	8,294	6,900
Poland	13,710	14,755	13,863	16,946	19,023	21,451	21,708	21,643
Romania	5,085	5,972	6,359	7,742	8,785	8,987	8,566	8,812
Yugoslavia	5,689	5,544	6,562	6,216	6,342	7,401	7,683	6,539
USSR	55,993	56,055	67,483	71,434	66,593	70,032	72,272	57,800
AFRICA	5,692	6,641	6,938	7,199	7,327	7,469	7,623	7,880(d)
ASIA								
China (Mainland)	240,759	269,231	274,808	280,424	286,038	291,083	294,211	298,000(d)
Japan	199,400	220,000	223,010	228,000	231,200	234,200	237,250	n.a.
	4,142	6,335	6,904	6,985	7,313	8,018	7,684	7,955
OCEANIA	2,558	3,190	3,423	4,001	3,990	3,246	2,937	2,900(d)
Australia	1,712	2,398	2,590	3,199	3,259	2,505	2,195	2,160

(a) Annual average.
(b) Figures relate to numbers or estimated numbers at the beginning of the year in question. Selected countries' figures of major interest are shown underneath the relevant regional totals.
(c) Official census—data may not be comparable to previous years.
(d) MLC estimate
n.a. Not available.

Pig production is a relatively quick and efficient way of producing meat. Under good management and sound husbandry practices, sows can produce two litters each year, which will give approximately fifteen piglets weaned per sow per year. These pigs can be ready for slaughter at about 5 months of age. Such pigs convert food at a rate of approximately 1 lb (0·45 kg) live-weight gain per 3½ lb (1·6 kg) food. This compares with food conversion ratios for cattle of approximately 1 lb (0·45 kg) per 10 lb (4·5 kg) feed, but with considerable variations according to age and the type of feeding system.

The bulk of world trade in live pigs and pork is within Europe. China exports a considerable number of live pigs, but exact figures are difficult to obtain. Pig numbers in the various countries, and the general demand for meat, are important in determining the direction and volume of trade. For example, in recent years France has tended to have a shortage of home-produced pigs and in both France and Western Germany demand for pig meat has been strong because of the general scarcity and high prices of beef. As a result large numbers of live pigs have been imported into France and West Germany particularly from Denmark, the Netherlands, and Belgium. France has also imported large quantities of pork, particularly from other EEC countries. The United Kingdom imports very little pork, but is the world's major importer of bacon and hams. Denmark accounts for approximately three-quarters of the bacon and hams entering the export trade and Poland accounts for approximately half of the remainder.

United Kingdom

It has already been stated that the tendency throughout the world is for the wetter parts of a country to support cattle, while the drier and less fertile areas are given over to the rearing of sheep. Sheep will also be found on hillsides, because of the lesser rainfall and the consequent poorness of vegetation. Applying such knowledge to this country we shall have a general idea of the distribution of food animals. The prevailing winds sweeping the British Isles are those from the southwest, which, coming across the Atlantic Ocean without any obstruction, will be full of moisture and ready to precipitate it as rain. Again, most of the mountains are to be found in the north and west, so one naturally expects these to be areas of greatest rainfall, and the precipitation to become less as one travels to the east. This is indeed the case, for in the western parts of the British Isles the rainfall reaches as much as 40 in (100 cm) during an average year while the amount falling in London and eastern counties hardly ever exceeds 20 in (50 cm).

TABLE 53

Regional distribution of livestock in the United Kingdom (June 1969)

Region	Cattle		Sheep and lambs		Pigs	
	Numbers (000)	Per 100 acres of crops and grass in region	Numbers (000)	Per 100 acres of crops and grass in region	Numbers (000)	Per 100 acres of crops and grass in region
Eastern	527·3	13·8	293·0	7·7	1582·7	41·4
South-eastern	939·9	31·5	1282·1	43·0	850·6	28·5
East Midland	819·0	27·5	1174·3	39·4	525·4	17·6
West Midland	1299·3	46·2	1853·1	65·9	659·1	23·4
South-western	2049·6	48·6	2628·0	62·3	984·4	23·3
Northern	1171·5	48·9	3233·9	134·9	365·9	15·3
Yorks. and Lancs.	828·1	38·7	1536·0	71·8	937·5	43·8
Wales	1343·5	52·1	6051·5	234·9	244·4	9·5
Scotland	2152·5	50·1	7617·0	177·2	600·3	14·0
N. Ireland	1242·0	60·1	946·0	45·8	1053·0	50·9

Table 53 shows how cattle are to be found evenly spread over the North and West with the highest density in Northern Ireland, whereas sheep are predominantly found in the upland areas of Wales, the North, and Scotland. Pig production which is not affected by the same climatic considerations takes place particularly in the Eastern and Yorkshire and Lancashire regions of England and Northern Ireland.

Since the first livestock census about a century ago, cattle have shown a persistent tendency to increase in number. However there was a gradual decrease in sheep numbers up to 1920, when a slow recovery started. Losses in the national flock due to severe winters have caused considerable fluctuations in sheep numbers over the years.

Following the Second World War there was a considerable emphasis on meat production, and Table 56 indicates the changing pattern of meat supplies. Whilst before the war only 51 % of the carcase meat and offals (excluding bacon) were home produced; by 1973, the overall figure had increased to almost 75%, the figures for beef and veal being 24% imported and 76% home produced.

The cattle population has increased from 8·8 million in 1938 to over 13 million in 1976.

In the case of sheep, there was a steady increase in the national flock from 26·8 in 1938 to 30 million in 1966. This figure declined to 26·6 million in 1969, but has since increased, and now stands at about 19 million (provisional figure, 1976).

Over the years, the pig population tended to fluctuate in a cyclical pattern, with a peak being reached every 4 or 5 years. This was because it was relatively easy for a producer to shift into or away from pig production, in response to a changing market situation. Government action and changing structure has tended to dampen the 'Pig Cycle' in recent years. In 1938 the pig population was about 4·4 million. A peak in pig population occurred during 1965 (over 8 million) followed by a drop and gradual recovery.

In 1976 (June) the provisional figures stood at about 8 million, a slight increase as compared with December 1975. In relating pig population to annual kill, the relatively short gestation period and rapid growth must be borne in mind, and the slaughter numbers may be almost twice that of the pig population. For example it is estimated that the ratio of pigs slaughtered to the pig population in 1974 (June) is in the order of 1·8 to 1.

Table 54 illustrates the present tendency to demand younger animals and smaller joints with less fat content.

TABLE 54

Average dressed carcase weights (estimated)

Year	Cattle (lb)	Sheep (lb)	Pigs (lb)
1908	672	67	160
1925	628	60	160
1962	585	55	140
1968	555	42	136

TABLE 55

Livestock numbers—United Kingdom (thousand head)
(Source: M.A.F.F.)

	Dec. 1975	Dec. 1976 (g)	% change Dec. 1976/ Dec. 1975
CATTLE			
Cows and heifers in milk:			
dairy herd (b)	2,574	2,627	+ 2
beef herd (c)	825	809	− 2
Cows in calf but not in milk:			
dairy herd (b)	668	692	+ 4
beef herd (c)	997	947	− 5
Total of above	5,064	5,075	—
Heifers in calf (1st calf):			
dairy herd (b)	502	454	−10
beef herd (c)	252	231	− 8
Bulls for service (d)	63	91	− 2
Other:			
2 years and over	1,029	1,028	—
1 year to 2 years	3,309	3,031	− 8
6 months to 1 year	2,140	2,113	− 1
Under 6 months	1,528	1,649	+ 8
Total (a)	13,915	13,672	− 2
SHEEP			
Ewes for breeding (e)	12,746	12,709	—
Rams for service	344	343	—
Other sheep 1 year and over	731	726	− 1
Sheep and lambs under 1 year:			
Ewe lambs retained for breeding	2,365	2,591	+10
Others under 1 year	3,349	3,529	+ 5
Total (a)	19,536	19,899	+ 2
PIGS			
Sows in pig	496	537	+ 8
Gilts in pig	122	111	− 9
Other sows for breeding	226	238	+ 5
Total breeding sows (a)	845	886	+ 5
Boars for service:	41	43	+ 5
Gilts over 50 kg. (110 lb.) but not yet in pig	102	90	−12
Other:			
110 kg. (240 lb.) and over (f)	101	145	+44
80 kg. (175 lb.) and under 110 kg. (240 lb.)	628	705	+12
50 kg. (110 lb.) and under 80 kg. (175 lb.)	1,766	1,851	+ 5
20 kg. (45 lb.) and under 50 kg. (110 lb.)	2,281	2,411	+ 6
Under 20 kg. (45 lb.)	1,905	2,034	+ 7
Total (a)	7,668	8,169	+ 7

(a) Because of individual rounding, figures do not necessarily add up to totals shown.
(b) Intended mainly for producing milk or rearing calves for the dairy herd.
(c) Intended mainly for rearing calves for beef.
(d) Including bull calves being reared for service.
(e) Including shearling ewes.
(f) Including barren sows for fattening.
(g) Provisional.

Table 56

Sources of United Kingdom meat supplies

	Pre-war		1961		1968		1973	
	000 tons	% of total supplies	000 tons	% of total supplies	000 tons	% of total supplies	000 tons	% of total supplies
Beef and veal—								
Imports	612	51	357	24	257	22	266	24
Home production	578	49	891	76	891	78	864	76
Total*	1190	100	1179	100	1148	100	1130	100
Mutton and lamb—								
Imports	344	64	348	57	347	59	261	53
Home production	195	36	263	43	243	41	230	47
Total*	539	100	611	100	590	100	491	100
Pork—								
Imports	58	21	18	4	18	3	24	3
Home production	220	79	444	96	567	97	671	97
Total*	278	100	462	100	585	100	695	100
Offal—								
Imports	48	31	87	36	110	41	93	41
Home production	105	69	155	64	158	59	136	59
Total*	153	100	242	100	268	100	229	100

*Because of individual rounding, figures do not necessarily add up to totals shown.

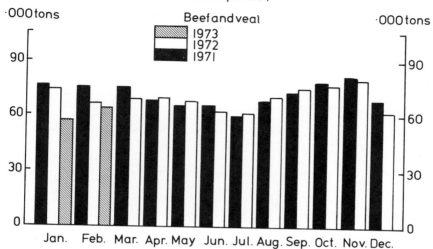

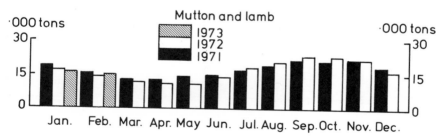

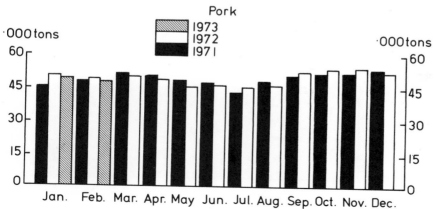

Fig. 58 Seasonal trends in meat production (*MLC*)

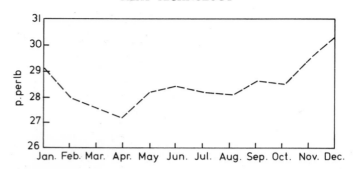

Fig. 59 Seasonal trends in United Kingdom wholesale prices (p per lb) for Scottish killed side of beef

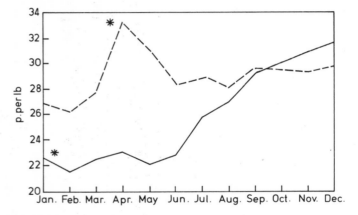

Fig. 60 Seasonal trends in United Kingdom wholesale prices (p per lb) for English and New Zealand lamb. English lamb is shown by broken line, New Zealand by full line. Asterisks denote new-season lamb

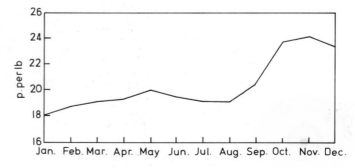

Fig. 61 Seasonal trends in United Kingdom wholesale price (p per lb) English pigs (120 to 160 lb 54 to 73 kg)
(Source: Average of mean price range quoted each day at Smithfield Market, London, 1973)

Table 57

Consumption of meat in the EEC, (MLC)

Consumption per head (kg) per annum	Beef and Veal						
	1960/69*	1970	1971	1972	1973	1974	1975
France	28·9	29·9	29·6	28·5	28·7	29·5	30·2
Belgium & Luxembourg	24·6	26·9	27·3	27·0	26·1	30·8	30·6
Irish Republic	16·8	19·0	19·1	19·6	18·4	22·6	28·9
UNITED KINGDOM	24·2	23·5	22·9	23·5	21·1	24·0	25·2
Western Germany	22·0	24·7	24·7	23·4	22·6	23·3	23·3
Italy	19·0	24·5	25·7	26·0	27·8	24·8	23·1
Netherlands	20·8	21·8	21·9	20·2	20·6	21·3	22·4
Denmark	17·9	19·7	19·3	16·2	14·7	14·7	15·6

Consumption per head (kg) per annum	Pig meat						
	1960/69*	1970	1971	1972	1973	1974	1975
Western Germany	39·5	45·6	47·9	49·0	48·1	50·5	51·3
Denmark	32·2	29·4	30·8	34·0	34·6	34·9	38·5
Belgium & Luxembourg	28·2	33·7	34·5	35·7	38·4	39·0	36·3
Netherlands	26·0	28·6	32·1	32·3	30·4	34·2	35·3
France	28·0	30·6	32·0	32·7	32·6	33·2	34·0
Irish Republic	25·2	30·9	30·9	30·5	30·8	31·8	27·2
UNITED KINGDOM	26·2	26·9	28·3	28·0	26·7	26·1	23·0
Italy	9·4	12·7	14·1	14·7	15·8	17·0	17·8

Consumption per head (kg) per annum	Mutton/Lamb and Goat meat						
	1960/69*	1970	1971	1972	1973	1974	1975
Irish Republic	10·9	10·9	11·1	10·9	10·5	11·0	11·2
UNITED KINGDOM	11·0	9·9	10·3	9·5	8·4	7·8	8·4
France	2·6	3·0	3·2	3·3	3·5	3·5	3·6
Belgium & Luxembourg	0·5	0·7	0·9	0·9	1·1	1·2	1·3
Italy	0·9	1·2	1·1	1·1	1·1	0·9	1·1
Western Germany	0·2	0·2	0·3	0·3	0·4	0·4	0·6
Denmark	0·3	0·4	0·4	0·4	0·4	0·4	0·4
Netherlands	0·2	0·2	0·2	0·2	0·2	0·2	0.2

*1960/1969 Annual Average.

Table 57 (*cont.*)

Consumption per head (kg) per annum	Poultry meat						
	1960/69*	1970	1971	1972	1973	1974	1975
Italy	8·4	11·8	12·2	13·4	14·7	15·3	16·4
France	10·4	12·2	12·0	13·2	14·0	14·3	14·1
UNITED KINGDOM	7·6	10·9	10·8	12·5	11·9	11·9	11·3
Irish Republic	7·2	9·9	10·4	11·9	12·8	11·3	10·6
Belgium & Luxembourg	7·6	8·7	9·1	9·0	9·5	9·4	9·9
Western Germany	6·1	8·4	8·7	8·9	9·0	8·6	9·1
Denmark	3·7	5·1	5·0	5·4	6·8	7·1	7·7
Netherlands	3·9	6·2	6·3	7·0	7·0	6·8	7·0

Consumption per head (kg) per annum	Offal						
	1960/69*	1970	1971	1972	1973	1974	1975
Irish Republic	10·8	12·9	13·8	12·6	12·8	16·2	23·3
France	8·0	8·6	8·9	8·8	8·8	9·3	9·4
Belgium & Luxembourg	5·1	6·3	7·9	7·0	6·4	7·2	7·2
Denmark	6·2	6·7	7·0	6·6	5·6	6·3	6·5
UNITED KINGDOM	4·7	4·3	4·3	4·4	4·2	4·2	5·0
Western Germany	4·5	4·7	4·7	4·5	4·6	4·8	5·0
Netherlands	3·8	4·5	4·9	4·9	4·3	5·4	4·9
Italy	2·0	2·8	3·1	3·1	3·1	3·2	3·0

Consumption per head (kg) per annum	All meat and offal						
	1960/69*	1970	1971	1972	1973	1974	1975
Irish Republic	70·9	83·6	85·3	85·6	86·2	92·0	101.4
Western Germany	73·2	84·6	87·2	87·0	85·7	88·7	90·4
France	84·0	91·9	93·3	94·4	95·1	97·5	99·3
Belgium & Luxembourg	70·5	81·5	83·5	84·3	87·5	92·3	90·4
UNITED KINGDOM	74·5	76·3	77·3	77·3	72·6	74·5	73·0
Netherlands	56·5	63·8	66·9	67·1	65·3	71·5	72·4
Denmark	61·5	62·1	63·4	63·5	62·9	64·0	69·6
Italy	41·9	56·5	59·5	61·2	66·2	65·3	65·2

*1960/1969 Annual Average

21   Some EEC Trading Terms

Whilst most members of the meat trade will be familiar with such terms as FOB, CIF, ex-store and other abbreviations, entry into the EEC has given rise to a new trade nomenclature. The following is a glossary of those commonly employed, as defined by the MLC* (1973).

Basic Price (Pigmeat)

Fixed annually to apply throughout a 12-month period commencing November 1st, at a level designed to stabilize prices without leading to surplus production in the Community. Price levels for support buying and private storage are set in relation to the basic price.

Customs Duty (Beef and veal, mutton and lamb)

A fixed percentage charge made on specific products imported into the EEC.

Export Restitution Payment (Beef and veal, pigmeat)

A payment made to an EEC exporter to enable him to compete on world export markets where prices are at lower level.

GATT

General agreement on tariffs and trade.

Guide Prices (Beef and veal)

Fixed annually for cattle and calves to apply throughout a 12-month period, normally commencing April 1st. Guide prices are set at a level

*Livestock and meat in the EEC. A guide to the regulations, MLC June 1973.

which is considered desirable for producers to obtain, under normal market conditions. Guide prices are used as a basis for determining variable levies and support buying prices.

Jumelage 'Twinning'

A scheme whereby buyers in the EEC must match tonne for tonne supplies from other exporting countries with those purchased from the EEC.

Monetary Compensatory Amount (Beef and veal, pigmeat)

A charge or refund made by individual EEC member states to compensate for the effects of currency movements in relation to the official parity with the unit of account.

Reference Price (Beef and veal, pigmeat)

The official average weekly market price. For cattle and calves, the reference price is calculated for each member state from fatstock prices at selected representative markets. For pigs, the reference price is based upon Grade 11 pig carcase quotations. The EEC reference prices are based on weighted averages of the national figures.

Sluice Gate Price (Pigmeat)

Represents the cost of producing pigmeat in non-EEC countries. If the free at frontier offer price falls below the sluice gate price, a supplementary levy may be charged.

Support Buying (Cattle and beef)

Calves and veal are excluded. Direct purchases of specified commodities may be made by the intervention authority* in the member states. There is also provision for the payment of aids to enable private meat traders to take beef off the market and store it for release when the market strengthens. There are three methods of support buying:

(1) The intervention authorities will buy fresh or chilled beef of defined qualities. The intervention price is related to 93% of the guide price.

---

*In the United Kingdom the Intervention Board for Agricultural Produce is the Intervention Authority. The Meat and Livestock Commission are, however, acting as their agents for livestock and meat.

(2) Discretionary support buying may also be introduced when the EEC reference price for adult cattle is less than 98 % of the guide price and at the same time, the average market price for one or more grades in a member state is below 93 % of the guide price.

(3) Compulsory support buying throughout the whole Community is carried out when the EEC reference price for adult cattle falls below 93 % of the guide price. The maximum buying-in price is also 93·5 % of the guide price adjusted by the appropriate coefficient.

Pigmeat

The support buying price for pigmeat carcases is normally specified for the standard quality, but the Community system provides for support prices to be specified for other qualities.

The pigmeat regulations include provision for two types of intervention. Direct purchases may be made by the intervention authority in the member state; or aid can be provided to enable private meat traders to put pigmeat into store.

When the reference price (the average price of carcases of reference quality) falls below 103 % of the basic price and is likely to remain at that level, support buying measures may come into operation.

In these circumstances direct support buying may be undertaken by the intervention authorities at prices between 85 % and 92 % of the basic price.

Transitional compensatory amounts (Beef and veal, pigmeat)

These bridge the gap between the different price levels of the Six and new member states during the transitional period. This means a charge on exports into EEC countries with higher market prices, and a payment on inter-Community exports to countries with lower prices.

Unit of Account

The monetary unit used by the EEC.

Variable Levy (Beef and veal, pigmeat)

A charge on imports which may be varied depending on the movement of prices within and outside the Community.

22　Metric Trading in the Meat Industry

At the time of writing (December 1976), the position of the change from imperial to metric measurements, would appear to be as follows.

Fatstock Sales from 3rd January 1977

Sales on auction markets will be based on metric weights of fatstock from Monday 3rd January 1977.

The weight unit of one kilogram is recommended to replace the current units of hundredweights and quarters for cattle and scores and pounds for pigs.

The sale weights and bidding units recommended for use from that date are:

	Sale Weight	Bidding Units
Cattle	Kilograms	p per kg
Pigs	Kilograms, with any additional $\frac{1}{2}$ kg included	p per kg
Sheep	None, as sheep will continue to be sold per head	£ per head

Bidding for Cattle

The bidding intervals used will be influenced by market conditions. It is possible that individual bids might be taken in steps of 0·2p per kg. This represents about £1 to the total price of an animal, and thus approximates to current bids of 10p per cwt.

Bidding for Pigs

If the most usual current practice is followed, the bidding for pigs will take place in steps of 0·5p per kilogram.

The total value added to one pig by each increment of 0·5p per kg will be about 45p per head, based upon an average weight of 90 kg.

Bidding for Sheep

The live weight of a single sheep, or a pen of sheep, will be recorded in kilograms, with any additional $\frac{1}{2}$ kg noted. The *estimated* dressed carcase weight will also be recorded to the nearest complete half kilogram.

Example 4 sheep in one lot:

Total liveweight	154 kg	
Average	$38\frac{1}{2}$ kg	
'Halfweight' per sheep	19 kg	
Adjustment per sheep to arrive at the estimated dressed carcase weight, say— 1 kg		say, + $\frac{1}{2}$ kg
Average estimated dressed carcase weight (basis of guarantee payment)	18 kg	$19\frac{1}{2}$ kg

Market Prices

Market price reports relating to liveweight sales will be based on metric units from the 3rd January 1977. The following categories of stock will be affected. Fat cattle, fat sheep, fat pigs, fat cows, fat sows and store cattle.

It is intended that deadweight prices for all classes of stock reported by the MLC will be expressed in terms of metric units from the same time.

It is recommended that wholesale meat prices should be reported on the basis of metric weights from 3rd January 1977.

No arrangements have yet been made for the metrication of *retail meat sales.*

Support Buying of Beef

As part of the common agricultural policy for beef, there is provision for market prices to be supported by direct purchase by a nominated government agency. In the United Kingdom the nominate agency is the Intervention Board for Agricultural Produce (the 'Board') which operates through its agents, the Meat & Livestock Commission (the 'MLC') in Great Britain and the Department of Agriculture for Northern Ireland ('DANI') in Northern Ireland. These arrangements are derived directly from EEC Regulations.

Eligible Beef

Beef which may be bought by the Board must be of the quality specified, and must be dressed and presented in accordance with the specifications set out. The beef must also be:

(a) Chilled. Chilling should begin immediately after slaughter and should be undertaken gradually so that a maximum internal temperature of the meat (at the deepest part) 7°C or 45°F is achieved in not less than 24 hours and not more than 48 hours. The meat should be held at a temperature not exceeding this maximum until taken over by the Board.

(b) Free from characteristics indicating that it is not fit to be stored or used.

(c) Derived from cattle reared in the community.

(d) From adult cattle, slaughtered not more than 6 days previously.

(e) Not from emergency slaughtered cattle.

(f) Slaughtered and handled in accordance with the provisions specified. The directive requires the beef inter alia, to be from the cattle slaughtered in export approved premises and to be:

1. Inspected by an official veterinarian not more than 24 hours before slaughter and immediately after slaughter and found satisfactory;

2. Stamped as conforming with the Directive;

3. Loaded under conditions and transported in vehicles which conform with the hygiene standards set up in the Directive;

4. Accompanied by a health certificate signed by an official veterinarian.

(g) Dressed in accordance with the requirements of the EEC regulations.

Qualities and grades of beef which can be purchased into intervention Great Britain

Beef from the following basic qualities can be purchased into intervention in Great Britain:

1. Steers (medium), yielding carcases of 250 to 300 kg, approximately 485 to 560 kg (live weight).

2. Steers (heavy), yielding carcases of over 300 kg approximately equivalent to 570 kg and over (live weight).

3. Heifers (medium and heavy), yielding carcases of over 215 kg approximately equivalent to 420 kg and over (live weight).

Beef within these qualities will be assessed at the abattoir and, provided it falls within grade 'A' or 'B' as defined below, it may be accepted into intervention. Grade 'A' will be purchased at a higher price than that of Grade 'B'. The carcase weights quoted above are all ex-KCF.

GRADE A. Very good carcase: compact and heavily fleshed throughout. Fat covering even, not patchy or excessive.

GRADE B. Good commercial carcase: well fleshed throughout. May be fatter than 'A' but not excessively so.

Northern Ireland

Beef from the following basic qualities can be purchased into intervention in Northern Ireland:
1. Steers L (medium), yielding carcases weighing 196 to 270 kg;
2. Steers L (heavy), yielding carcases weighing 271 kg and over;
3. Steers T, yielding carcases weighing 196 kg and above;
4. Heifers T, yielding carcases weighing 168 kg and above.
    The carcase weights quoted above are exclusive of key knob and channel fat.
The quality definitions are as follows:
(a) Grade LM and LH: Very good to good conformation and fleshing, thin to medium and evenly distributed fat covering. Short to relatively short neck and shanks;
(b) Grade T: Good conformation and good to reasonably good general fleshing. Fat covering from thin to thicker than the maximum requirements for quality L but not very fat. Neck and shanks may be longer and thinner than for the L quality.
    Beef accepted into intervention within these qualities will be assessed at the abattoir and beef derived from leaner carcases graded B, will be purchased at a higher price than beef derived from carcases graded A.

Dressing Specifications

Offers must relate to meat dressed in accordance with the following specifications:
(a) Cut symmetrically along the spine, without head, feet, tail, kidneys and kidney fat, pelvis fat (i.e. channel fat), spinal cord, thin skirt udder, penis, and thick skirt. The throat must be clean and properly trimmed;
(b) Having been well bled and properly flayed, the skin in no way peeling, bloodstained, suffused or bruised. Superficial fat must not be torn. The pleura must be undamaged.

Presentation specifications

Offers must be one of the following presentations:

(a) Carcases, sides or compensated quarters (i.e. 1 forequarter and 1 hindquarter of the same quality and matching cut).

(b) Forequarters – cut from the carcase after cooling off, straight 1 rib cut.

(c) Hindquarters – cut from the carcase after cooling off, straight 3 rib cut.

Appendix

Fifty thought questions

1. Name and describe five British breeds of cattle.
2. What indication of age and quality would you look for when selecting cattle?
3. How would you calculate the carcase cost per lb/kg, from the price per live animal?
4. What names are applied to male and female cattle of various ages? What does each denote?
5. Compile a list of the edible and inedible offals of the ox.
6. What hygienic precautions are essential when slaughtering cattle?
7. Describe the various operations involved in killing and dressing a beast.
8. Compare and contrast a side of beef from an ox and a heifer.
9. Name and give the positions of the main lymphatic nodes in a side of ox beef.
10. What range of bone percentage would you expect in a hindquarter and forequarter of beef?
11. Name the bones of the ox and state in which joints they are found.
12. What do you understand by the term maturing, as applied to beef?
13. Indicate the main factors involved in the preservation of meat.
14. How may the dew-point affect carcase quality?
15. Define the term rigor mortis.
16. On a calorie cost basis, which is the cheapest portion of a side of beef.
17. Why does meat form such an important part of the human diet?
18. What characteristics would you look for in selecting a wrapping film for (a) fresh beef, (b) frozen meat, (c) pickled meat?
19. Indicate the main factors influencing meat spoilage.
20. Describe the digestive system of a ruminant.
21. What indication of probable quality would you look for in a side of beef?

381

22. How does the French method of cutting beef differ from that of the London and Home Counties style?
23. What weight of boneless cuts, prepared for retail sale, would you expect from a good side of beef weighing 300 lb (136 kg)?
24. Describe the various methods which may be employed to tenderize beef.
25. What precautions should be taken in order to reduce the risk of 'bone-taint'?
26. In what way does a weight percentage analysis assist in costing?
27. Compare and contrast the Suffolk with a Scotch Black Face.
28. What seasonal variations occur in the supply of home-killed mutton and lamb?
29. Describe the method of slaughtering and plain dressing a lamb carcase.
30. Compare the lamb carcase grading system of New Zealand, with that of Australia.
31. How would you judge the quality of a lamb carcase?
32. Give the dental formulae of an adult sheep.
33. Name the joints of a lamb carcase and state their approximate percentages of the whole carcase.
34. To what extent can the proportion of total fat vary in lamb carcases?
35. How does the conformation of a Hill lamb differ from that of a Devon?
36. Name and describe four breeds of pigs.
37. How does the digestive system of a pig differ from that of a sheep?
38. What are the main factors in a pork carcase which influence the yield of prepared cuts?
39. What percentage of the carcase of a pig is represented by (a) legs, (b) loins, (c) hands and bellies?
40. How does the per capita consumption of pig meat compare with that of mutton and lamb in the United Kingdom?
41. Compare the pluck of a porker pig with that of a lamb.
42. What are the main considerations in judging a pork carcase?
43. To what extent does the carcase weight of a pig influence its price?
44. How would you prepare a costing system?
45. Describe in detail how you would bone and roll a forequarter of veal.
46. What are the essentials of a well-balanced diet?
47. How do you account for the variation in muscle colour in bovines?
48. Discuss the advantages and disadvantages of young bull beef.
49. How would you obtain an indication of probable age from the bones of a beef carcase?
50. What factors can influence the colour of beef fat?

Twenty suggestions for the student

1. Visit markets and study breeds, crosses, and relative values in relation to types.
2. Visit slaughterhouses, examine live animal, and grade according to score card.
3. Study methods of slaughter, and judge carcase according to score card, and check with estimate of live animal.
4. Compile a list of the edible and inedible offals and state their commercial destination and application.
5. Calculate (a) dressing percentage of carcase, (b) percentage of edible offal, (c) percentage of inedible offal, (d) percentage of loss.
6. If possible, assist in slaughtering and dressing.
7. In carcase markets examine beef, mutton, pork, and veal from the aspect of conformation, finish and sex. Obtain experience in estimating weights.
8. Cut representative carcases and quarters, complete a chart showing cuts, then compile a percentage analysis showing loss in preparation for sale, and estimate the potential sale value on current prices.
9. Study the effect of rigor mortis, noting its duration under different conditions (a rabbit is a convenient animal for this purpose).
10. Visit a modern cold store and observe type of plant, refrigerant used, type of condenser and evaporator, insulation and storage temperatures, and methods of stacking and storing various commodities.
11. Visit plants handling dried blood, horns, bone, edible and inedible fat, and compare dry rendering with the steam process.
12. Visit a hide and skin merchant or tannery and consider the results of bad flaying and the effects of parasites.
13. Visit a firm dealing with the preparation and vacuum packing of prime cuts.
14. Visit and, if possible, assist in a small goods factory, dealing with fresh and cooked products.
15. On a small scale map mark in the retail butchers' shops and supermarkets in a given area, and study 'shopping centres', side of street, proximity of railway stations, bus stops, etc., and the trading neighbours. Select good and poor shops, and attempt to analyse the reasons for it.
16. Attempt to obtain a holiday assisting on a good mixed stock farm and consider production methods.
17. Visit a bacon factory and follow the processes through from the pig to the finished product.
18. Visit, several times if possible, the condemned meat room of an

abattoir, and with the aid of an inspector examine the various diseases and conditions found in food animals.

19. Visit a refrigerated container vessel and compare stowage space of the various products and the temperatures employed.

20. Remember that knowledge acquired, though it may seem but distantly related to our immediate interest, may prove of definite practical value in some future activity.

The Food, Drink, and Tobacco Industry Training Board are taking an active interest in systematic training within the meat industry. This will no doubt result in a widening in the scope of trade education and training, and the Institute of Meat will consider the provision of specialist courses, including those for management and for operatives.

The Institute of Meat

The Institute of Meat was founded in 1946 and is the national organization concerned with technical education and training in every facet of the meat industry.

The main courses are based upon a 3 tier pattern and, whilst each section is in itself distinctive, they can form a basis for an extension into higher levels of study.

1. MEAT INDUSTRY GENERAL CERTIFICATE. To provide the student with an introductory study of the Meat Industry in terms of its structure, raw materials and processing which will equip him for skilled craft or higher operative responsibilities and make him aware of adequate safety and hygiene practice. Specialized studies in the abattoir, wholesale, retail and processing sectors are available. Successful candidates can continue and extend their studies through the Meat Trades Final/Craftsman's Certificate.

2. MEAT TRADES FINAL/CRAFTSMAN'S CERTIFICATES. To provide the student with knowledge of basic business and management studies and of more detailed meat technology appropriate to the wider responsibilities of a supervisory nature. It is also intended to lay a foundation for the more advanced studies in management and meat technology provided in the Advanced Certificate syllabus.

3. ADVANCED CERTIFICATE IN MEAT TECHNOLOGY. This is intended for students aspiring to a position of responsibility, such as production manager, quality controller and other managerial posts in meat processing plants; and for other executive posts in distributive units in the meat industry.

Meat Industry General Certificate I

Compulsory subjects	Optional subjects
1A—The Meat Industry 1B—Calculations, Communications and Documentation 1C—Meat Science	1D(A)—Abattoir Organization 1D(M)—Manufacturing Plant Organization 1D(R)—Retail Shop Organization 1D(S)—Supermarket Depot Organization 1D(W)—Wholesale Depot Organization 1E—Practical (Abattoir) 1E—Practical (Manufacturing) 1E—Practical (Retail) 1E—Practical (Wholesale) (One 1D and One 1E option must be completed)

1A. The Meat Industry (Teaching time: 35 hours)

Objective: On completion the student will have a basic understanding of the aspects of the Meat Industry, identified in the syllabus.
Livestock—Slaughtering—Meat Type & Quality—Wholesaling—Retailing—Offals—Manufacturing and Processing—Legislation—Hygiene and Safety—Associated Studies

1B. Calculations, Communications and Documentation (Teaching time: 35 hours)

Objective: On completion of this module the student will:
(a) Have an understanding of the calculations and simple accounting procedures used in the Meat Industry in terms of cost and profits;
(b) Have an improved ability to communicate and interpret oral and written instructions;
(c) Be able to keep accurate records and understand simple documentation.
Calculations—Communications—Documentation—Costing

1C. Meat Science (Teaching time: 35 hours)

Objective: On completion of this module, the student will have:
(a) A basic scientific knowledge of the structure and composition of meat;
(b) An elementary knowledge of microbiology and its implications for good hygienic practice and the control of meat spoilage and storage.
Hygiene—Preservation and Storage—Meat Quality

1D(A). Abattoir Organization (Teaching time: 35 hours)

Objective: On completion of this module, the student will have a basic knowledge of the functions and operations of a slaughtering establishment.
Hygiene—Safety—Law—Provision of Slaughtering Facilities—Livestock—Methods of Slaughter—Carcase Cooling and Storage—By-Products

1D(M). Manufacturing Plant Organization (Teaching time: 35 hours)

Objective: On completion of this module, the student will have a basic understanding of the operation and organization of a manufacturing plant.
Hygiene—Safety—Law—Fundamental Operations—Raw Materials used in Manufactured Products—Basic Recipes, Preparation and Manufacture of Products

1D(R). Retail Shop Organization (Teaching time: 35 hours)

Objective: On completion of this module, the student will have a basic understanding of the operation and organization of a retail unit.
Hygiene—Safety—Law—Supplies—Display and Selling—Stock Control

1D(S). Supermarket Meat Section Organization (Teaching time: 35 hours)

Objective: On completion of this module, the student will have a basic understanding of the functions and operations of the meat section of a supermarket.
Hygiene—Safety—Law

1D(W). Wholesale Depot Organization (Teaching time: 35 hours)

Objective: On completion of this module, the student will have a basic understanding of the organization and operation of a wholesale depot.
Hygiene—Safety—Law—Structure of the Meat Industry—Types of Wholesale Outlets—Basic Organizational Structure of Wholesale Company and Meat Depot—Operation of a Wholesale Meat Depot—Principles of Wholesale Pricing and Market Trends

1E(A). Practical Demonstration and Participation—Abattoir (Teaching time: 70 hours)

DEMONSTRATE, SLAUGHTER AND DRESSING: Cattle—Sheep—Pig
Pre-slaughter procedure; reception, lairaging, casualities—
Methods of stunning/sticking/bleeding, including legal requirements—
Various methods of dressing and evisceration, with special references to hygiene—
EEC export requirements—Indications of carcase quality—Dressing Percentages—Offals—By-Products

1E(R). Practical Demonstration and Participation—Retail (Teaching time: 70 hours)

Cut, bone and prepare for sale:
  (a) Forequarter of beef
  (b) Lamb
Demonstration of cutting, boning and preparation for sale:
  (a) Hindquarter of Beef
  (b) Pig
  (c) Rabbits and Poultry
  (d) Minced Meat
Indications of Quality—Cuts—Offals—Manufactured Products

1E(W). Practical Demonstration and Participation—Wholesale (Teaching time: 70 hours)

Cut and prepare for sale:
  (a) Side of Beef
  (b) Lamb, fresh or imported
  (c) Pig
Carcase Assessment:
  (a) Sex, weight, age, conformation, degree of finish.
  (b) Grades, marks, classification schemes.
  (c) Percentage of cuts and ratios.
  (d) Identification of cuts.
  (e) Pricing and costings.
  (f) Seasonal variations in supply and demand.
Offals:
  (a) Indication of quality.
  (b) Identification points.
  (c) Grades, marks, country of origin.
  (d) Seasonal variations.

Meat Trade Final/Craftsman's Certificate 2

Compulsory subjects	Optional subjects

2A The Meat Industry
2B Business Organization
2C Meat Technology
2D Anatomy and Physiology
      of Meat Animals.
	2E(A) Abattoir Supervision
	2E(M) Manufacturing Plant
	          Supervision
	2E(R) Retail Shop Supervision
	2E(S) Supermarket Supervision
	2E(W) Wholesale Depot Supervision
	2F Accounts
	2G Chemistry and Microbiology
	2H Meat Hygiene and Inspection
	2J Practical (A)
	               (M)
	               (R)
	               (S)
	               (W)
	(One 2E and one 2J option must be
	completed (plus one from either 2F,
	2G or 2H)

2A. The Meat Industry (Teaching time: 70 hours)

Objective: On completion of this module, the student will have an adequate understanding of the aspects of the Meat Industry identified in the syllabus, sufficient to appreciate and benefit from his specialist options.
Livestock—Meat Type and Quality—Manufacturing and Processing—Meat Marketing

2B. Business Organization (Teaching time: 70 hours)

Objective: On completion of this module, the student will have a general knowledge and understanding of the nature and purpose of commercial activity, including distribution and marketing.
Economic Background—Business Units—Main Branches of Industry—Main Branches of Commerce and Trade—Transport and Storage—Banking and Finance—Insurance—Marketing—Channels of Distribution—Taxation—Law

2C. Meat Technology (Teaching time: 70 hours)

Objective: On completion of this module, the student will have a general understanding of scientific principles relevant to various technological aspects of the Meat Industry, together with an appreciation of the factors contributing to the acceptability of meat and meat products.

Solutions—Refrigeration—Electricity—Chemistry of meat and meat products—Packing of meat and meat products—Enzymes—Metabolism—Microbiology and Hygiene

2D. Anatomy and Physiology of Meat Animals (Teaching time: 70 hours)

Objectives: On completion of this module, the Student:

(a) Will have a sufficient understanding of anatomy and physiology to benefit from the study of pathology and meat inspection in the Meat Hygiene module.

(b) Will have a sufficient understanding of anatomy to know the position of:

(i) the different organs in the animal's body cavities and

(ii) the position of the main, lymph nodes, blood vessels and fat deposits in a carcase.

(c) Will know the relationship between muscles and skeleton and the position and method of articulation of the joints.

(d) Will have an understanding of the comparative physiology of ruminant mammals, non-ruminant mammals and domestic fowls.

(e) Will understand the most humane and efficient methods of stunning, bleeding and dressing slaughter animals.

Introduction—Histology—Circulatory System—Digestive System—Urinary System—Respiratory System—Reproductory System—Endocrine System—Skeletal System—Muscular System—Skin—Anatomy and Physiology of the Fowl

2E(A). Abattoir Supervision (Teaching time: 70 hours)

Objective: On completion of this module, the student will have a knowledge of the construction, operation and supervision of slaughtering establishments.

Personnel Management—Siting and Construction—Legal Operational Requirements—Hygiene—Slaughter and Dressing—Storage and Processing—Utilization of by-products—Meat Marketing—Legal rights and responsibilities of employees and employers

2E(M). Manufacturing Plant Supervision (Teaching time: 70 hours)

Before commencing this module, the student *must* have a basic product and processing knowledge.

Raw materials, recipes and costings—Machines and Equipment—Organization of manufacturing techniques—Quality control—Personnel management—Meat and meat products' marketing—Finance and financial control—Legislation—Safety and hygiene

2E(R). Retail Shop Supervision (Teaching time: 70 hours)

Objective: On completion of this module, the student will have:
  (a) A comprehensive knowledge of the management and organizational requirements sufficient to be responsible for a traditional retail unit.
  (b) A general understanding of the considerations necessary to
    (i) re-design or re-equip
    (ii) start on own account.
Hygiene and Safety — Legislation — Personnel/Staff — Commodity — Procuration and Control—Finance—Sales—Small Goods Production

2E(W). Wholesale Depot Supervision (Teaching time: 70 hours)

Objective: To provide the student with a broad outline knowledge of meat importing and wholesaling, a basic knowledge of the factors affecting wholesale meat prices and sales policy, and a knowledge of various aspects of the management of a wholesale depot, including the main points of relevant law.
Meat Importation—Meat Marketing—Wholesale Meat Prices—Sales Policy—Operation of a Wholesale Depot—Management of Staff—Law

2F. Accounts (Teaching time: 70 hours)

Objective: On completion of this module, the student will have a basic understanding of the principles of Accounts and appreciate the role and need for accounts in any business organization.
Accounts—Interpretation of accounts—Accounting procedure—Pricing, margins and mark-ups—Concept of manufacturing accounts—Capital and Revenue expenditure—Stock Valuation—Depreciation—Credit Control—Bank reconciliation statements—VAT—Wages/PAYE—Budgets, targets and controls

2G. Food Chemistry and Microbiology (Teaching time: 70 hours)

Objective: On completion of this module, the student will have a general knowledge of the structure and biochemical properties of the main consituents of food, which is necessary to understand the changes that occur during growth, processing and storage of food with special reference to meat and meat products.

Proteins — Enzymes — Carbohydrates — Lipids — Vitamins — Microbiology—Microbial Spoilage of Food

2H. Meat Hygiene and Inspection (Teaching time: 70 hours)

Objective: On completion of this module, the student:

(a) Will have an elementary knowledge of pathological conditions and disease processes occurring in meat animals and their probable effect of fitness for food;

(b) Will know the importance of hygiene standards for the slaughter and dressing of animals for human consumption and how adequate standards may be effected;

(c) Will have a general knowledge of the legislation covering meat inspection animal welfare in slaughterhouses, and hygiene in the Meat Trade;

(d) Will have an appreciation of the duties of a meat inspector.

Meat Inspection—Pathology—Specific Diseases—Legislation

Advanced Certificate in Meat Technology.

Subjects offered include Meat Production and Marketing; Anatomy, Physiology and Meat Inspection; Principles of Management and, as optional subjects, Food Microbiology and Hygiene; Food Chemistry and Nutrition; Factory Abattoir Operations.

For the purpose of examination, the first three are compulsory with an elected optional subject. The two remaining optional subjects may also be included in the examinations and successful candidates have these as endorsements to the main certificate.

At the time of going to press, we are informed that work has commenced on the revision of the syllabuses for the Advanced Certificate in Meat Technology, for planned implementation in the autumn of 1978.

Alphabetical guide to Meat Trade Classes

The following list gives the names of centres (in alphabetical order, under the name of the town or city concerned) providing, or likely to provide, classes leading to the examinations of the Institute of Meat. In some cases the availability of classes depends on enrolments and this list does not guarantee or imply that classes will be provided in any particular year. For the same reason it is not practicable to state whether any particular centre operates a particular course at a particular time.

Full details of the courses available, fees, and hours of study should be obtainable from the Registrar of the various centres listed.

BARROW-IN-FURNESS: College for Further Education, Howard Street, Barrow-in-Furness, Lancashire.

BELFAST: The College of Business Studies, Brunswick Street, Belfast, Northern Ireland.

BIRKENHEAD: Birkenhead Technical College, Borough Road, Birkenhead L42 9QD.

BIRMINGHAM: College of Food & Domestic Arts, Summer Row, Birmingham 3

BLACKPOOL: Blackpool College of Technology & Art, Palatine Road, Blackpool, Lancs.

BOLTON: Bolton Technical College, Manchester Road, Bolton BL2 1ER.

BRISTOL: Brunel Technical College, Ashley Down, Bristol BS7 9BU.

BURNLEY: Burnley Municipal College, Ormerod Road, Burnley, Lancs.

CARDIFF: Cardiff College of Food Technology & Commerce, Colchester Avenue, Cardiff CF3 7XR.

CHELTENHAM: North Gloucestershire College of Technology, The Park, Cheltenham Glos GL50 2RR.

CHESTERFIELD: Chesterfield College of Technology, Infirmary Road, Chesterfield S41 7NG.

COLWYN BAY: Llandrillo Technical College, Llandudno Road, Rhos-on-Sea, Colwyn Bay, North Wales.

DARLINGTON: Darlington College of Technology, Cleveland Avenue, Darlington, Co. Durham.

DERBY: Derby College of Art & Technology, Kedleston Road, Derby DE3 1GB.

DURHAM: Durham Technical College, Framwellgate Moor, Durham.

GUILDFORD: Guildford Technical College, Stoke Park, Guildford, Surrey.

HITCHIN: Hitchin College, Cambridge Road, Hitchin, Herts SG4 0JD.

HUDDERSFIELD: Huddersfield Technical College, New North Road, Huddersfield HD1 5NN.

HULL: Hull College of Technology, Queens Gardens, Kingston-upon-Hull HU1 3DG.

LEEDS: Thomas Danby College, Kildare Terrace, Whitehall Road, Leeds LS12 1DB.

LEICESTER: South Fields College of Further Education, Aylestone Road, Leicester.

LINCOLN: Lincoln College of Technology, Cathedral Street, Lincoln.

LIVERPOOL: College of Crafts and Catering, Colquitt Street, Liverpool L1 4DB.

LONDON: College for the Distributive Trades, Briset House, Briset Street, London EC1M 5SL.

MANCHESTER: Hollings College, Wilmslow Road, Manchester M14 6HR.

MIDDLESBROUGH: Kirby College of Further Education, Roman Road, Middlesbrough, Teeside.

NEWCASTLE-UPON-TYNE: College of Arts & Technology, Sandyford Road, Newcastle-upon-Tyne.

NORWICH: Norwich City College, Ipswich Road, Norwich, Norfolk NOR 67D.

NOTTINGHAM: Clarendon College of Further Education, Pelham Avenue, Nottingham NG5 1AL.

OXFORD: Oxford College of Further Education, Oxpens Road, Oxford OX1 1SA.

PETERBOROUGH: Peterborough Technical College, Park Cresent, Peterborough, Northants.

PLYMOUTH: Plymouth College of Further Education, Tavistock Road, Plymouth, Devon PL4 8AA.

READING: Reading College of Technology, Kings Road, Reading, Berks RG1 4HJ.

SALFORD: Salford College of Technology, Frederick Road, Salford, Lancs. M6 6PU.

SCARBOROUGH: Scarborough Technical College, Lady Edith's Drive, Scalby Road, Scarborough, Yorks. YO12 5RN.

SHEFFIELD: Granville College of Further Education, Granville Road, Sheffield S2 2RL.

SOUTHAMPTON: Southampton Technical College, St Mary Street, Southampton SO9 3WX.

STOKE-ON-TRENT: North Staffordshire Polytechnic, College Road, Stoke-on-Trent ST4 2DE.

SWANSEA: College of Further Education, Tycoch, Swansea SA2 9EB.

TORQUAY: South Devon Technical College, Newton Road, Torquay, Devon TQ2 5BY.

TROWBRIDGE: Trowbridge Technical College, College Road, Trowbridge, Wiltshire.

WALSALL: Walsall & Staffordshire Technical College, St Paul's Street, Walsall WS1 1XN.

WOLVERHAMPTON: Wulfrum College of Further Education, Paget Road, Wolverhampton.

Details of the apprenticeship scheme for slaughtermen can be obtained from: Mr W. H. P. Whatley, Union of Shop, Distributive and Allied Workers, 188 Wilmslow Road, Manchester MI4 6LV.

N.B. Courses for the Institute of Meat examinations are not available outside the United Kingdom, but arrangements could be made for the local examination of persons residing abroad who have covered the appropriate syllabus through private study.

Some educational centres overseas

AUSTRALIA: The William Angliss Food Trades School, 555 Latrobe Street, Melbourne, Victoria.

The Wembley Trade School, Salvado Road, Wembley, Western Australia.

The East Sydney Technical College, Forbes Street, Darlinghurst, N.S.W. 2010.

NEW ZEALAND: Central Institute of Technology, Petone, N.Z.

CANADA: The Canadian Meat Training Institute, 116 Dundass Street West, Toronto 3, Ontario.

BELGIUM: Centre National de Recherches et de Perfectionnement pour la Boucherie-Charcuterie, 14 Rue Ropsy Chaudron, Anderlecht, Bruxelles.

Antwerpse Runds en Varken Beenhouwersband, Lange Lobroekstraat 89, Antwerp.

DENMARK: Danish Meat Research Institute, Roskilde.

FRANCE: Ecole Superieure des Metiers de la Viande, 37 Boulevard Sault, Paris Xlle.

IRISH REPUBLIC: School of Commerce and Retail Distribution, 18 Parnell Square, Dublin.

NETHERLANDS: Slagervakschool, Veermarktplein, Utrecht.

SOUTH AFRICA: School of Meat Cutting, Private Bag 23, Johannesburg.

SWITZERLAND: Fleischer-Fachschule, Oberlandstrasse 29, Spietz.

UNITED STATES: American Meat Institute, 59 East Van Buren Street, Chicago, Illinois 60605.
WEST GERMANY: Praktische Fleischer-Fachschule, Rodern Strasse 31, Offenbach am Main.

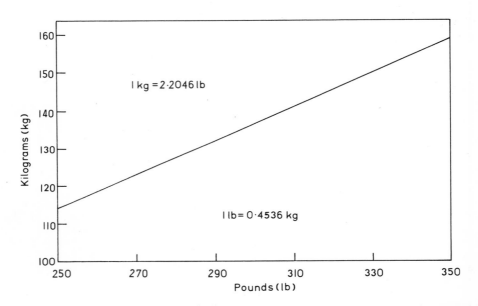

Fig. 62   Graph for conversions from lb to kg and vice versa

Index